STUDY GUIDE

Principles of Human Physiology

Cory Etchberger
Longview Community College

Margaret Nordlie
University of Mary

Patricia Munn (Chapter 22)
Longview Community College

Benjamin
Cummings

San Francisco   Boston   New York
Cape Town   Hong Kong   London   Madrid   Mexico City
Montreal   Munich   Paris   Singapore   Sydney   Tokyo   Toronto

Publisher: Daryl Fox
Project Editor: Claire Brassert
Publishing Assistant: Marie Beaugureau
Managing Editor: Wendy Earl
Production Supervisor: David Novak
Composition: Marian Hartsough Associates
Manufacturing Buyer: Stacey Weinberger
Marketing Manager: Lauren Harp
Cover Illustration: Tomo Narashima

ISBN: 0-8053-5684-3
1 2 3 4 5 6 7 8 9 10—BTP—05 04 03 02 01
www.aw.com/bc

Preface

Welcome to the study guide for *Principles of Human Physiology!* This guide is designed to provide you with a variety of questions that test your understanding of concepts covered in physiology. Below you will find a description of the contents of this guide, as well as helpful hints for successful studying.

The order of topics, key terms, and objectives covered in this study guide correspond to the chapters found in *Principles of Human Physiology* by William Germann and Cindy Stanfield, making it easy for you to refer back to the text. Each chapter contains different types and levels of questions, including completion, matching, labeling, short answer, multiple choice, and true/false questions, which review information you learned in the text. Challenge and Clinical Application questions are more difficult and test your ability to apply what you've learned to new situations. Concept Maps check your understanding of the relationships between concepts. Flow Chart questions test your comprehension of cause and effect relationships in physiological processes. Sequence questions ask you to put physiological processes into their appropriate order. Answers to all of the questions may be found at the end of the study guide.

Helpful Hints for Successful Studying

Over the years, we have asked successful physiology students what suggestions they might have for future students taking physiology. Their suggestions are listed below with our comments. By following these suggestions, you can increase your chances for success.

Write out a study schedule on a calendar. Creating a schedule will help you to establish short- and long-term goals.

Read the assigned sections in your textbook before class. As you are reading, jot down questions for your instructor that you can ask in class.

Outline the material in the chapter. Outlining gives you a sense of how the material is organized and shows you the "big picture."

Be an active learner. By listening and asking questions in class you will master the material.

Study the figures and figure legends. The figures in the text correlate directly to the text itself, and help to explain concepts visually. Use the figures to ensure that you understand concepts discussed in the text.

Re-read the key concepts in the textbook immediately after class and write them in your own words. Once you can articulate the material in writing, it shows you *know* the material. This technique will help you determine which concepts you still need to study.

Form a study group. Working with other students to understand material will increase your comprehension. By explaining concepts to others who don't understand them, you will clarify your own understanding. If you don't understand a concept, one of your fellow students may be able to help you!

We encourage you to send comments, suggestions, or corrections, so that we may improve the guide in future editions.

Happy studying!

Cory Etchberger, Margaret Nordlie, and Patricia Munn
c/o Benjamin Cummings
1301 Sansome Street
San Francisco, CA 94111

Contents

1 Introduction to Physiology

Objectives

We recommend that you review the **Objectives** for this chapter, found on page 1 of *Principles of Human Physiology*. The **Objectives** outline what you should know from each chapter.

Key Terms

body fluid compartment
cell
conduction
connective tissue cell
core temperature
effector
epithelia
epithelial cell
epithelium
error signal
evaporation
extracellular fluid (ECF)
homeostasis

hyperthermia
hypothermia
input
integrating center
internal environment
interstitial fluid (ISF)
intracellular fluid (ICF)
lumen
muscle cell
negative feedback
neuron
organ system
organ

output
physiology
plasma
positive feedback
radiation
regulated variable
sensor
set point
thermoregulation
tissue
total body water (TBW)

ORGANIZATION OF THE BODY

Matching

1. In the list below, indicate whether each cell type, location, or function describes a neuron (N), muscle cell (M), epithelial cell (E), or connective tissue cell (C).

   a. _____ red blood cells

   b. _____ contracts the heart

   c. _____ skin surface

   d. _____ bones

   e. _____ nerve cells

   f. _____ receives information from the outside environment and transmits the information to the brain

Completion

Fill in the blanks to complete the following narratives.

2. The body is composed of **(a)** major tissue types. **(b)** tissue is used for movement of both voluntary and **(c)** muscles. **(d)**, or nerve cells, conduct electrical information between various cells of the body. **(e)** is the most diverse tissue type and includes blood and bone. **(f)** tissue consists of a continuous sheetlike layer of cells in combination with a basement membrane.

   a. _____   d. _____

   b. _____   e. _____

   c. _____   f. _____

3. The **(a)** environment is separated from the interior of the body by **(b)** tissue. The body's **(c)** environment is composed of a number of body fluid environments: **(d)** is the portion of the extracellular fluid that bathes most cells of the body, **(e)** is the liquid portion of the blood, **(f)** is the fluid compartment present inside the cell, and **(g)** is the entire volume of fluid that is contained within the body.

   a. _____   e. _____

   b. _____   f. _____

   c. _____   g. _____

   d. _____

Short Answer

Answer the following questions in 1–4 sentences.

4. Define *physiology*.

5. The various cells of the body need to obtain oxygen and nutrients while getting rid of carbon dioxide and other waste products. To do so, these substances (and many others) need, at some point, to move across epithelial tissue. Describe the semipermeable nature of epithelial tissues.

6. Arteries and veins are organs of the cardiovascular system. As such, they are composed of several tissue types. a) Which tissue type is present on the inside of arteries and veins and is in direct contact with the blood? b) Which tissue type present in arteries and veins aids in constricting the blood vessels? c) Which tissue type present on the outside of arteries and veins helps to protect the blood vessels and anchor them to surrounding tissues?

Multiple Choice

Select the best answer from the choices given.

7. Ligaments and tendons are composed of which tissue type?

   a. epithelial   c. nervous   e. part of the plasma

   b. muscle   d. connective

8. Which of the following tissue types lines the inside of the lumen?

   a. nerve tissue   d. muscle tissue

   b. epithelial tissue (endothelium)   e. connective tissue and muscular tissue

   c. connective tissue

9. Which of the following fluids directly surround the blood cells?

   a. intracellular fluid   c. interstitial fluid   e. plasma

   b. extracellular fluid   d. total body water

10. Which of the following is not an organ of the cardiovascular system?

    a. heart   c. veins   e. capillaries

    b. arteries   d. blood

11. Tubule reabsorption occurs in which of the following organs?

    a. kidneys   c. heart   e. skin

    b. stomach   d. lungs

12. Which of the following is the term for the entry of fluid into the kidney tubules?

    a. absorption   c. filtration   e. diffusion

    b. reabsorption   d. excretion

13. Elimination of cellular waste products, salts, and water from the body occur at the _____ in a process known as _____.

    a. gastrointestinal tract : absorption   d. gastrointestinal tract : secretion

    b. kidneys : excretion   e. respiratory system : absorption

    c. cardiovascular system : filtration

14. In the digestive system, nutrients are transported from the lumen to the bloodstream. What is this process called?

    a. absorption   c. reabsorption   e. selective filtration

    b. filtration   d. excretion

15. Erythrocytes are produced in the _____ in response to the hormone _____.

    a. kidneys : oxytocin   c. brain : glucagon   e. liver : erythropoietin

    b. pancreas : insulin   d. bone marrow : erythropoietin

16. The testes are part of the reproductive system because they produce the sperm cells necessary for continuing life into the next generation. The testes also produce the hormone testosterone and are therefore also considered part of the _____ system.

    a. endocrine   c. immune   e. urinary

    b. cardiovascular   d. digestive

True/False

Label the following statements as true (T) *or false* (F). *If false, change the statement to make it true.*

17. _____ Muscle cells are generally elongated and line the inside of hollow organs.

18. _____ Capillaries are highly permeable to most substances in the blood except proteins.

19. _____ Most cells of the body are in direct contact with the external environment.

20. _____ Intracellular fluid contains many proteins and is rich in potassium.

21. _____ When air enters the lungs, it is considered to be outside of the body.

Labeling

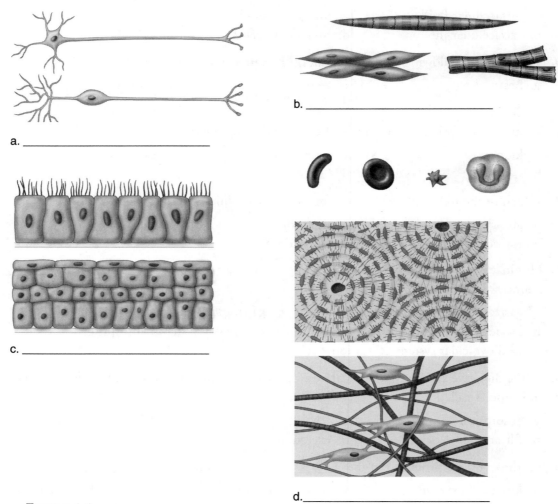

a. _____

b. _____

c. _____

d. _____

FIGURE 1.1

22. Label each cell type in Figure 1.1 and provide one function or characteristic for each cell type.

Sequencing

23. Place the following levels of organization in the correct order from the most simple to the most complex.

    a. organ,   b. cell,   c. organ system,   d. tissue

    Sequence: _____

Challenge Question

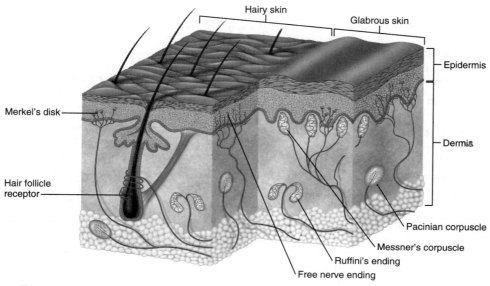

FIGURE 1.2

24. The skin is an excellent example of an organ. Examine Figure 1.2 and explain why the skin is considered an organ, taking into consideration its various components and functions.

Concept Map

25. Fill in the blanks in the following concept map, which shows the relationship of the various fluid compartments within the body.

Total Body Fluid

a. _____ 66%	Extracellular fluid	
	b. _____ 26%
	c. _____ 7%

HOMEOSTASIS

Matching

26. Match the following list of words with the descriptions below: sensor (S), effector (E), integrating center (IC), set point (SP), error signal (ES).

a. _____ cells that respond to signals from the integrating center

b. _____ compares the regulated variable to the set point and initiates the appropriate response

c. _____ the difference between the set point and the value determined by the sensor

d. _____ the desired value of the regulated variable

e. _____ sensitivity to changes in the body's environment, sending signals to the integrating center

27. Label the following descriptions as examples of negative feedback (NF) or positive feedback (PF).

a. _____ You have just suffered a bad laceration in your leg and have lost a significant amount of blood. Your blood pressure drops due to the blood loss. Your body responds by constricting blood vessels and increasing your blood pressure.

b. _____ While going outside on a cold morning, your skin temperature drops slightly. Your body responds by shivering in an effort to warm up.

c. _____ You have cut yourself and clotting factors are released into the bloodstream. Your body responds by releasing more clotting factors to form a clot.

d. _____ A nerve cell begins to open a few channels to allow sodium to enter the cell. The nerve cell responds by opening more channels to allow more sodium to enter.

e. _____ A woman is about to deliver a baby. Her uterus stretches, sending a signal to the brain to release the hormone oxytocin. Oxytocin travels in the blood to the uterus, stimulating it to contract.

Completion

Fill in the blanks to complete the following narrative.

28. Homeostasis in the body is typically maintained through the mechanism known as **(a)**. This occurs when there is a change in the actual value of the regulated variable, called the **(b)**. In other words, a/an **(c)** has occurred. This change is detected by a/an **(d)** that sends a signal to the **(e)**, which responds by sending a signal to the appropriate **(f)**.

a. _____   d. _____

b. _____   e. _____

c. _____   f. _____

Short Answer

Answer the following questions in 1–4 sentences.

29. Define *homeostasis*.

30. If homeostasis is properly maintained within the body, which three aspects of the extracellular fluid show very little change?

31. Describe each of the three types of thermoregulatory effectors and how they respond to a drop in body temperature.

Multiple Choice

Select the best answer from the choices given.

32. Which of the following is **not** a physiological change resulting from aerobic training?
  a. resting heart rate increases
  b. bone density increases
  c. heart size increases
  d. the abundance of sweat glands increases
  e. ability of airways to widen increases

33. During perspiration, what do the sweat glands act as?
  a. effector
  b. integrating center
  c. set point
  d. sensor
  e. regulated variable

34. Which of the following two organs receive first priority in the delivery of blood?
  a. liver and kidneys
  b. lungs and skeletal muscles
  c. heart and brain
  d. lungs and kidneys
  e. most endocrine glands and the liver

35. Which of the following is a response to hypothermia?
  a. increased blood flow to the skin
  b. increased sweat production
  c. positive feedback
  d. increased breathing rate
  e. shivering

True/False

Label the following statements as true (T) *or false* (F). *If false, change the statement to make it true.*

36. _____ Positive feedback responses are more common in the body than negative feedback.

37. _____ The interaction of estrogen and LH to initiate LH surge is a good example of positive feedback.

38. _____ Radiation energy is the transfer of thermal energy between objects that are in direct contact with each other.

39. _____ The body's thermoregulatory center is the pituitary gland.

40. _____ Evaporation is heat loss due to loss of water and helps to cool the body.

41. _____ When your body tries to lose heat, blood flow to the skin increases.

42. _____ Insensible water loss is the loss of water through sweat glands.

43. _____ Negative feedback is characterized by a response of the effector in the opposite direction of the stimulus detected by the sensor.

44. _____ Poikilothermic animals can regulate their body temperatures within a narrow range.

Sequencing

45. Place the following events associated with negative feedback in the correct sequence.

   a. Sensors detect an error signal.
   b. The integrating center determines the appropriate response and sends signals to the effectors.
   c. The effectors act to alter the error signal back to set point.
   d. The new set point is stable.
   e. The integrating center receives information.
   f. The set point is stable.

Sequence: _____

Clinical Question

46. A mother is concerned because her daughter woke up with a slight fever and a runny nose, and considers giving the child some children's aspirin to reduce the fever. Before she does this, she calls you, the pediatrician, to ask your advice. Explain the mechanism of the fever and the benefits of a fever in fighting infections.

Challenge Questions

47. Compare and contrast the general physiological roles of positive and negative feedback in maintaining homeostasis in the body.

48. After a grueling semester of physiology, Mary Jane decides to visit the Sonoran desert during the summer. Predict how the three types of thermoregulatory effectors in her body will respond to this hot, arid environment.

49. Convection ovens tend to cook food more evenly than conventional ovens. What do these ovens have inside of them to ensure more even cooking? What does this have to do with physiology?

Concept Map

50. Fill in the blanks in the following concept map that shows homeostasis through negative feedback.

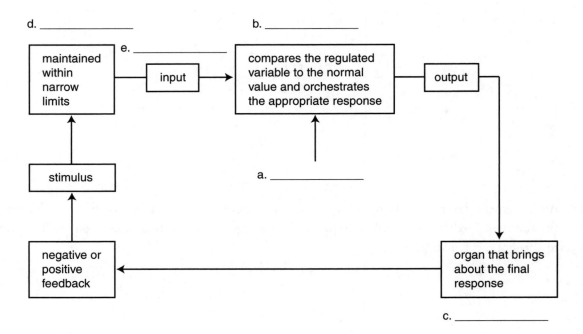

2 The Cell: Structure and Function

Objectives

We recommend that you review the **Objectives** for this chapter, found on page 21 of *Principles of Human Physiology*. The **Objectives** outline what you should know from each chapter.

Key Terms

amino acid
amphipathic
anabolism
biomolecule
carbohydrate
catabolism
cellular transport
cellulose
chromatin
chromosome
coated pit
codon
cristae
cytoplasm
cytoskeleton
cytosol
deoxyribonucleic acid (DNA)
desmosome
disaccharide
eicosanoid
electron transport system
endocytosis
endoplasmic reticulum
exocytosis
fatty acid
fibrous protein
gap junction
gene
genetic code
globular protein
glucose

glycerol
glycogen
Golgi apparatus
human genome
inclusions
integral membrane protein
intermediate filament
intermembrane space
interphase
law of complementary base
    pairing
leader sequence
lipid
lysosome
meiosis
messenger RNA (mRNA)
metabolism
microfilament
microtubule
microvilli
mitochondria
mitochondrial matrix
mitosis
monosaccharide
nuclear envelope
nuclear pore
nucleic acid
nucleotide
nucleus
organelle
peptide

peripheral membrane protein
peroxisome
phagocytosis
phospholipid
pinocytosis
plasma membrane
polypeptide
polysaccharide
post-translational processing
promoter sequence
protein
R group (residual group)
receptor-mediated endocytosis
replication
ribonucleic acid (RNA)
ribosome
saturated fatty acid
secreted
secretory vesicle
starch
steroid
tight junction
transcription
transcytosis
translation
transmembrane protein
triglyceride
triplet
unsaturated fatty acid
vault
vesicle

BIOMOLECULES

Matching

1. Match the following list of biomolecules with their descriptions or examples below: carbohydrates (C), lipids (L), proteins (P), nucleotides (N). Each can be used once or more than once.

   a. _____ composed of polar molecules with a 1:2:1 ratio of carbon, hydrogen, and oxygen

   b. _____ form the genetic material of cells

   c. _____ polypeptides form these biomolecules and their subunits are amino acids

   d. _____ primarily carbon and hydrogen atoms linked by nonpolar covalent bonds

   e. _____ phospholipids and steroids are examples of this biomolecule type

   f. _____ polysaccharides such as starch and cellulose are examples of this biomolecule type

Completion

Fill in the blanks to complete the following narrative.

2. **(a)** are molecules that are synthesized by living organisms and contain carbon atoms. These molecules are of four basic types. **(b)** are important in energy transfer within cells and also make up both **(c)** and RNA. **(d)** are sources of energy for the body and include examples such as glucose, lactose, and glycogen. **(e)** are a group of biomolecules that contain an amine group and a carboxyl group, and can form polymers called **(f)**. **(g)** are nonpolar and are therefore poorly soluble in water; two examples are triglycerides and eicosanoids.

   a. _____   e. _____

   b. _____   f. _____

   c. _____   g. _____

   d. _____

Short Answer

Answer the following questions in 1–4 sentences.

3. Describe the difference between saturated and unsaturated fatty acids.

4. Describe a polypeptide and include the chemical bonds associated with it.

5. A single strand of DNA has the following base sequence: AATTGCAATGA. a) What is the base sequence of the complimentary strand of DNA? b) What is the base sequence of an RNA molecule made from the DNA base sequence of AATTGCAATGA? c) How many total pyrimidines and total purines are present in the RNA base sequence?

Multiple Choice

Select the best answer from the choices given.

6. Some individuals are lactose intolerant and cannot digest lactose properly. Which of the following biomolecule types are these individuals intolerant to?

a. saturated fatty acids
b. proteins
c. nucleotides
d. eicosanoids
e. disaccharides

7. Which of the following is derived from a 20-carbon fatty acid and contains a 5-carbon ring in the middle?

a. thromboxane
b. sucrose
c. DNA
d. myoglobin
e. glycoprotein

8. Which of the following does **not** have cholesterol as a precursor?

a. calcitriol
b. cortisol
c. estradiol
d. testosterone
e. DNA

9. Which of the following polymers is properly paired with its repeating subunit?

a. DNA : RNA
b. polypeptide : pyrimidine
c. cellulose : ATP
d. glycogen : glucose
e. protein : nucleotide

10. Which of the following are generally nonpolar?

I. glucose
II. saturated fatty acids
III. triglycerides
IV. glycerol

a. I only
b. II only
c. III only
d. II and IV
e. II, III, and IV

True/False

Label the following statements as true (T) *or false* (F). *If false, change the statement to make it true.*

11. _____ Amphipathic means that a molecule has both covalent and ionic bonds.

12. _____ A phospholipid bilayer forms the main part of cell membranes.

13. _____ Micelles are formed from a single layer of phospholipids and function to transport nonpolar molecules.

14. _____ Eicosanoids are modified fatty acids that are part of the genetic material of cells.

15. _____ cAMP and cGMP are important chemical messengers within the cell.

Clinical Question

16. After two days of painful cramps in your lower abdomen you seek medical attention at the local clinic. Following a routine examination, your physician diagnoses you with non-pathological (dietary) constipation. Which biomolecule type is he likely to suggest that you eat in greater quantities and why?

Challenge Questions

17. Several hormones in the body have carriers to transport them from their site of production to where they exert their effects. These carriers bind to the hormones and transport them in blood plasma; steroid hormones fall into this category of needing a carrier protein. Without these carriers, the hormones would partition into the cell membranes in preference to being free in solution. Thus without a carrier, they would be far less likely to reach their target tissue. Given what you know about the polarity of both steroids and plasma, why do you think carriers are necessary for steroid hormones?

18. Compare and contrast the structure, location, and function of DNA and RNA.

19. When globular proteins are exposed to conditions outside of their normal physiological range they may denature or lose their three-dimensional shape. The result is that these proteins can no longer perform their physiological function, which occurs because hydrogen bonds are sensitive to changes in pH or temperature. Describe the role of hydrogen bonds in the three-dimensional conformation of proteins.

20. Contrast the three-dimensional nature and function of proteins found in tendons versus the three-dimensional nature and function of myoglobin.

CELL STRUCTURE

Matching

21. Match each of the following as either a membranous (M) or nonmembranous (NM) organelle.

a. _____ endoplasmic reticulum

b. _____ Golgi body

c. _____ ribosome

d. _____ mitochondria

e. _____ vault

f. _____ centriole

g. _____ lysosome

h. _____ cytoskeleton

Completion

Fill in the blanks to complete the following narrative.

22. The plasma membrane of the cell is composed of a number of structures. The **(a)** forms the basic structure of the cell membrane and acts as a semipermeable barrier to a number of molecules. **(b)** are classified into two types: **(c)** span the entire width of the lipid bilayer, and **(d)**, which are embedded in the lipid bilayer. **(e)** are located at the surface of the plasma membrane and are often associated with the cytoskeleton. **(f)** can be covalently bound to either the membrane **(g)** or can be associated with proteins within the membrane.

a. _____

b. _____

c. _____

d. _____

e. _____

f. _____

g. _____

Concept Map

23. Fill in the blanks for each of the types of filaments and their examples.

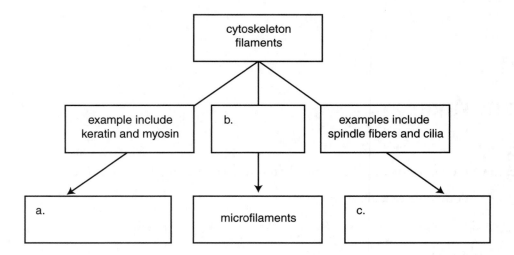

Short Answer

Answer the following questions in 1–4 sentences.

24. Explain why the structure of the plasma membrane is described as a "fluid mosaic."

25. Describe the two possible locations of protein synthesis and where the proteins travel to after they are synthesized.

26. Describe the organization of the membranes and compartments associated with a mitochondrion.

Multiple Choice

Select the best answer from the choices given.

27. The _____ face of the Golgi apparatus is closely associated with the _____.

    a. cis face : endoplasmic reticulum   d. outer : mitochondria

    b. trans face : lysosomes   e. lipid : water

    c. inner : nucleus

28. If a drug were to inhibit a cell from dividing its cytoplasm, which of the following organelles would most likely be affected by the drug?

    a. peroxisomes   c. Golgi apparatus   e. microfilaments
    b. vaults   d. ribosomes

29. Peroxisomes contain _____, which functions to _____.

    a. sucrase : serve as an energy source for the cell
    b. lactase : catalyze the breakdown of lactose
    c. catalase : catalyze the breakdown of hydrogen peroxide
    d. inhibin : synthesize ATP
    e. tubulin : modify substances from the endoplasmic reticulum

30. All of the following are associated with the nucleus **except**:

    a. chromatin   c. pores   e. nucleolus
    b. rRNA   d. ribosomes

31. _____ are masses that store energy in the form of triglycerides or glycogen.

    a. Tubulins   c. Mitochondria   e. Secretory vesicles
    b. Inclusions   d. Cristae

32. What is one function of microtubules?

    a. aid in muscle contraction
    b. assist in the separation of the cytoplasm during cell division
    c. provide strength to the cytoskeleton
    d. act as storage sites
    e. provide intracellular transport of materials

33. Which organelle is responsible for storing calcium in muscle cells?

    a. ribosomes   d. mitochondria
    b. Golgi apparatus   e. smooth endoplasmic reticulum
    c. rough endoplasmic reticulum

34. Which of the following is the function of secretory vesicles?

    a. structural support of the cell
    b. ATP synthesis
    c. engulf harmful particles on the outside of the cell
    d. storage and eventual release of molecules from inside the cell
    e. aid in cell division

True/False

Label the following statements as true (T) *or false* (F). *If false, change the statement to make it true.*

35. _____ The cytosol is the fluid present **only** inside the nucleus.

36. _____ Ribosomes can be free in the cytoplasm or associated with the Golgi apparatus.

37. _____ All cells of the body have roughly an equal number of mitochondria.

38. _____ Microfilaments provide structural support for microvilli.

39. _____ Each pair of microtubules in a cilium is connected by dynein arms.

40. _____ The thin, thread-like pieces of DNA are known as chromatin.

41. _____ Insulin is a chemical messenger that binds to membrane proteins on the outside of many cells in the body. The type of protein that insulin binds to is a peripheral membrane protein.

Labeling

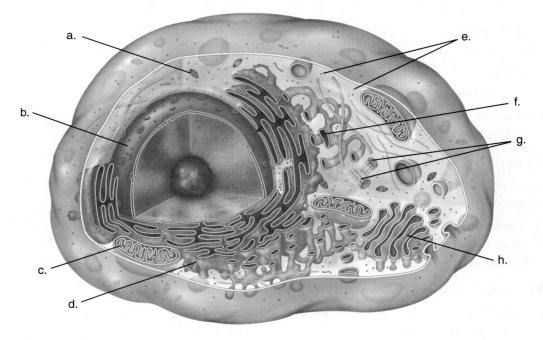

FIGURE 2.1

42. In the space below, identify the structures (a–h) on Figure 2.1 and provide at least one function for each organelle.

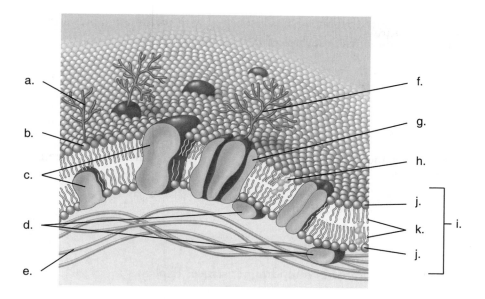

FIGURE 2.2

43. In the space below, identify the structures (a–k) on Figure 2.2 and provide one function for each structure.

Challenge Questions

44. Some drugs, such as nicotine, can disrupt the ability of cells to move substances along the cell surface. Which organelle is most likely affected by these drugs?

45. Why do you think that the carbohydrate chains associated with membrane lipids and membrane proteins are on the outside surface of the cell instead of on the inside?

46. Contrast the characteristics and functions of integral and peripheral membrane proteins.

47. Which organelle has been implicated in multidrug resistance? Explain.

CELL-TO-CELL ADHESIONS

Matching

48. In the list below, indicate if each cell junction type or location describes a tight junction (TJ), desmosome (D), or gap junction (GJ).

    a. _____ Cadherins are associated with this junction type.

    b. _____ These junctions allow free movement of ions from cell to cell.

    c. _____ Connexons and connexins are associated with this type of junction.

    d. _____ These junctions often occur between epithelial cells lining the inside of the lumen of hollow organs, restricting the movement of molecules between the cells.

    e. _____ These junctions form strong filamentous connections between cells that are often under stress.

    f. _____ Occludins are associated with this junction type.

Short Answer

Answer the following question in 1–4 sentences.

49. Contrast paracellular movement and transepithelial transport.

True/False

Label the following statements as true (T) *or false* (F). *If false, change the statement to make it true.*

50. _____ Gap junctions allow a signal from one cell to directly diffuse into an adjacent cell.

51. _____ In epithelial tissue, the only membrane facing the extracellular fluid is the apical membrane.

52. _____ Gap junctions are found between all epithelial cells.

53. _____ A plaque is formed at the site of each desmosome.

Labeling

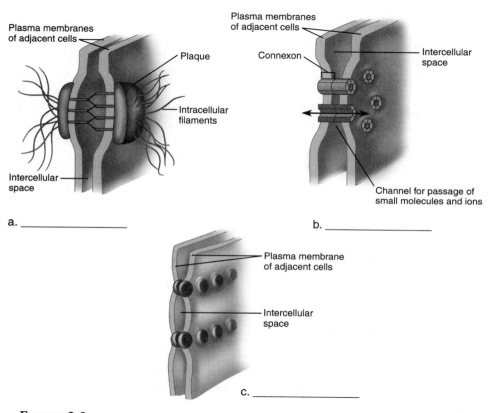

a. _____

b. _____

c. _____

FIGURE 2.3

54. Label each of the cell junctions on Figure 2.3. In the space below, list the types of membrane proteins that join the cells and one location where each junction can be found.

Clinical Question

55. You are a veteran nurse at a heart transplant unit of a hospital. One of your jobs is to orient new nurses to heart transplants. Upon first seeing a live, beating heart, the new nurses are amazed by the coordination between the rhythmical beating of the atria and the ventricles. They notice that first the atria contract and relax, and then the ventricles contract and relax. Explain to the new nurses why this organ is able to coordinate its function so precisely.

Challenge Question

56. Explain why tight junctions and occludin are important components of the epithelial tissue that lines hollow organs.

GENERAL CELL FUNCTIONS

Matching

57. Match the following list of membrane transport mechanisms with their location, function, or cells that utilize the form of transport: exocytosis (EX), phagocytosis (PH), pinocytosis (PI), receptor-mediated endocytosis (RME), transcytosis (T).

   a. _____ Epithelial cells can move compounds from one side of the epithelium to the other by this form of membrane transport.

   b. _____ ADH is released from cells in the brain using this form of membrane transport.

   c. _____ An endolysosome is formed during this membrane transport.

   d. _____ Bacteria are cleared from our bodies by this form of membrane transport.

   e. _____ An endocytic vesicle is formed during this form of membrane transport.

Completion

Fill in the blanks to complete the following narrative.

58. Transport of material within membrane-bound compartments can occur through two general processes, **(a)** or endocytosis. There are three forms of endocytosis: phagocytosis, pinocytosis, and **(b)**. Phagocytosis is used by white blood cells to surround foreign particles and form a/an **(c)**. In pinocytosis a/an **(d)** is formed, which brings extracellular fluid into the cell. Receptor-mediated endocytosis uses proteins in the plasma membrane that act as **(e)** to bring specific particles into the cell. To do this, the cell forms a/an **(f)**, which indents and brings the **(e)** and the particle into the cell.

a. _____

b. _____

c. _____

d. _____

e. _____

f. _____

Short Answer

Answer the following questions in 1–4 sentences.

59. Define *metabolism.*

60. Bagels are composed of starch. After you have eaten a bagel, the starch is broken down into its smaller subunits of glucose where it can be absorbed by the small intestine. What form of metabolism is exemplified by this reaction?

Multiple Choice

Select the best answer from the choices given.

61. The manufacturing of proteins at the ribosomes is an example of which of the following?

    a. exocytosis

    b. catabolism

    c. receptor-mediated endocytosis

    d. membrane transport

    e. anabolism

62. Which of the following forms a coated pit to transport substances?

    a. pinocytosis

    b. receptor-mediated endocytosis

    c. exocytosis

    d. transcytosis

    e. phagocytosis

63. Goblet cells are found in the epithelium of the trachea. The function of these cells is to produce and secrete mucus into the lumen of the trachea. Which membrane transport mechanism do they use to accomplish this?

    a. transcytosis

    b. exocytosis

    c. receptor-mediated endocytosis

    d. pinocytosis

    e. phagocytosis

64. After the hormone epinephrine is released from the adrenal gland, it travels to various cells in the body where it exerts its effects. When epinephrine arrives at its _____, it binds to _____.

    a. coated pit : the lysosome

    b. glycoprotein : the phagosome

    c. ion channel : the glycocalyx

    d. target cells : receptors

    e. gap junctions : (nonspecifically) the outside of the cell

65. During _____, the _____ fuses with phagolysosomes, and exposes the engulfed particle to the enzymes of the lysosome.

    a. receptor-mediated endocytosis : coated pit

    b. exocytosis : coated pit

    c. phagocytosis : phagocytic vesicle

    d. exocytosis : endolysosome

    e. phagocytosis : lysosome

True/False

Label the following statements as true (T) *or false* (F). *If false, change the statement to make it true.*

66. _____ Metabolic reactions are catalyzed by the presence of enzymes.

67. _____ Both endocytosis and exocytosis require an input of energy.

68. _____ The only function of transcytosis is to add components to the plasma membrane.

69. _____ Transcytosis is common to all tissue types.

Sequencing

70. Place the following statements of receptor-mediated endocytosis in the correct sequence.

    a. Endocytosis is triggered.

    b. Vesicle is formed after pinching off.

    c. Plasma membrane indents around the molecules.

    d. Vesicle enters the cell carrying the molecule.

    e. Proteins on the plasma membrane bind specific molecules.

    Sequence: _____

Challenge Question

71. Compare and contrast endocytosis and exocytosis.

Concept Map

72. Fill in the blanks on the following concept map, which shows each type of transport within membrane-bound compartments.

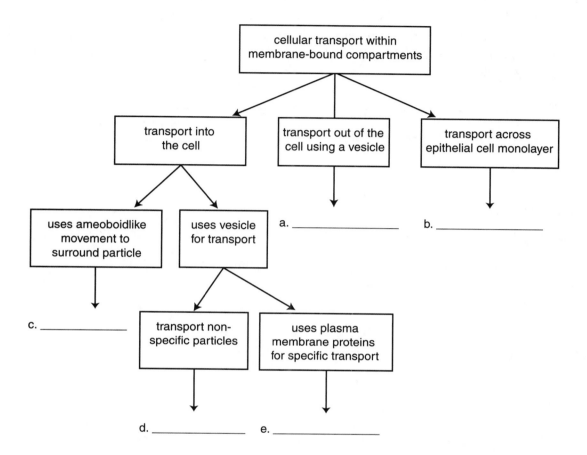

PROTEIN SYNTHESIS

Matching

73. Match the descriptions below with one of the two major steps of protein synthesis: transcription (TR) or translation (TL).

a. _____ associated with ribosomes

b. _____ DNA is the template.

c. _____ mRNA is synthesized.

d. _____ amino acids are assembled.

e. _____ RNA polymerase binds to DNA.

f. _____ tRNA carries the amino acid to the ribosome.

Completion

Fill in the blanks to complete the following narrative.

74. Proteins are synthesized in the **(a)** or in association with the **(b)**. For those proteins made in the **(a)**, the **(c)** determines whether the protein will remain in the **(a)** or enter a peroxisome, a **(d)**, or the nucleus. For those proteins synthesized in association with the **(b)**, the protein will eventually be packaged by the **(e)** and directed to the appropriate site in the cell, or will be secreted by the cell.

a. _____   d. _____

b. _____   e. _____

c. _____

Short Answer

Answer the following questions in 1–4 sentences.

75. Briefly describe transcription and translation, including where each occurs.

76. Define *gene*.

77. What is a polyribosome and why does it occur?

Multiple Choice

Select the best answer from the choices given.

78. What is the name for the three base sequence on a DNA molecule that codes for a single amino acid?

    a. codon   c. gene   e. promoter sequence
    b. triplet   d. chromosome

79. What is the name for the three base sequence on an mRNA molecule that is complimentary to the three base sequence on DNA?

    a. codon   c. gene   e. promoter sequence
    b. triplet   d. chromosome

80. What is the first step of translation?

   a. termination
   b. post-translational processing
   c. post-transcriptional processing
   d. initiation
   e. glycosylation

81. Which of the following molecules includes an anticodon?

   a. DNA
   b. mRNA
   c. RNA polymerase
   d. ribosomes
   e. tRNA

82. Which of the following is one function of RNA polymerase?

   a. carries the appropriate amino acid to the ribosome
   b. contains the base sequence called the anticodon
   c. binds to the promoter sequence on the DNA
   d. degrades proteins in the cytosol
   e. determines whether a protein will be synthesized in the cytosol or in association with the endoplasmic reticulum

83. Excess bases in a gene that do not code for the amino acids are called _____.

   a. exons
   b. anticodons
   c. initiation factors
   d. histones
   e. introns

84. During protein degradation, _____ directs the protein to the _____, which contains enzymes that degrade the protein into smaller peptide fragments.

   a. ubiquitin : protesome
   b. RNA polymerase : anticodon
   c. tRNA : RNA polymerase
   d. initiation factors : termination codon
   e. genetic code : tRNA

85. Assume that a muscle cell requires more protein. Transcription will _____.

   a. be repressed
   b. occur at the nucleus
   c. be induced
   d. occur by signal recognition proteins
   e. be directed by charged tRNA

True/False

Label the following statements as true (T) *or false* (F). *If false, change the statement to make it true.*

86. _____ Glycosylation occurs when carbohydrates are added to the growing polypeptide.

87. _____ In the cytosol, proteins are degraded by the enzyme RNA polymerase.

88. _____ The Golgi apparatus is an important site of post-translational processing.

89. _____ If you had the DNA triplet AAT, the mRNA codon would be TTA.

90. _____ Regulation of transcription usually can occur when RNA polymerase binds to DNA.

91. _____ If protein synthesis occurs at the rough endoplasmic reticulum, the leader sequence and associated ribosome will bind to the charged tRNA.

Sequencing

92. Place the following statements of protein synthesis in the correct sequence.

    a. mRNA moves from nucleus to cytosol.

    b. Peptide bond forms between the first two amino acids.

    c. Stop codon is reached.

    d. RNA polymerase binds to DNA.

    e. mRNA is assembled.

    f. Polypeptide chain detaches from ribosome.

    g. Ribosome continues to move down the length of mRNA.

    h. Leader sequence is clipped off.

    i. Second tRNA-amino acid complex attaches to adjacent codon on mRNA.

    j. tRNA carrying the first amino acid attaches to mRNA.

Sequence: _____

Clinical Question

93. Research indicates that the drug *clotrimazole* may inhibit initiation of translation in some cells. Where in the cell does this drug likely exert its effect?

Challenge Questions

94. Describe the function of each of the following in protein synthesis: DNA, RNA polymerase, mRNA, tRNA, ribosomes.

95. What is the difference in the function of a promoter sequence and a leader sequence?

96. Examine the following hypothetical mRNA sequence that codes for a sequence of amino acids: AUGCCAUCGCUAAAGGGACGCUUUUGA. a) How many codons are present in the mRNA molecule? b) How many amino acids are coded for by this mRNA sequence? Explain each of your answers.

Concept Map

97. Fill in the blanks of the general sequence of polypeptide post-translational processing.

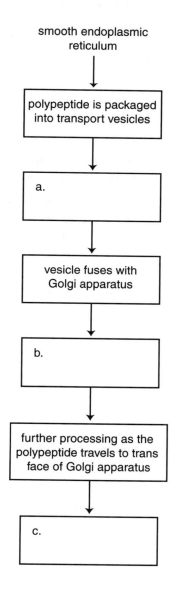

CELL DIVISION

Matching

98. Match the following stages of the cell cycle with its appropriate description below: interphase (I), prophase (P), prometaphase (PM), metaphase (M), anaphase (A), telophase (T), cytokinesis (C).

a. _____ Chromosomes align in the middle of the cell.

b. _____ Nuclear envelope breaks down.

c. _____ DNA replication occurs.

d. _____ New nuclear envelope develops.

e. _____ First stage that chromosomes are visible with a microscope.

f. _____ Chromosomes move toward opposite poles of the cell.

g. _____ cytoplasmic division

Completion

Fill in the blanks to complete the following narrative.

99. There are two types of cell division. **(a)** occurs only in the reproductive cells, while **(b)** occurs in the other cells of the body. The cell cycle can be divided into two main parts: **(c)** and interphase. Interphase is divided into four phases: G0, G1, **(d)**, and G2. During G0 the cell performs functions unrelated to **(c)**. During G1 the cell increases its rate of **(e)** synthesis. When the cell is in **(d)** phase DNA replication occurs and, finally, during G2, the cell **(f)** to get ready for mitosis.

a. _____   d. _____

b. _____   e. _____

c. _____   f. _____

Short Answer

Answer the following question in 1–4 sentences.

100. Define semiconservative replication of DNA and when in the cell cycle it occurs.

Multiple Choice

Select the best answer from the choices given.

101. Which of the following molecules positions and links the nucleotides together during DNA replication?

    a. RNA polymerase   c. protease   e. lactase

    b. ubiquitin   d. DNA polymerase

102. In a single chromosome, two _____ are linked together at the _____.

    a. histones : gene   d. nuclear envelopes : centriole

    b. chromatids : centromere   e. genes : histone

    c. spindle fibers : centriole

103. In which of the following phases of interphase does DNA replication occur?

    I. G0

    II. G1

    III. S

    IV. G2

    a. I only   c. III only   e. II and IV

    b. II only   d. IV only

True/False

Label the following statements as true (T) *or false* (F). *If false, change the statement to make it true.*

104. _____ Proto-oncogenes usually have no serious clinical effects on cells.

105. _____ During interphase, the DNA is in the form of chromatin.

106. _____ Mutations are molecular changes in the DNA sequence.

107. _____ Chromosomes are coiled around proteins called proteosomes.

Clinical Question

108. Cancer occurs when cells reproduce in an unregulated manner. Some anti-cancer drugs, such as Taxol®, operate by interrupting the spindle fibers or the centrioles. Explain how these drugs may help to prevent cells from dividing.

Challenge Questions

109. Describe why DNA replication is necessary after mitosis has occurred.

110. Contrast the functions of interphase, mitosis, and cytokinesis.

111. What would a cell look like if mitosis occurred, but cytokinesis failed to take place?

112. Explain why all of the cells of your body that have 23 pairs of chromosomes are identical in their genetic make-up. (Hint: they all came from a single fertilized egg cell).

Concept Map

113. Fill in the concept map of the various stages of the cell cycle.

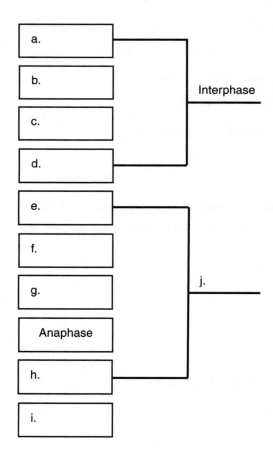

3 Cell Metabolism

Objectives

We recommend that you review the **Objectives** for this chapter, found on page 62 of *Principles of Human Physiology*. The **Objectives** outline what you should know from each chapter.

Key Terms

activation energy
activation energy barrier
active site
adenosine triphosphate (ATP)
adenosine diphosphate (ADP)
affinity
allosteric regulation
anabolic
ATP synthase
calorie
catabolic
catalytic rate
chemiosmotic coupling
coenzyme
cofactor
covalent regulation
dephosphorylation
electron transport chain

end-product
end-product inhibition
energy metabolism
enzyme
equilibrium
essential nutrient
feedback inhibition
feedforward activation
gluconeogenesis
glycogen
glycogenesis
glycogenolysis
glycolysis
hydrolysis
intermediate
kinetic energy
Krebs cycle
lactic acid
law of mass action
lipogenesis

lipolysis
metabolic pathway
metabolism
modulator
oxidative phosphorylation
oxidation
percent saturation
phosphatase
phosphorylation
potential energy
product
protein kinase
proteolysis
reactant
reduction
regulatory site
substrate
substrate specificity
substrate-level phosphorylation
vitamin

TYPES OF METABOLIC REACTIONS

Matching

1. Match the following equations to the type of chemical reaction each best represents: oxidation reaction (OR), reduction reaction (RR), hydrolysis reaction (HR), condensation reaction (CR), phosphorylation reaction (PR), dephosphorylation reaction (DR).

   Answers may be used more than once or not at all.

   a. _____ $HA—BH \rightarrow A = B + 2H$

   b. _____ $A—P \rightarrow A + P_i$

c. _____ $A-OH + H-B \rightarrow A-B + H_2O$

d. _____ $2\ H \rightarrow 2\ H^+ + 2\ e^-$

e. _____ $C_6H_{12}O_6 + 6\ O_2 \rightarrow 6\ CO_2 + 6\ H_2O$

f. _____ $2\ H^+ + 2\ e^- \rightarrow 2\ H$

Completion

Fill in the blanks to complete the following narrative.

2. In order for the human body to function normally, its cells must function normally. Cells can perform their work only if they have a source of **(a)**. This **(a)** comes from the **(b)** present in the food a person ingests. After extracting the energy in food, the body processes it and uses this energy for **(c)** or stores it for **(d)**. All of the chemical reactions involved in energy storage and utilization are known as **(e)**.

a. _____   d. _____

b. _____   e. _____

c. _____

Multiple Choice

Select the best answer from the choices given.

3. Which of the following does **not** correctly define an oxidation reaction?
   a. the removal of electrons from a molecule
   b. the reaction of any molecule with carbon
   c. the reaction of any molecule with oxygen
   d. the removal of hydrogen atoms from a molecule
   e. a reaction in which the oxidized molecule may become positively charged

Questions 4–6 refer to the following equation.

$$A + X \rightarrow B \rightarrow C \rightarrow D + Y$$

4. What does this equation best represent?
   a. a metabolic pathway   d. a hydrolysis reaction
   b. an oxidation-reduction reaction   e. a condensation reaction
   c. a phosphorylation reaction

5. Which letter or letters in the equation above represent(s) the end products?
   a. A + X   c. C   e. D + Y
   b. B   d. B and C

6. Which letter or letters in the equation above represent(s) the intermediates?
   a. A + X   c. C   e. D + Y
   b. B   d. B and C

7. Most metabolic reactions _____.

    a. proceed only in the forward direction
    b. proceed only in the reverse direction
    c. are bidirectional

    d. generate reactants from products
    e. require the use of energy

8. Which of the following reactions specifically involves the removal of a phosphate group from a molecule?

    a. condensation reaction
    b. oxidation reaction
    c. phosphorylation reaction

    d. dephosphorylation reaction
    e. reduction reaction

True/False

Label the following statements as true (T) *or false* (F). *If false, change the statement to make it true.*

9. _____ Hydrolysis reactions are anabolic reactions.

10. _____ A phosphorylation reaction involves the addition of a phosphorus atom to a molecule.

11. _____ Condensation reactions generate water as a product.

12. _____ Condensation reactions join smaller molecules together.

13. _____ A molecule that is reduced gains electrons.

14. _____ A hydrolysis reaction is the opposite of a condensation reaction.

Short Answer

Answer the following questions in 1–4 sentences.

15. Define *metabolism*.

16. Distinguish between catabolism (catabolic reactions) and anabolism (anabolic reactions).

Challenge Questions

17. Oxidation reactions can be described in a number of different ways (refer to Question 3). Explain why so many different definitions can be used to describe this type of reaction.

18. When describing a chemical reaction, we often say the reaction is going forward or in reverse. What do these terms mean when applied to the direction of a chemical reaction?

Clinical Question

19. Your roommate Sara recently came down with the stomach flu, and she's having a hard time keeping food down. The nurse at Student Health tells her she shouldn't eat any solid food for 24 hours, but she should drink water or Gatorade® (a low-calorie electrolyte replacement) as tolerated. During this time period, where will most of the energy come from that Sara's cells need in order to perform work? What are two examples of catabolic metabolic reactions that may be occurring in her body at this time?

Labeling

20. Label the **reactants** and **products** in the following equation.

$$A + B \rightarrow C + D$$

METABOLIC REACTIONS AND ENERGY

Matching

21. Match the following statements as to whether they apply to energy-releasing (ERL) reactions or energy-requiring (ERQ) reactions.

a. _____ reactants contain more energy than products

b. _____ may proceed spontaneously in the reverse direction

c. _____ have a positive ΔE

d. _____ proceed in the forward direction when energy is added to the reaction

e. _____ proceed spontaneously in the forward direction

f. _____ are typically catabolic reactions

Completion

Fill in the blanks to complete the following narrative.

22. Metabolic reactions in the body provide the cells with energy and are also important in transforming **(a)** into molecules useable by the body. The energy produced is used to perform many different types of work, including the formation of **(b)** by the kidneys, generating the **(c)** action of the heart, the **(d)** of cells during tissue repair, and the **(e)** of skeletal muscle tissue when you walk.

a. _____   d. _____

b. _____   e. _____

c. _____

Multiple Choice

Select the best answer from the choices given.

23. What does the following statement describe? "Energy can be neither created nor destroyed, but instead can only change form."

    a. the law of mass action
    b. the first law of thermodynamics
    c. activation energy
    d. thermal motion
    e. potential energy

24. A reaction in which the conversion of reactants to products and products to reactants occurs at the same rate is said to be _____.

    a. in transition
    b. experiencing an activation energy barrier
    c. in equilibrium
    d. experiencing the law of mass action
    e. an energy-releasing reaction

25. Energy that can be stored and that is not associated with motion is best described as _____.

    a. potential energy
    b. kinetic energy
    c. transitional energy
    d. activation energy
    e. molecular energy

26. What is the term for the difference between the energy of the transition state and the energy of the reactants or products of a reaction?

    a. concentrated energy
    b. kinetic energy
    c. potential energy
    d. transitional energy
    e. activation energy

27. The activation energy barrier is important to cellular functioning because it _____.

    a. affects whether or not a metabolic reaction will proceed
    b. determines the number of collisions that will occur between molecules within cells
    c. limits how fast metabolic reactions can proceed
    d. b and c are correct
    e. a and c are correct

True/False

Label the following statements as true (T) *or false* (F). *If false, change the statement to make it true.*

28. _____ The products of anabolic reactions contain more energy than the reactants.

29. _____ Kinetic energy can be described as the energy of motion.

30. _____ An increase in the concentration of reactants relative to products will cause a reaction to proceed spontaneously in the reverse direction.

31. _____ The transition state is the high energy state in which products exist after an energy-releasing reaction has occurred.

32. _____ The direction in which a chemical reaction proceeds is determined by the energy change of the reaction.

Short Answer

Answer the following questions in 1–4 sentences.

33. What is meant by the "coupling" of anabolic and catabolic reactions?

34. Define *thermal motion*.

35. Define ΔE.

Challenge Questions

36. Why do energy-releasing reactions require the input of activation energy in order to proceed?

37. Define the *law of mass action*. Explain why this phenomenon occurs.

38. How do molecules acquire the energy they need to overcome the activation energy barrier?

REACTION RATES

Matching

39. Indicate whether each of the conditions listed below will increase (I) or decrease (D) the forward rate of a chemical reaction. Note that questions preceded by an ^{E} are specific to enzyme-catalyzed reactions.

a. _____ decreased temperature

b. _____ increased concentration of products relative to reactants

c. _____ decreased height of the activation energy barrier

^{E}d. _____ increased catalytic activity of the enzyme

^{E}e. _____ decreased enzyme concentration

^{E}f. _____ decreased substrate concentration

Completion

40. Fill in the term that corresponds to each of the following definitions.

Definition	Term
A biomolecule specialized to act as a catalyst	a.
A nonprotein component attached to an enzyme that is necessary to its function	b.
The reactant molecule in an enzyme-catalyzed reaction	c.
A molecule that directly participates in an enzyme-catalyzed reaction by assisting the reaction in some (non-catalytic) way	d.
The site on an enzyme to which the substrate binds	e.
The site on an enzyme to which a modulator binds	f.
A molecule that, when bound to an enzyme, changes the shape of the active site	g.

True/False

Label the following statements as true (T) *or false* (F). *If false, change the statement to make it true.*

41. _____ The chemical composition of an enzyme is altered by the chemical reactions in which it participates.

42. _____ Enzymes are not specific for the substrates with which they interact.

43. _____ As long as the substrate concentration in an enzyme-catalyzed reaction continues to increase, the rate of the reaction will continue to increase.

44. _____ The higher an enzyme's affinity for substrate, the faster the rate of the enzyme-catalyzed reaction.

45. _____ Dephosphorylation reactions are typically catalyzed by protein kinases.

46. _____ The rate at which metabolic pathways function can be controlled by feedback inhibition or feedforward activation.

Multiple Choice

Select the best answer from the choices given.

47. Which of the following statements is **not** true of enzymes?

    a. Enzymes are usually proteins.
    b. Enzymes speed up the rate of chemical reactions.
    c. Enzymes lower the activation energy barrier of chemical reactions.
    d. Enzymes are often monosaccharides.
    e. More than one of the above statements is incorrect.

48. Which of the following is a coenzyme that carries electrons within cells?

    a. coenzyme A   d. copper
    b. FAD (flavin adenine dinucleotide)   e. vitamin A
    c. iron

49. Enzyme regulation in which an enzyme's activity is altered by the chemical binding of a specific chemical group to the enzyme is known as _____.

    a. covalent regulation   c. modulatory regulation   e. feedforward activation
    b. allosteric regulation   d. feedback inhibition

50. Which of the following is true regarding allosteric regulation of enzyme activity?

    a. A modulator binds to the active site on an enzyme, changing the shape of the active site.
    b. A substrate molecule binds to the active site on an enzyme, changing the shape of the regulatory site.
    c. A modulator binds to the regulatory site on an enzyme, changing the shape of the active site.
    d. A modulator binds to the active site on an enzyme, changing the shape of the substrate.
    e. A modulator binds to the regulatory site on an enzyme, changing the shape of the substrate.

51. Which of the following is **not** a mechanism by which metabolic reaction rates could be sped up or slowed down to meet the needs of the body?

    a. Cellular enzyme concentrations could be increased or decreased.
    b. The activation energies of the reactions could be increased.
    c. Enzyme activity could be regulated by feedforward activation.
    d. Enzyme activity could be modified by feedback inhibition.
    e. Enzyme activity could be modified by end-product inhibition.

Labeling

52. Label the *binding step*, the *catalytic step*, and the *enzyme-substrate complex* in the following equation.

$$E \;+\; S \;\Leftrightarrow\; E\bullet S \;\rightarrow\; P \;+\; E$$

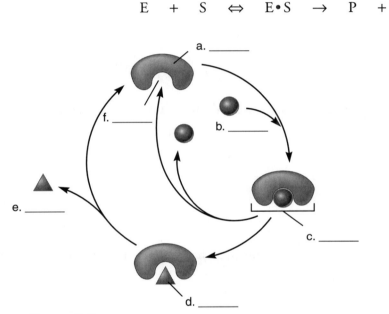

FIGURE 3.1

53. Label the *enzyme, substrate, enzyme-substrate complex, active site,* and *product* in Figure 3.1.

Short Answer

Answer the following questions in 1–4 sentences.

54. Define *net rate* of a chemical reaction.

55. Define *affinity* as it applies to enzymes.

Challenge Questions

56. Compare and contrast feedback inhibition and feedforward activation.

57. Substrate specificity is the result of the complementary fit between substrates and the active sites on enzymes with which they interact. Is it more accurate to describe the concept of complementary fit using the *lock-and-key model*, or using the *induced-fit model*? Explain your answer.

58. Why would increasing the temperature at which a chemical reaction occurs increase the rate of the reaction?

59. Why does increasing the concentration of reactants in a chemical reaction increase the rate of the reaction?

Clinical Question

60. You are working in the emergency room when 4-year-old Bob is admitted. He is unconscious and has rapid respiratory and heart rates. His father says he thinks Bob ate an entire bottle of children's aspirin (acetylsalicylic acid). Based on what you learned in this chapter about the relationship between pH and cellular functioning, what effect might this have on Bob's cells?

Concept Map

61. Fill in the blanks on the concept map below.

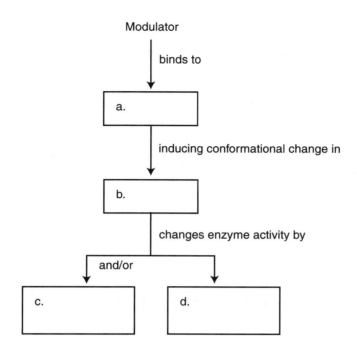

Modulator

binds to

a.

inducing conformational change in

b.

changes enzyme activity by

and/or

c.

d.

GLUCOSE OXIDATION: THE CENTRAL REACTION OF ENERGY METABOLISM

True/False

Label the following statements as true (T) *or false* (F). *If false, change the statement to make it true.*

62. _____ The oxidation of one mole of glucose requires the input of 686 kcal of energy.

63. _____ The 38 moles of ATP synthesized as the result of glucose oxidation require the input of 266 kcal energy.

64. _____ The process of glucose oxidation utilizes oxygen.

Short Answer

Answer the following questions in 1–4 sentences.

65. What is the primary purpose of glucose oxidation within human cells?

66. List the products and quantities produced when one molecule of glucose is oxidized.

67. What is the purpose of ATP in human cells?

68. What is the chemical name of ATP?

69. Write out the chemical reaction that occurs when energy is released from ATP. Is this a hydrolysis or a condensation reaction?

Challenge Question

70. Why must glucose oxidation and ATP synthesis be linked? (Refer to Figure 3.12 in your text, if necessary.)

Clinical Question

71. Your buddy Joe is running his first marathon. As time goes by, Joe feels warmer and warmer and his body temperature increases. Based on your knowledge of glucose oxidation and ATP synthesis, what would explain this phenomenon?

STAGES OF GLUCOSE OXIDATION: GLYCOLYSIS, THE KREBS CYCLE, AND OXIDATIVE PHOSPHORYLATION

Matching

72. Match the following components of glucose oxidation to the location in which they occur: cytosol (C), mitochondrial matrix (MM), intermembrane space of mitochondrion (ISM), or inner mitochondrial membrane (IMM).

Answers may be used more than once.

a. _____ electron transport chain

b. _____ Krebs cycle

c. _____ site at which movement of hydrogen ions down the concentration gradient begins

d. _____ glycolysis

e. _____ linking step

Sequencing

73. List the following stages of glucose oxidation in the proper order.

    a. oxidative phosphorylation, b. linking step, c. glycolysis, d. Krebs cycle

    Sequence: _____

74. List the following events in the order in which they occur during glucose oxidation.

    a. The processing of acetyl CoA results in the formation of ATP, carbon dioxide, NADH and FADH$_2$ molecules.
    b. Glucose is converted to pyruvate.
    c. NADH and FADH$_2$ donate electrons to the electron transport chain.
    d. Pyruvate is converted to acetyl CoA.
    e. Water is formed.
    f. Electrons travel along the electron transport chain.

    Sequence: _____

Completion

75. For each of the stages of glucose oxidation listed below, indicate the net number of molecules produced for every one molecule of glucose oxidized.

	Glycolysis	Linking Step	Krebs Cycle	Oxidative Phosphorylation
NADH	a.	e.	i.	m.
FADH$_2$	b.	f.	j.	n.
CO$_2$	c.	g.	k.	o.
ATP	d.	h.	l.	p.

Multiple Choice

Select the best answer from the choices given.

76. ATP that is generated when an enzyme transfers a phosphate group from one substrate to another is generated by _____.

    a. oxidative phosphorylation
    b. chemiosmosis
    c. the electron transport chain
    d. substrate-level phosphorylation
    e. active transport

77. Which of the following components of glucose oxidation uses oxygen?

    a. glycolysis
    b. the electron transport chain
    c. chemiosmosis
    d. the Krebs cycle
    e. the production of lactic acid

78. For every pair of electrons donated to the electron transport chain by NADH, _____ molecules of ATP are produced.

    a. 1
    b. 2
    c. 3
    d. 4
    e. 5

79. For every pair of electrons donated to the electron transport chain by $FADH_2$, _____ molecules of ATP are produced.

    a. 1
    b. 2
    c. 3
    d. 4
    e. 5

80. How many times does the Krebs cycle turn for every molecule of glucose oxidized?

    a. 1
    b. 2
    c. 3
    d. 4
    e. 5

81. What happens in the linking step of glucose oxidation?

    a. Glucose is converted to pyruvate.
    b. $FADH_2$ is produced.
    c. Pyruvate is converted to acetyl CoA.
    d. Acetyl CoA is converted to pyruvate.
    e. Pyruvate is converted to ATP.

82. Which of the following is a mobile electron carrier that participates in the electron transport chain?

    a. coenzyme Q
    b. cytochrome molecules
    c. heme molecules
    d. iron-sulfur proteins
    e. ATP synthase

83. Which of the following statements about the events of oxidative phosphorylation is **not** true?

    a. As electrons released to the electron transport chain from NADH and $FADH_2$ travel along the chain, energy is released.
    b. Oxygen serves as the final electron acceptor at the end of chemiosmosis.
    c. Energy released via the electron transport chain is used to transport hydrogen ions into the intermembrane space of the mitochondrion.
    d. Hydrogen ions move along their concentration gradient from the intermembrane space into the mitochondrial matrix through ATP synthase complexes.
    e. ATP synthase generates ATP by oxidative phosphorylation.

84. In an anaerobic environment, how many net molecules of ATP are generated per molecule of glucose?

    a. 0   c. 2   e. 38

    b. 1   d. 20

85. In the absence of oxygen, pyruvate _____.

    a. is converted to acetyl CoA   d. enters the electron transport chain

    b. enters the Krebs cycle   e. is converted to lactate

    c. is converted to glucose

Labeling

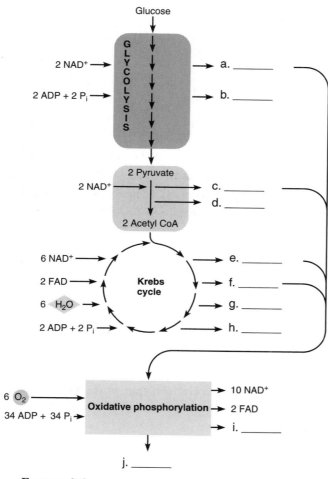

FIGURE 3.2

86. Fill in the blanks in Figure 3.2, indicating the products produced by each stage of glucose oxidation.

Challenge Questions

87. Why is oxygen essential to life?

88. How are sugars other than glucose utilized by cells for energy?

Clinical Questions

89. You are working in the emergency room one night when a patient in cardiac arrest is admitted. The physicians and nurses work to resuscitate him for 20 minutes, at which time his heart beat and respirations resume. The physician orders that his blood gas be analyzed, which indicates (among other things) that the pH of his blood is 7.30 (normal is 7.35–7.45). Explain this finding.

90. The poison *cyanide* works by blocking the activity of the electron transport chain. Explain why this action would result in death.

True/False

Label the following statements as true (T) *or false* (F). *If false, change the statement to make it true.*

91. _____ Oxidative phosphorylation involves two simultaneous processes: the electron transport chain and chemiosmotic coupling.

92. _____ The Krebs cycle produces the majority of NADH generated during glucose oxidation.

93. _____ The anaerobic production of ATP occurs in the mitochondrial matrix.

94. _____ The Krebs cycle generates ATP by oxidative phosphorylation.

95. _____ Glycolysis produces one molecule of pyruvate for every molecule of glucose that enters it.

96. _____ ATP synthase is involved in the anaerobic production of ATP.

Concept Map

97. Fill in the blanks in the following concept map representing aerobic and anaerobic cellular respiration.

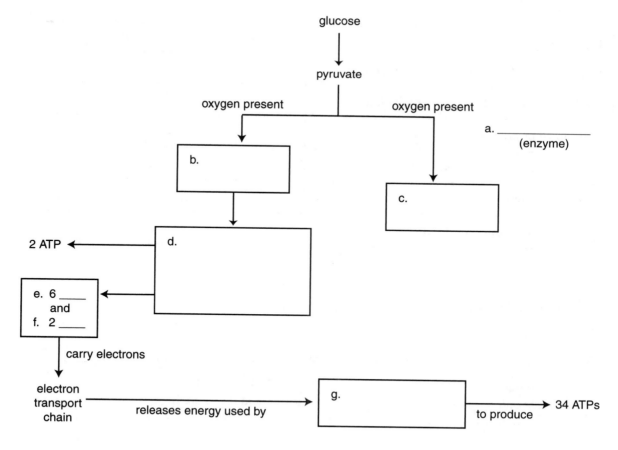

ENERGY STORAGE AND UTILIZATION: METABOLISM OF CARBOHYDRATES, FATS, AND PROTEINS

Matching

98. Match the following definitions to the appropriate molecule: glycogen (G), triglyceride (T), ketone (K), or ammonia (A).

    a. _____ compound synthesized from acetyl CoA as a by product of the breakdown of fats

    b. _____ a polymer composed of glucose molecules

    c. _____ a fat molecule

    d. _____ a compound produced as a result of amino acid deamination when proteins are broken down

Completion

99. Fill in the name of the process that corresponds to each of the following definitions. In the third column, indicate whether or not the process is catabolic (C) or anabolic (A).

Definition	Process	Reaction type
break down of fats into fatty acids and glycerol	a.	g.
synthesis of glucose from noncarbohydrates	b.	h.
breakdown of proteins into amino acids	c.	i.
breakdown of glycogen to glucose	d.	j.
synthesis of glycogen from glucose	e.	k.
synthesis of fats from non-lipids	f.	l.

Multiple Choice

Select the best answer from the choices given.

100. The breakdown of fats and proteins for energy use will occur in the body when _____.

    a. amino acid levels are low
    b. fatty acid levels are low
    c. glucose levels are low
    d. glycerol levels are high
    e. fatty acid levels are high

101. Glycogen is synthesized in cells when _____.

    a. amino acid levels are low
    b. fatty acid levels are low
    c. glucose levels are low
    d. glycerol levels are high
    e. glucose levels are high

102. Fats are broken down into _____.

    a. amino acids and glucose
    b. amino acids and glycerol
    c. fatty acids and glucose
    d. fatty acids and glycerol
    e. amino acids and fatty acids

103. What is an essential amino acid?

    a. an amino acid that is necessary to the body but cannot be synthesized by the cells
    b. an amino acid that must be obtained in the diet
    c. an amino acid that is synthesized by the cells when it is essential to a metabolic process
    d. a and b are correct
    e. a and c are correct

104. Molecules that can be converted into glucose during the process of gluconeogenesis include _____.

    a. fructose and sucrose
    b. glycerol, lactate, and some amino acids
    c. glycerol and fatty acids
    d. some amino acids, lactate, and fructose
    e. some amino acids, glycerol, and fatty acids

105. Which of the following molecules **cannot** be converted to glucose?

    a. fatty acids
    b. glycerol
    c. glycogen
    d. pyruvate
    e. most amino acids

106. Ammonia is ultimately converted into which waste product that is eliminated from the body by the kidneys?

    a. glucose
    b. amino acids
    c. urea
    d. lactate
    e. triglycerides

107. The cells of which organs of the body are the primary stores of glycogen molecules?

    a. liver and skin
    b. skeletal muscle and smooth muscle
    c. liver and brain
    d. skeletal muscle and liver
    e. skeletal muscle and brain

108. Which of the following molecules **cannot** enter the Krebs cycle (some may need to be converted into other molecules before entering the cycle)?

    a. glucose
    b. urea
    c. ketones
    d. amino acids
    e. triglycerides

109. Which of the following molecules can be used by the nervous system as a partial alternative to glucose?

a. glycogen
b. urea
c. fatty acids
d. glycerol
e. ketones

True/False

Label the following statements as true (T) *or false* (F). *If false, change the statement to make it true.*

110. _____ There is no reverse reaction from acetyl CoA to glucose.

111. _____ Not all amino acids can be converted to glucose.

112. _____ Proteins are broken down directly into amino acids and urea.

113. _____ Fats and proteins can be used as energy substitutes for glucose.

114. _____ All amino acids can be converted to glucose.

115. _____ One way in which gluconeogenesis occurs is that pyruvate travels the glycolysis pathway in reverse.

116. _____ Carbohydrates and fats can be used to synthesize some amino acids.

Short Answer

Answer the following question in 1–4 sentences.

117. What is meant by a bypass reaction?

Challenge Questions

118. Are the one-way reactions illustrated in Figure 3.23 of your textbook truly irreversible? Explain your answer.

119. If fats and proteins can be used by most tissues as energy substitutes for glucose, why might a person faint in response to a low blood glucose level?

Clinical Questions

120. In your practice as a dietician, you are working with two clients who are trying to lose weight. Both eat about the same volume of food each day, but one is consistently losing weight and the other is holding steady. After having each client keep a food diary for three days, you discover that the client who is losing weight is eating mainly foods rich in carbohydrates and protein, while the one whose weight is remaining steady eats many foods high in fat. What would explain the difference in their weight loss patterns?

121. You are working with another client who is trying to lose weight, but she has decided to take a more aggressive approach by following a very low-calorie diet. Although she is losing weight rapidly, her breath has a strange odor and she feels tired and sluggish. Trace what has been happening metabolically in her cells since the first day of her diet.

Concept Map

122. Fill in the blanks in the following concept map, diagramming the various pathways amino acids can follow when proteins are broken down. Shaded boxes indicate metabolic processes, while open boxes indicate chemical compounds.

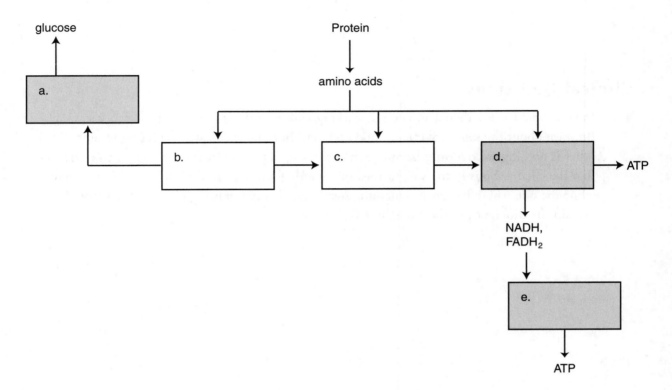

4 Cell Membrane Transport

Objectives

We recommend that you review the **Objectives** for this chapter, found on page 100 of *Princicples of Human Physiology*. The **Objectives** outline what you should know from each chapter.

Key Terms

absorption
active transport
apical membrane
basement membrane
basolateral membrane
carrier
channel
chemical driving force
concentration gradient
cotransport
countertransport
diffusion
electrical driving force

electrochemical driving force
electrochemical gradient
equilibrium potential
facilitated diffusion
flux
hyperosmotic
hypertonic
hypo-osmotic
hypotonic
iso-osmotic
isotonic
mediated transport
membrane potential

osmolarity
osmosis
osmotic pressure
passive transport
permeability
primary active transport
pump
secondary active transport
secretion
simple diffusion
sodium-potassium pump

FACTORS AFFECTING THE DIRECTION OF TRANSPORT

Matching

For this question, assume that the cell membrane potential is negative.

1. In the list below, indicate if each phrase describes passive transport (PT) or active transport (AT).

    a. _____ movement of molecules from an area of low concentration to an area of high concentration

    b. _____ requires energy

    c. _____ movement of molecules from an area of high energy to an area of low energy

    d. _____ movement of molecules through the lipid bilayer

    e. _____ Protein pumps move molecules against the concentration gradient.

Completion

Fill in the blanks to complete the following narrative.

2. Transported molecules are generally affected by three types of driving forces: 1) **(a)** driving forces, which are due to the presence of concentration gradients, 2) **(b)** driving forces, which result from the cell membrane's potential on the movement of ions, and 3) **(c)** driving forces, which are a combination of **(a)** and **(b)** driving forces that represents the **(d)** movement acting on molecules.

a. _____   c. _____

b. _____   d. _____

Short Answer

Answer the following questions in 1–4 sentences.

3. What happens to diffusion of a molecule when the equilibrium potential is equal to zero?

4. Define *membrane potential.*

5. Distinguish between cations and anions. Provide some examples of each.

6. Assume that calcium has a greater electrochemical energy inside the cell than outside the cell. If the cell were to gain more calcium (that is, if calcium were to move into the cell), which transport mechanism would it have to use? Explain.

Multiple Choice

Select the best answer from the choices given.

7. In a muscle cell, which of the following has the greatest electrical driving force?

    a. Ca^{++} c. glucose   e. K^+

    b. Cl^- d. Na^+

8. Which of the following is an anion?

    a. glucose   c. Ca^{++} e. K^+

    b. Cl^- d. Na^+

9. Which of the following is repelled by the charge inside of a nerve cell?

   a. glucose   c. Ca^{++} e. K^+

   b. Cl^- d. Na^+

10. Which of the following is the difference in voltage across a cell membrane?

    a. concentration gradient   d. electrochemical driving force

    b. chemical driving force   e. membrane potential

    c. electrical driving force

11. Which of the following is the total force acting on ions?

    a. concentration gradient   d. electrochemical driving force

    b. chemical driving force   e. membrane potential

    c. electrical driving force

Labeling

TABLE 4.1   MILLIMOLAR CONCENTRATIONS OF SELECTED SOLUTE IN INTRACELLULAR FLUID (ICF) AND EXTRACELLULAR FLUID (ECF)

Solute	ICF (mM)	ECF (mM)
K^+	140.0	4.0
Na^+	15.0	145.0
Mg^{2+}	0.8	1.5
Ca^{2+}	<0.001*	1.8
Cl^-	4.0	115.0
HCO_3^-	10.0	25.0
P_i	40.0	2.0
Amino acids	8.0	2.0
Glucose	1.0	5.6
ATP	4.0	0.0
Protein	4.0	0.2

*Refers to calcium ions free in the cytoplasm. A significant quantity of intracellular calcium is sequestered in membrane-bounded organelles and/or bound to proteins.

12. Refer to Table 4.1. In the table below, indicate the directions of the electrical and chemical driving forces for the following ions: K^+, Na^+, and Cl^-.

Ion	Direction of Electrical Driving Force	Direction of Chemical Driving Force
K^+	a.	d.
Na^+	b.	e.
Cl^-	c.	f.

True/False

Label the following statements as true (T) *or false* (F). *If false, change the statement to make it true.*

13. _____ The inside of most cells of the body have a net neutral charge associated with them.

14. _____ Passive transport requires energy.

15. _____ The chemical driving force is always down the concentration gradient.

16. _____ The membrane potential is the difference in the charges across a cell membrane.

17. _____ If the electrical and chemical driving forces are equal and in the same direction, then an equilibrium potential exists.

Sequencing

18. Assume that Na^+, Ca^{++}, and Cl^- are being transported through ion channels in a cell membrane. Place these three ions in order from the smallest driving force to the largest.

    Sequence: _____

Clinical Question

19. Cholera is an acute intestinal infection caused by the bacterium *Vibrio cholerae.* The bacterium enters the body, usually in contaminated water or in food that has been washed in contaminated water. It has a short incubation period (from less than one day to five days) and produces cholera toxin that causes a copious, watery diarrhea that can quickly lead to severe dehydration and death if not treated promptly. This toxin causes the cells lining the intestines to secrete chloride ions (Cl^-) into the intestinal lumen, which is then followed by the movement of sodium ions (Na^+). Explain why sodium ions and water enter the lumen of the intestines.

Challenge Questions

20. Compare and contrast the roles of passive and active transport in cell membrane transport.

21. Contrast chemical driving force and electrical driving force.

Concept Map

22. Refer to Table 4.1 in Question 12. Use arrows to indicate the direction of the electrical and chemical driving forces for the following ions: Mg^{++}, Ca^{++}, and HCO_3^-.

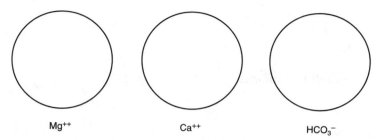

Mg⁺⁺   Ca⁺⁺   HCO₃⁻

FACTORS AFFECTING THE RATE OF TRANSPORT

Matching

23. In the list below, indicate if each condition will increase (I) or decrease (D) the rate of transport of molecules across a cell membrane.

    Passive transport

    a. _____ the surface area of the membrane is decreased by one half

    b. _____ the difference in concentration of an ion across the membrane has increased by 25%

    c. _____ membrane permeability has increased

    Active transport

    d. _____ increased numbers of active individual pump proteins

    e. _____ the number of active protein pumps is decreased on the cell membrane

Completion

Fill in the blanks to complete the following narrative.

24. The rate at which molecules move across a membrane is known as **(a)**. The flow of molecules in one direction is **(b)** flux, and the difference between two of these is known as **(c)** flux. For substances that are transported passively across a cell membrane, the rate of transport depends on three factors: the **(d)** of the driving force, membrane **(e)**, and the **(f)** of the membrane to that particular substance. For substances moved by active transport, two factors determine the rate of movement: the rate at which individual **(g)** proteins transport the substance, and the **(h)** of pumps on the membrane.

    a. _____   e. _____

    b. _____   f. _____

    c. _____   g. _____

    d. _____   h. _____

Short Answer

Answer the following questions in 1–4 sentences.

25. Define *net flux*.

26. Define *permeability* as it relates to cell membranes.

Multiple Choice

Select the best answer from the choices given.

27. Which of the following is the term that describes when there is no net transfer of molecules from one side of a cell membrane to the other?

a. flux
b. diffusional equilibrium
c. pulmonary edema
d. unidirectional flux
e. active transport

28. Assume that sodium is moving into a cell by simple diffusion. Suddenly, the concentration of sodium on the outside of the cell is increased by twice as much. What will initially happen to the rate of transport of sodium into the cell after the change in concentration? (Assume that no other factors change other than the concentration gradient of sodium).

a. The rate of simple diffusion will be twice as fast.
b. The rate of simple diffusion will be ten times as fast.
c. Simple diffusion will no longer occur.
d. The rate of simple diffusion will be reduced by one-half.
e. The rate of simple diffusion will not change.

True/False

Label the following statements as true (T) or false (F). If false, change the statement to make it true.

29. _____ The more active protein pumps that are in the membrane, the faster active transport takes place.

30. _____ Once a cell and its environment come to equilibrium, diffusion no longer takes place.

31. _____ If the extracellular fluid is more highly concentrated with a permeable substance, then the next flux of that substance will be *into* the cell.

32. _____ The greater the concentration difference between the inside and the outside of the cell, the slower diffusion takes place.

33. _____ Individual protein pumps have no effect on the rate of actively transported substances.

Labeling

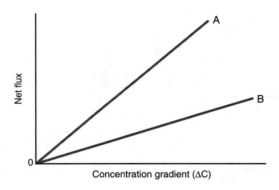

FIGURE 4.1

34. On Figure 4.1, label which of the lines (A or B) indicates lower permeability of the cell membrane and which indicates higher permeability. Explain your answer.

Clinical Question

35. Donald has smoked two packs of cigarettes per day for 37 years and has been diagnosed with emphysema. Emphysema is characterized by the destruction of alveolar cells of the lungs, which is where the gases in the lungs are exchanged with the gases in the blood. At the alveoli, oxygen diffuses from the lungs into the red blood cells where it is transported to the cells of the body, and carbon dioxide diffuses from the blood into the lungs to be exhaled. As the alveoli of the lungs become inflamed, gas exchange becomes more difficult. Explain why.

Challenge Question

36. A cell contains a 15.0 mM concentration of Na^+ and the extracellular fluid has a 140 mM concentration of Na^+. Assuming the membrane is permeable to Na^+, in which direction(s) will Na^+ flux occur? In which direction(s) will a net flux occur?

Concept Map

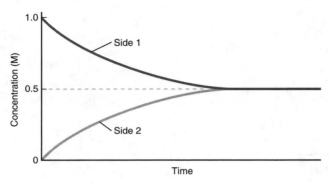

FIGURE 4.2

37. Figure 4.2 is the rate of diffusion of a molecule across an epithelial membrane. What would this graph look like if the surface area of the membrane were reduced? Explain your answer.

SIMPLE DIFFUSION: PASSIVE TRANSPORT THROUGH THE LIPID BILAYER

Matching

38. In the list below, indicate whether the statement describes higher permeability (HP) or lower permeability (LP) conditions.

   a. _____ a small lipid-soluble molecule versus a small non-lipid-soluble molecule

   b. _____ a very warm temperature versus a colder temperature

   c. _____ a thick epithelial layer that is many cell layers thick versus an epithelial layer that is a single layer thick

   d. _____ a large, irregularly shaped molecule versus a small, regularly shaped molecule

Short Answer

Answer the following questions in 1–4 sentences.

39. Define *simple diffusion* and briefly describe the four factors that affect membrane permeability in simple diffusion.

40. Explain why substances such as fatty acids, steroid hormones, and vitamin E are able to diffuse through the lipid bilayer, while many other substances must use different transport mechanisms.

41. Assuming all factors are equal, what will have the strongest influence on membrane permeability?

Labeling

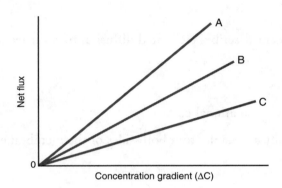

FIGURE 4.3

42. Refer to Figure 4.3. Line B represents the normal permeability of an epithelial tissue. a) Which line represents the permeability of an epithelial tissue that had its surface area reduced by one-half? b) Which line represents the permeability of very small molecules across the epithelial tissue? c) Which line represents the permeability of larger, irregularly shaped molecules across the epithelial tissue? Briefly state your reason for each answer.

Clinical Question

43. Many drugs (such as those found in birth control pills) are able to make their way into the cells more effectively because of their chemical composition. Predict the chemical nature of these drugs.

Challenge Question

44. While studying for a physiology test, your study partner says, "I understand diffusion! Individual molecules always move down their concentration gradient, and that is how diffusion takes place." Is she right? Explain.

FACILITATED DIFFUSION: PASSIVE TRANSPORT THROUGH MEMBRANE PROTEINS

Matching

45. In the list below, indicate whether the statement describes facilitated diffusion by a carrier (CR) or a channel (CH) protein.

a. _____ uses pores to transport substances

b. _____ transports substances due to a conformational change

c. _____ has binding sites that are generally accessible from both sides of the membrane at the same time

Completion

Fill in the blanks to complete the following narrative.

46. Facilitated diffusion involves two types of transport proteins : **(a)** and channels. **(a)** transport substances by binding to molecules and transporting them to the other side of the membrane by means of a **(b)** change. Channels have **(c)** that extend from one side of the membrane to the other. In facilitated diffusion, membrane permeability is determined by the **(d)** rate of individual carriers or channels, and the **(e)** of carriers or channels in the membrane.

a. _____   d. _____

b. _____   e. _____

c. _____

Short Answer

Answer the following questions in 1–4 sentences.

47. Describe how carrier proteins operate.

48. Explain the importance of facilitated diffusion.

Multiple Choice

Select the best answer from the choices given.

49. Ion channel proteins typically show which of the following characteristics?
   a. lower transport rates than pumps
   b. movement of molecules up the concentration gradient
   c. active transport
   d. energy is required
   e. passive transport

50. Carrier proteins typically show which of the following characteristics?
   a. active transport
   b. higher transport rates than ion channels
   c. no net flux occurs across the membrane
   d. saturation
   e. no transport protein required

51. Which of the following is a distinguishing characteristic between facilitated diffusion and simple diffusion?
   a. In simple diffusion, molecules pass through the lipid bilayer; in facilitated diffusion, they pass through a protein.
   b. In simple diffusion, molecules move up their concentration gradient; in facilitated diffusion, they move down their concentration gradient.
   c. In simple diffusion, hydrophilic molecules cross the membrane; in facilitated diffusion, hydrophobic molecules cross the membrane.
   d. In simple diffusion, active transport is used; in facilitated diffusion, it is not.
   e. In simple diffusion, energy is not required; in facilitated diffusion, energy is required.

52. Which of the following does not determine membrane permeability in facilitated diffusion?
   a. concentration gradient
   b. temperature
   c. size of the molecules
   d. number of carriers or channels on the membrane
   e. energy available to the cell

True/False

Label the following statements as true (T) or false (F). If false, change the statement to make it true.

53. _____ Facilitated diffusion requires a carrier or channel protein.

54. _____ Channel proteins are open at both ends at the same time.

55. _____ Facilitated diffusion transports substances up their concentration gradient.

56. _____ Hydrophobic substances are generally transported by facilitated diffusion.

57. _____ Both channels and carriers are usually specific for the substances that they transport.

Sequencing

58. Place the following events of facilitated transport using carrier proteins into the proper sequence.

    a. Carrier undergoes a conformational change.
    b. Molecule binds to binding site on carrier.
    c. The molecule is free to be released.
    d. Binding site on the other side of the membrane is exposed.

    Sequence: _____

Clinical Question

59. A 25-year-old man is brought into the emergency room. The patient had dined at a local seafood restaurant where he ate shrimp cocktail and steamed clams and, after dinner, he noticed a tingling sensation that affected his mouth and lips and then spread to his neck and face. The patient also reported numbness and difficulty walking in a coordinated fashion. The emergency room physician immediately recognized this as paralytic shellfish poisoning, a condition caused by saxitoxin. Saxitoxin is a neurotoxin (produced by particular marine microorganisms) that blocks the ability of human nerve cells to transport Na^+ into the cell. This inhibits nerve impulses, which may cause tingling as well as muscular paralysis. Describe the form of transport that is used by human nerve cells to gain Na^+, and how saxitoxin effects this form of transport, thus causing the symptoms described above.

Challenge Question

60. You observe a cell transporting substances across its membrane. The following are determined: a) the cell uses proteins to transport the substance, b) the substance travels down its concentration gradient, and c) the cell has binding sites that are accessible on both sides of the membrane available at the same time. Which form of transport is the cell using? Explain.

Concept Maps

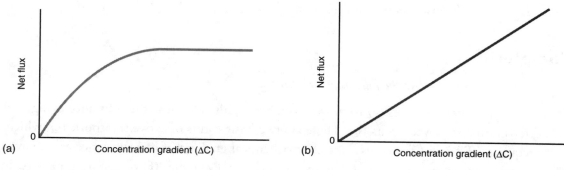

FIGURE 4.4

61. One of these graphs represents simple diffusion and the other represents facilitated diffusion. Explain whether Figure 4.4 a or b represents facilitated diffusion. How can you tell?

62. On the concept map below, fill in the boxes that represent the events of facilitated transport of glucose using a carrier.

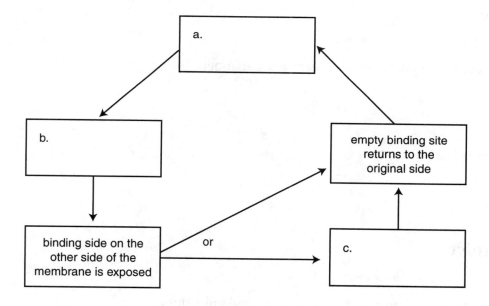

ACTIVE TRANSPORT

Matching

63. In the list below, indicate if each phrase describes primary active transport (PAT) or secondary active transport (SAT).

a. _____ Transport of one substance is coupled to the transport of another.

b. _____ Glucose can be transported this way.

c. _____ ATP is the primary energy source for transport.

d. _____ Transports Na^+ and K^+ in a 3/2 ratio.

Completion

Fill in the blanks to complete the following narrative.

64. Active transport requires **(a)** to move substances. This is because the substance being transported is moved up its **(b)**. There are two basic forms of active transport: **(c)**, which requires ATP, and **(d)** that uses the electrochemical gradient of one substance as a source of **(e)** to drive the active transport of another. **(d)** may involve either **(f)** or countertransport. In countertransport, two substances are moved in the **(g)** direction, whereas in **(f)**, two substances are moved in the **(h)** direction.

a. _____   e. _____

b. _____   f. _____

c. _____   g. _____

d. _____   h. _____

Short Answer

Answer the following questions in 1–4 sentences.

65. Distinguish between primary and secondary active transport.

66. Why do cells leak substances?

Multiple Choice

Select the best answer from the choices given.

67. Which of the following transport processes moves molecules through the lipid bilayer?

a. simple diffusion
b. facilitated diffusion with channels
c. facilitated diffusion with carriers
d. primary active transport
e. secondary active transport

68. Which of the following transport processes uses energy to transport two molecules in opposite directions?

a. simple diffusion
b. facilitated diffusion with channels
c. facilitated diffusion with carriers
d. primary active transport
e. secondary active transport

69. Which of the following transport processes uses no energy and is open at both ends of the membrane?

  a. simple diffusion
  b. facilitated diffusion with channels
  c. facilitated diffusion with carriers
  d. primary active transport
  e. secondary active transport

70. Which of the following is a characteristic of the Na^+/K^+ pump?

  a. It uses simple diffusion.
  b. No energy is necessary to operate the pump.
  c. It transports three Na^+ ions out of the cell and transports two K^+ ions into the cell.
  d. It binds Na^+ and K^+ nonselectively.
  e. It helps to maintain equal concentrations of Na^+ and K^+ on either side of the cell membrane.

71. A cell has an intracellular concentration of amino acids of 8.0 mM and 3.0 mM concentration on the outside of the cell. Which of the following mechanisms does it use to obtain more amino acids?

  a. simple diffusion
  b. facilitated diffusion with channels
  c. facilitated diffusion with carriers
  d. passive transport
  e. secondary active transport

72. Which of the following transport processes counteracts the leaking of Na^+ and K^+?

  a. simple diffusion
  b. facilitated diffusion with channels
  c. facilitated diffusion with carriers
  d. primary active transport
  e. secondary active transport

True/False

Label the following statements as true (T) *or false* (F). *If false, change the statement to make it true.*

73. _____ The Na^+/K^+ pump does not require energy.

74. _____ During the sodium-proton exchange of Na^+ and H^+, Na^+ moves into the cell and H^+ moves out of the cell.

75. _____ Glucose can be transported by secondary active transport.

76. _____ Na^+ and K^+ are transported by primary active transport.

77. _____ Primary active transport is used when a substance needs to be transported down its concentration gradient.

Sequencing

78. Place the following events of primary active transport of the Na^+/K^+ pump in the proper sequence.

  a. The binding of three Na^+ triggers phosphorylation of the pump by ATP.
  b. Intracellular Na^+ binds to the pump protein.

c. Extracellular K^+ binds to the pump protein, which triggers the release of the phosphate group.

d. K^+ is released to the inside of the cell.

e. Protein returns to its original conformation.

f. A conformational change in the protein releases Na^+ to the extracellular fluid.

Sequence: _____

Challenge Questions

79. Calcium is an important ion necessary for muscle contractions. It is stored in the endoplasmic reticulum (called the sarcoplasmic reticulum) of muscle cells where it is in high concentration in relation to the intracellular fluid. Explain how the muscle cell is able to concentrate calcium in an organelle when the concentration of calcium in the intracellular fluid is so low.

80. If the primary active transport pumps in a cell were to fail, what would eventually happen to the concentrations of Na^+ and K^+ on either side of the membrane?

81. How can you tell whether a substance is being transported actively or passively?

82. Explain the mechanism that allows intestinal cells to obtain glucose.

Concept Map

83. Fill in the blanks in the following concept map of the various transport processes into and out of cells.

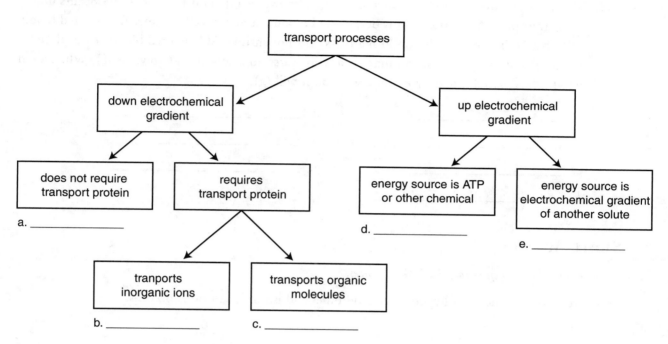

OSMOSIS: PASSIVE TRANSPORT OF WATER ACROSS MEMBRANES

Matching

84. Match the following list of words with their definitions below: osmolarity (O), iso-osmotic (IO), hypo-osmotic (HPO), hyperosmotic (HPR), tonicity (T), isotonic (I), hypotonic (HOT), hypertonic (HPT). Note that designations are relative to a cell containing 300 mOsm solutes, which are assumed to be impermeant. Conditions refer to what occurs at steady state.

a. _____ concentration of impermeant solutes relative to intracellular fluid

b. _____ total concentration of permeant and impermeant solutes

c. _____ greater than 300 mOsm of impermeant solutes

d. _____ less than 300 mOsm of permeant and impermeant solutes

e. _____ 300 mOsm (impermeant solutes)

f. _____ 300 mOsm of permeant and impermeant solutes

g. _____ greater than 300 mOsm of permeant and impermeant solutes

h. _____ less than 300 mOsm (impermeant solutes)

Completion

Fill in the blanks to complete the following narrative.

85. When water moves across a cell membrane it is known as **(a)**. This process always occurs due to **(b)** transport. A solution's **(c)** is determined by how it affects cell volume. When a red blood cell is placed in a/n **(d)** solution, it neither swells nor shrinks. When a red blood cell is placed in a/n **(e)** solution it swells, and may eventually burst, in a condition known as **(f)**. When a red blood cell is placed into a hypertonic solution it will **(g)**.

a. _____   e. _____

b. _____   f. _____

c. _____   g. _____

d. _____

Short Answer

Answer the following questions in 1–4 sentences.

86. Describe the effects of hypertonic, hypotonic, and isotonic solutions on cells.

87. Define *osmosis*.

Multiple Choice

Select the best answer from the choices given.

88. Which of the following sodium chloride solutions would cause a red blood cell to shrink?
    a. 50 mOsm   c. 200 mOsm   e. 400 mOsm
    b. 100 mOsm   d. 300 mOsm

89. Which of the following sodium chloride solutions would cause red blood cells to swell?
    a. 50 mOsm   c. 350 mOsm   e. 400 mOsm
    b. 300 mOsm   d. 375 mOsm

90. When a solution dehydrates a cell, what can we say about the osmolarity of the solution?
    a. It is hypotonic.   d. It is hypertonic.
    b. It is isotonic.   e. It is iso-osmotic relative to the ICF.
    c. It is hypo-osmotic relative to the ICF.

91. Which of the following sodium chloride solutions is iso-osmotic relative to intracellular fluid in the body?

    a. 50 mOsm
    b. 100 mOsm
    c. 200 mOsm
    d. 300 mOsm
    e. 400 mOsm

True/False

Label the following statements as true (T) *or false* (F). *If false, change the statement to make it true.*

92. _____ Osmotic pressure increases as the osmolarity increases.

93. _____ Water moves from areas that are hyperosmotic to areas that are hypo-osmotic.

94. _____ Water transport is always passive.

Clinical Question

95. A child is admitted to the hospital after a severe case of vomiting. After careful analysis, it is determined that the solute concentration of the child's blood is 300 mOsm. a) Is the child's blood hyperosmotic, hypo-osmotic, or iso-osmotic relative to normal blood? b) What do these findings tell you about the solute composition of the vomit?

Challenge Questions

96. Explain why a 300 mOsm intravenous bag of glucose has approximately the same osmolarity as a 150 mOsm intravenous bag of sodium chloride (NaCl).

97. Solution A and B are separated by a semipermeable membrane. Over time, the level of fluid on side B increases and the level of fluid on side A decreases. Which solution initially had the higher concentration of solutes?

Concept Map

98. Draw arrows below that show net water movement through cells when placed in hypertonic, isotonic, and hypotonic solutions.

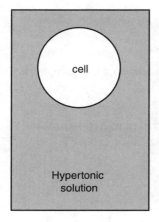

Hypertonic
solution

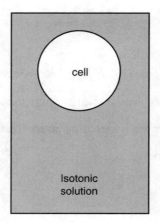

Isotonic
solution

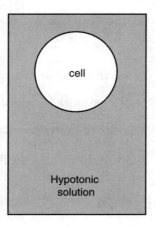

Hypotonic
solution

MOVEMENT OF MOLECULES ACROSS TWO MEMBRANES: EPITHELIAL TRANSPORT

Matching

For this question assume that the epithelial cells are the kind that absorb nutrients in the intestines.

99. In the list below, indicate whether the statement describes the apical membrane (AM) or the basolateral membrane (BM).

a. _____ is closest to the lumen

b. _____ exchanges material with the blood

c. _____ has sodium leak channels

d. _____ has K^+ leak channels

e. _____ has Na^+/K^+ pumps

Completion

Fill in the blanks to complete the following narrative.

100. Epithelial tissue forms barriers between the **(a)** and **(b)** environments. The border of the cell that faces the lumen is known as the **(c)**, while the portion of the cell that rests on the basement membrane is known as the **(d)**. **(e)** and secretion are accomplished across certain **(f)** tissue. This occurs because these cells are **(g)**.

a. _____

b. _____

c. _____

d. _____

e. _____

f. _____

g. _____

Short Answer

Answer the following question in 1–4 sentences.

101. Why is water transport across epithelia considered "secondary to" solute transport?

Multiple Choice

Select the best answer from the choices given.

102. During glucose absorption in the intestines, which of the following is transported in the same direction as glucose?

a. Ca^{++} c. urea   e. Cl^-

b. Na^+ d. K^+

103. In the absorptive intestinal epithelia, which of the following contains Na^+ leak channels?

a. basolateral membrane   d. interstitial spaces

b. apical membrane   e. tight junctions

c. basement membrane

104. Which of the following contains Na^+/K^+ pumps in intestinal epithelial cells?

a. basolateral membrane   d. interstitial spaces

b. apical membrane   e. tight junctions

c. gap junctions

True/False

Label the following statements as true (T) *or false* (F). *If false, change the statement to make it true.*

105. _____ In absorptive intestinal epithelial tissues, K^+ leak channels are located along the basolateral membrane.

106. _____ Glucose is moved into intestinal epithelial cells by passive transport.

107. _____ Water flows across epithelial tissue by osmosis.

108. _____ In absorptive intestinal epithelial tissues, Na^+ leak channels exist in the apical membrane.

109. _____ Gap junctions occur between all epithelial cells.

110. _____ In epithelial tissues, water is moved up the osmotic gradient.

Labeling

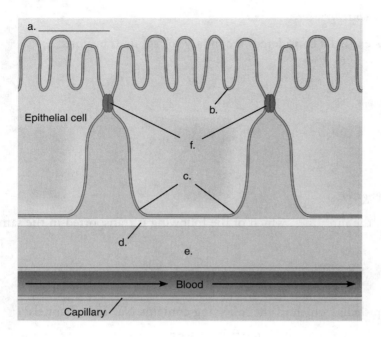

a. _____

Epithelial cell

b.

f.

c.

d.

e.

Blood

Capillary

FIGURE 4.5

111. In the space below, identify the structures (a–f) in Figure 4.5, and describe their functions.

Sequencing

112. Place the following events of epithelial absorption of water in the proper sequence.

    a. Osmotic pressure gradient across epithelium exists.

    b. Pumps in the basolateral membrane actively transport Na^+ into the interstitial fluid, and Cl^- follows.

    c. Water flows from the lumen to the interstitial space.

    d. Solute concentration of the interstitial fluid rises.

    e. Apical Na^+ ion channel opens, and Na^+ enters cell.

    Sequence: _____

Clinical Question

113. You are in a lifeboat after your sailboat capsized at sea. After three days without any water you decide to drink some seawater. Is this a good idea? Explain.

Challenge Question

114. Why do you suppose it is important for epithelial cells to have tight junctions between them?

Concept Map

115. Fill in the blanks in this chart of transport of water across an epithelial membrane.

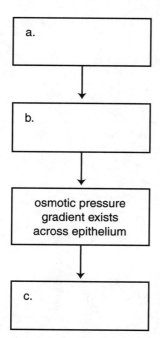

a.

b.

osmotic pressure
gradient exists
across epithelium

c.

5 Chemical Messengers and the Endocrine System

Objectives

We recommend that you review the **Objectives** for this chapter, found on page 131 of *Principles of Human Physiology*. The **Objectives** outline what you should know from each chapter.

Key Terms

additive
adenylate cyclase
adrenal cortex
adrenal gland
adrenal medulla
adrenocorticoid
affinity
agonist
amine
antagonism
antagonist
autocrine
calmodulin
cascade
catecholamine
channel-linked receptor
circadian rhythm
covalent modulation
cytokine
eicosanoid
endocrine gland
enzyme-linked receptor

G protein
G protein-linked receptor
G protein-regulated enzyme
G protein-regulated ion channel
glucocorticoid
half-life
hormone
hypothalamic-pituitary portal system
hypothalamus
ligand-gated channel
lipophobic
mineralocorticoid
neurohormone
neuron
neurotransmitter
pancreas
paracrine
parathyroid gland
peptide
permissiveness

phosphatidyl inositol
pineal gland
pituitary gland - anterior lobe
pituitary gland - posterior lobe
postsynaptic cell
primary endocrine organ
protein kinase
receptor
second messenger
secondary endocrine organ
secretion
secretory cell
sex hormone
signal transduction mechanism
steroid
synaptic signaling
synergistic
target cell
thymus
thyroid gland
tropic hormone

INTERCELLULAR COMMUNICATION

Completion

Fill in the blanks to complete the following narrative, which describes the general process of cellular communication using chemical messengers.

1. A cell using a chemical method of communication would initiate the process by **(a)** a chemical into the interstitial fluid. Another cell will then respond to that chemical message; this cell is

called the **(b)** cell. This cell is able to respond to the chemical message because it contains **(c)** that are able to specifically bind that chemical. Once stimulated by a chemical message, cells can respond to the message in a variety of ways, which are referred to as **(d)**. The strength of the **(b)** cell response depends on the number of **(c)** to which the chemical messenger is bound. This number depends on the concentration of **(e)** in the interstitial fluid and the concentration of **(c)** on the responding cell.

a. _____   d. _____

b. _____   e. _____

c. _____

Multiple Choice

Select the best answer from the choices given.

2. A molecule that binds reversibly to a receptor site on a protein is a _____.
   a. ligand   c. connexin   e. cholesterol molecule
   b. receptor   d. connexon

3. Which of the following is **not** true of gap junctions?
   a. They allow direct cell-to-cell communication.
   b. They are essentially channels formed by connexons.
   c. They allow muscle cells to contract as a unit.
   d. They work by utilizing chemical messengers to signal adjacent cells.
   e. They are found in cardiac muscle cells, smooth muscle cells of blood vessels and the intestines, and in some glands and neurons.

Short Answer

Answer the following question in 1–4 sentences.

4. What is the difference between connexins and connexons?

Challenge Question

5. Why is it important for cells to be able to communicate with each other? List five examples of different physiologic situations in which cellular communication would be essential.

CHEMICAL MESSENGERS

Matching

6. Match the following definitions to the functional category of chemical messenger they best describe: paracrines (P), autocrines (A), cytokines (C), neurotransmitters (NT), hormones (H), and neurohormones (NH). Use each answer once.

a. _____ chemical messengers that are often secreted by white blood cells, are involved in the immune response, and include interleukins and interferons

b. _____ chemical messengers that are released from endocrine glands

c. _____ chemicals that communicate with neighboring cells

d. _____ chemical messengers secreted by neurosecretory cells

e. _____ chemical messengers that act on the cells that secreted them

f. _____ chemical messengers released from neurons that communicate via synaptic signaling

7. Match each of the following chemical messengers to its primary mode of transport within the body: most catecholamines (CA), paracrines (P), peptides and amines (except thyroid hormones) (P, A), autocrines (AU), most cytokines (CY), and steroids and thyroid hormones (S, T). Answers may be used more than once or not at all.

a. _____ simple diffusion through interstitial fluid

b. _____ transported in the blood bound to carrier proteins

c. _____ transported dissolved in blood

Multiple Choice

Select the best answer from the choices given.

8. Cells that release neurotransmitters are _____ and are called _____.

   a. neurons : postsynaptic cells   d. glands : neurosecretory cells

   b. neurons : presynaptic cells   e. glands : endocrine cells

   c. neurons : target cells

9. Which of the following chemical messengers is lipophilic?

   a. amino acid messengers

   b. catecholamines and most other amine messengers

   c. peptide messengers

   d. protein messengers

   e. eicosanoid messengers

10. Which of the following is **not** an example of an amine messenger?

   a. thyroid hormones   c. prostaglandins   e. epinephrine

   b. histamine   d. serotonin

11. Steroid hormones are derived from _____.

    a. arachadonic acid   c. a nucleic acid   e. an amino acid

    b. a fatty acid   d. cholesterol

12. Which of the following chemical messengers does **not** usually get to its target cell by diffusion?

    a. neurohormone   c. cytokine   e. paracrine messenger

    b. neurotransmitter   d. autocrine messenger

13. In the case of hydrophobic hormones, as the amount of hormone bound to target cell receptors increases, the amount of hormone _____.

    a. encased in secretory vesicles increases

    b. released from secretory vesicles increases

    c. released from secretory vesicles decreases

    d. released from carrier proteins in the blood increases

    e. released from carrier proteins in the blood decreases

14. Which of the following chemical messengers can be synthesized in advance and stored until needed?

    a. GABA   c. epinephrine   e. all of the above

    b. prostaglandins   d. a and c

15. Which of the following chemical messengers is **not** released from storage vesicles by exocytosis when it is needed?

    a. epinephrine   c. steroids   e. amino acid neurotransmitters

    b. norepinephrine   d. peptides

16. Which of the following enzymes is involved in the synthesis of prostaglandins?

    a. cyclooxygenase

    b. lipoxygenase

    c. dopa decarboxylase

    d. glutamic acid decarboxylase

    e. phenylethanolamine N-methyl transferase (PNMT)

17. Which of the following enzymes is involved **specifically** in the synthesis of epinephrine?

    a. cyclooxygenase

    b. lipoxygenase

    c. dopa decarboxylase

    d. glutamic acid decarboxylase

    e. phenylethanolamine N-methyl transferase (PNMT)

18. Which of the following enzymes begins the process of eicosanoid synthesis by catalyzing the release of arachadonic acid from membrane phospholipids?

    a. tyrosine ß-hydroxylase   c. PNMT   e. lipoxygenase

    b. dopa decarboxylase   d. phospholipase A_2

True/False

Label the following statements as true (T) *or false* (F). *If false, change the statement to make it true.*

19. _____ The term lipophilic refers to molecules that are lipid soluble, easily cross the plasma membrane, and are soluble in water.

20. _____ The majority of chemical messengers are polypeptides.

21. _____ Hormones travel to their target cells through the blood.

22. _____ Histamine is an example of an autocrine messenger.

23. _____ Cytokines can be paracrines, autocrines, or hormones.

24. _____ Neurohormones are secreted specifically by endocrine cells.

25. _____ Glutamate, aspartate, glycine, and gamma-amino butyric acid (GABA) are eicosanoid messengers.

26. _____ Glutamate and aspartate are released from vesicles by exocytosis when needed.

27. _____ Prostaglandins, leukotrienes, prostacyclins, and thromboxanes are all synthesized and released by cells on demand.

28. _____ Dopa decarboxylase is involved in the synthesis of dopamine, norepinephrine, and epinephrine.

29. _____ All carrier proteins are specific for particular hormones.

30. _____ Neurotransmitters diffuse through the interstitial fluid in the synapse to reach their target cells.

Completion

31. For each of the following chemical messengers, list the chemical from which it is derived and the chemical category into which it fits.

Chemical Messenger	Chemical from which it is directly derived	Chemical Category
Dopamine	a.	f.
Glycine	b.	g.
Leukotrienes	c.	h.
Glutamate	d.	i.
GABA	e.	j.

Labeling

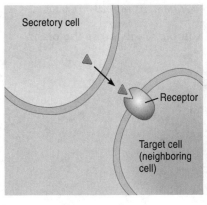

a. _____

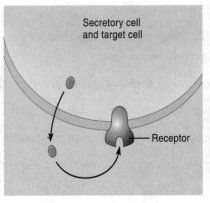

b. _____

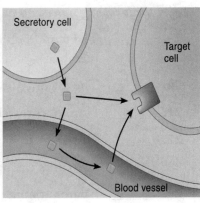

c. _____

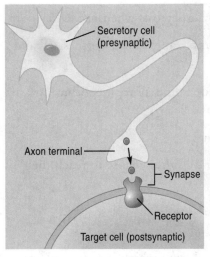

d. _____

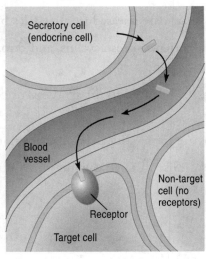

e. _____

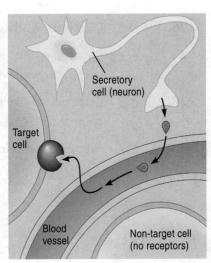

f. _____

FIGURE 5.1

32. Under each of the illustrations in Figure 5.1, indicate the functional category of chemical messenger depicted in the drawing.

Sequencing

33. Put the following terms in order.

a. synapse,   b. postsynaptic cell,   c. presynaptic cell

Sequence: _____

34. List the following chemicals in the order in which they are synthesized.

a. norepinephrine,   b. dopamine,   c. epinephrine,   d. tyrosine

Sequence: _____

Short Answer

Answer the following questions in 1–4 sentences.

35. What type(s) of cell or cells can be presynaptic cells? Postsynaptic cells?

36. What is meant by the biological half-life of a hormone? How long is the typical biological half-life of hydrophilic hormones? What is the typical biological half-life of hydrophobic hormones?

Challenge Questions

37. Since hormones travel in the blood to their target cells, they must come into contact with virtually every cell in the body. Why do they only affect specific target cells?

38. Why must hydrophobic chemical messengers be synthesized on demand?

39. Do chemical messengers such as paracrines and neurotransmitters act indefinitely when they are released from cells? Do they have an effect on cells throughout the body or just cells near their site of release? Explain your answer.

Clinical Questions

40. Physicians often treat allergy symptoms by giving the patient a prescription for an antihistamine. What symptoms would antihistamines help, and why? Do antihistamines cure the allergy?

41. You are a hematologist, and a patient of yours has a longer than normal blood clotting time. Tests show that the patient's clotting factors are all normal, but you discover that she produces a much lower than normal level of cyclooxygenase within her blood cells. Why might this affect her blood clotting process?

SIGNAL TRANSDUCTION MECHANISMS

Completion

Fill in the blanks to complete the following narrative.

42. Lipophilic chemical messengers bind to receptors located in the **(a)** or **(b)**. Binding of a lipophilic messenger to its receptor results in an alteration in the **(c)** of a specific protein or proteins. Lipophobic messengers bind to receptors located on the **(d)**. Binding of these messengers generally results in changes in the **(e)** of intracellular proteins. The duration of the response to lipophilic messengers is generally relatively **(f)**, while the duration of response to lipophobic receptors is relatively **(g)**.

a. _____   e. _____

b. _____   f. _____

c. _____   g. _____

d. _____

Matching

43. Match the following substances to the listed functions: calcium (C), diacylglycerol (D), tyrosine kinase (TK), adenylate cyclase (AC), phospholipase C (PC), and cyclic adenosine monophosphate (cAMP). Some functions will have more than one answer.

a. _____ enzyme-linked receptor

b. _____ second messenger

c. _____ enzyme that catalyzes the formation of a second messenger

Multiple Choice

Select the best answer from the choices given.

44. Which of the following is **not** true of target cell receptors?

    a. Each type of receptor generally binds only one messenger or class of messengers.
    b. A single messenger can often bind to more than one type of receptor.
    c. The affinity of different receptors for a single messenger often varies.
    d. A single target cell may have receptors for more than one type of messenger.
    e. Target cell receptors will be less likely to bind a messenger for which they have a greater affinity.

45. The strength of binding between a messenger and its receptor is termed _____.

    a. specificity
    b. saturation
    c. agonistic binding
    d. antagonistic binding
    e. affinity

46. Down-regulation of receptors tends to occur _____.

    a. when the specificity of target cell receptors for messenger increases
    b. when the specificity of target cell receptors for messenger decreases
    c. when messenger concentration is higher than normal for a prolonged period of time
    d. when messenger concentration is lower than normal for a short period of time
    e. more than one of the above is correct

47. The magnitude of a target cell's response to a chemical messenger depends on the messenger's concentration, the number of target cell receptors, and _____.

    a. the affinity of the receptors for the messenger
    b. the specificity of the receptors for the messenger
    c. up-regulation
    d. down-regulation
    e. the degree of saturation of the receptors

48. The region of the DNA to which a lipophilic hormone-receptor complex binds is called a _____.

    a. G protein
    b. second messenger
    c. first messenger
    d. hormone response element
    e. channel-linked receptor

49. Once the hormone-receptor complex binds to the area indicated in Question 48, the response that occurs is:

    a. activation or inactivation of a gene, which will increase or decrease the synthesis of a specific protein or proteins
    b. activation or inactivation of a gene, which will increase or decrease the synthesis of all proteins within the cell
    c. activation or inactivation of a gene, which will directly activate or inactivate an existing protein or proteins within the cell
    d. direct activation or inactivation of a G protein, which will activate or inactivate a protein or proteins within the cell
    e. direct activation or inactivation of a second messenger, which will activate or inactivate a protein or proteins within the cell

50. Which of the following is **not** a type of receptor to which extracellular lipophobic messengers normally bind?

a. channel-linked receptors
b. nuclear receptors
c. enzyme-linked receptors
d. G protein-linked receptors
e. receptors associated with ligand-gated channels

51. Which subunit of a G protein most commonly activates or inactivates enzymes that catalyze the synthesis of second messengers?

a. alpha
b. beta
c. delta
d. gamma
e. theta

52. Which of the following substances is the second messenger used most often by human cells?

a. ATP
b. G proteins
c. GTP
d. cAMP
e. cGMP

53. The ability of small changes in the concentration of chemical messenger to cause large responses in target cells is called _____.

a. the phosphatidyl inositol system
b. signal transduction
c. protein phosphorylation
d. hormone-mediated response
e. signal amplification

True/False

Label the following statements as true (T) *or false* (F). *If false, change the statement to make it true.*

54. _____ Binding of a chemical messenger to a target cell receptor does not always trigger a response in the target cell.

55. _____ The presence of an antagonist will increase the likelihood that a chemical messenger will bind to the target cell and produce a response.

56. _____ Up-regulation refers to an increase in the number of receptors on a target cell.

57. _____ Alpha$_1$ receptors have a greater affinity for norepinephrine than for epinephrine.

58. _____ Down-regulation makes a target cell more responsive to a chemical messenger.

59. _____ The effects of lipophilic messengers usually occur quite rapidly.

60. _____ An intracellular messenger produced by the binding of an extracellular messenger to a receptor is called a second messenger.

61. _____ Enzyme-linked receptors function as both enzymes and G proteins.

62. _____ Calcium exerts its effect as a second messenger by binding to a nuclear protein kinase.

Short Answer

Answer the following questions in 1–4 sentences.

63. Define *specificity*.

64. What is meant by *cascade*, as it applies to signal amplification?

65. Why don't G proteins stay active very long?

Labeling

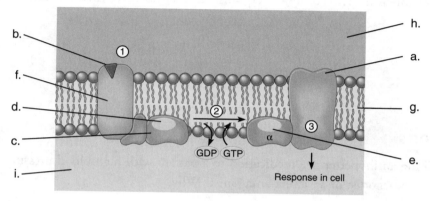

FIGURE 5.2

66. In the space below, identify the structures (a–i) in Figure 5.2. Which of the events depicted in the figure directly activates the G protein?

Sequencing

67. From the list of statements below, select those statements that are part of the process by which enzyme-linked receptors exert their effects, and put them in their proper order.

a. Target cell response occurs.
b. Enzyme is activated.
c. Enzyme is inactivated.
d. Messenger binds to the receptor located on the cytosolic side of the plasma membrane.
e. Messenger binds to the outer surface of the receptor located in the plasma membrane.
f. Binding of the messenger changes the conformation of the receptor.
g. Enzyme (if tyrosine kinase) catalyzes phosphorylation of an extracellular protein.
h. Enzyme (if tyrosine kinase) catalyzes phosphorylation of an intracellular protein.

Sequence: _____

Challenge Questions

68. How does the magnitude of a target cell's response relate to the concentration of messenger present? Will this response continue indefinitely if the concentration of messenger continues to increase?

69. Define a ligand-gated channel. Compare and contrast fast ligand-gated ion channels and slow ligand-gated ion channels in terms of how they work, and the speed of their response to a chemical messenger.

Clinical Questions

70. If you are prescribing antihypertensive medication to a patient with high blood pressure, would you prescribe an alpha-agonist or an alpha-antagonist? Why?

71. A patient of yours has been ingesting large amounts of calcium supplements over the past month, and has come to you complaining of weakness, lethargy, and fatigue. Blood work shows that she is hypercalcemic. In general cell signaling terms, why might having a higher than normal calcium level in her blood result in her physical symptoms?

72. A patient of yours, who has been complaining of a racing heart beat and difficulty sleeping, is a college student who has been drinking 10–12 cups of coffee per day for the past week in order to maintain the energy level he needed to complete a lengthy term paper. You tell him that his symptoms are probably due to an excessive caffeine intake, and should resolve if he stops drinking coffee and other caffeinated beverages. The student is a premed biology major, and he asks you to explain what caffeine does to the body at the cellular level. How would you respond?

Concept Maps

73. Fill in the steps in the following concept map, which illustrates the mechanism by which cAMP works as a second messenger.

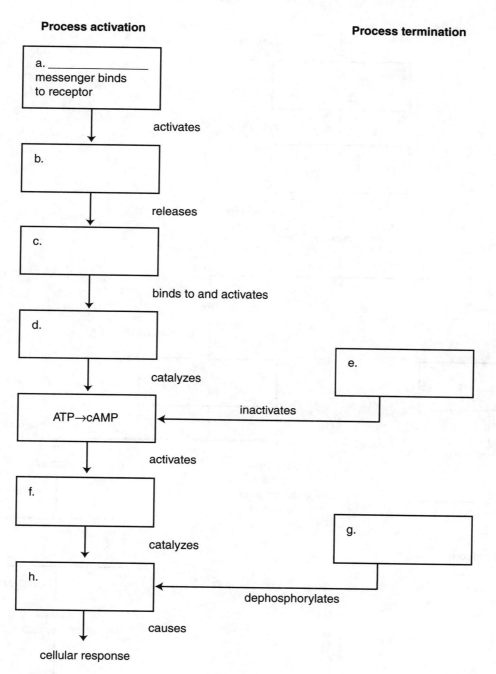

74. Fill in the missing steps in the following concept map, which illustrates the events that occur during signal transduction via the phosphatidyl inositol system.

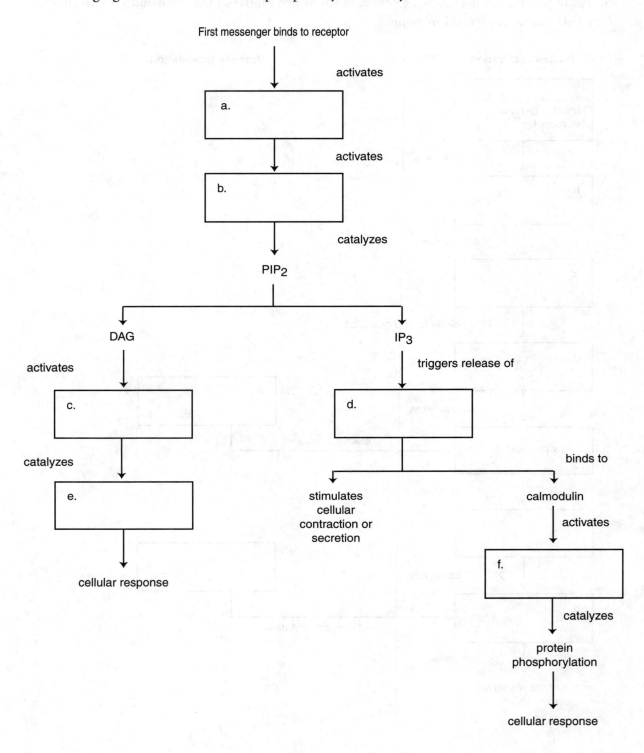

LONG-DISTANCE COMMUNICATION VIA THE NERVOUS AND ENDOCRINE SYSTEMS

Short Answer

Answer the following questions in 1–4 sentences.

75. What is the basic difference between the way most neurotransmitters produce responses in their target cells and the mechanisms used by hormones?

76. Compare examples of typical activities in the body that the nervous system would have primary control over with those that would typically be controlled by the endocrine system.

77. Compare the activities of the nervous and endocrine systems in terms of the speed with which signals are transmitted and the duration of the effect of the signals.

ENDOCRINE GLANDS

Matching

78. Match each hormone in the following list to its primary function: corticotropin releasing hormone (CRH), melatonin (M), T_3 and T_4 (T_3 and T_4), insulin (I), oxytocin (O), thyroid stimulating hormone (TSH), and epinephrine (E).

    a. _____ lowers blood glucose levels

    b. _____ stimulates the "fight-or-flight" response

    c. _____ regulates circadian rhythms

    d. _____ stimulates the release of ACTH

    e. _____ stimulates uterine contractions

    f. _____ increase basal metabolic rate

    g. _____ stimulates the secretion of thyroid hormones

Labeling

79. Label the primary and secondary endocrine organs on Figure. 5.3

Primary Endocrine Organs

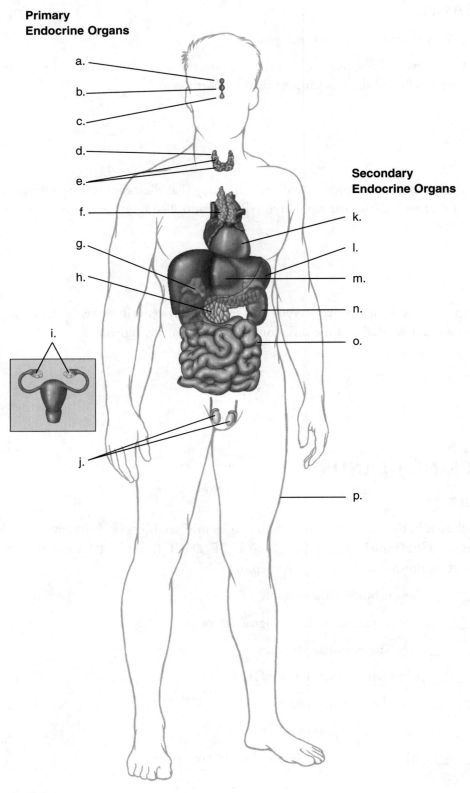

a.
b.
c.
d.
e.
f.
g.
h.
i.
j.

Secondary Endocrine Organs

k.
l.
m.
n.
o.
p.

FIGURE 5.3

True/False

Label the following statements as true (T) *or false* (F). *If false, change the statement to make it true.*

80. _____ Epinephrine is secreted by the posterior pituitary gland.

81. _____ Follicle stimulating hormone (FSH) is secreted by the ovaries.

82. _____ Calcitonin is secreted by the thyroid gland.

83. _____ Antidiuretic hormone (ADH) is secreted by the hypothalamus.

84. _____ Glucagon is secreted by the adrenal cortex.

85. _____ Most of the hypothalamic and anterior pituitary hormones are peptides.

86. _____ The inhibition of a hypothalamic tropic hormone by the anterior pituitary hormone whose secretion it stimulates is called long loop negative feedback.

87. _____ Mineralocorticoids are produced by cells in the zona glomerulosa of the adrenal cortex.

Multiple Choice

Select the best answer from the choices given.

88. Which of the following primary endocrine organs would be considered structurally and functionally separate glands?

    a. adrenal glands and the kidneys

    b. anterior and posterior pituitary glands

    c. adrenal cortex and adrenal medulla

    d. individual parathyroid glands

    e. a and b

    f. b and c

89. The hypothalamic-pituitary portal system is a system of _____ that interconnects the _____.

    a. neurosecretory cells : hypothalamus and anterior pituitary gland

    b. neurosecretory cells : hypothalamus and posterior pituitary gland

    c. capillaries : hypothalamus and anterior pituitary gland

    d. capillaries : hypothalamus and posterior pituitary gland

    e. capillaries : anterior and posterior pituitary glands

90. A tropic hormone is _____.

    a. a hormone found only in people who live in warm climates

    b. a hormone that acts only on the hypothalamus

    c. the last hormone secreted in a pathway

    d. a hormone that regulates the secretion of other hormones

    e. a hormone secreted by the gonads

91. Which of the following hormones is released in direct response to thyrotropin releasing hormone?

    a. thyroid stimulating hormone

    b. thyroid hormone

    c. parathyroid hormone

    d. calcium

    e. luteinizing hormone

92. Posterior pituitary gland hormones _____.

   a. are synthesized by the anterior pituitary gland and transported to the posterior pituitary gland through portal capillaries
   b. are synthesized by neurons within the hypothalamus and travel within secretory vesicles to the neural endings in the posterior pituitary gland
   c. are synthesized by neurons within the hypothalamus and travel to the posterior pituitary through a portal capillary system
   d. are synthesized by cells within the posterior pituitary gland
   e. are synthesized by endocrine cells within the hypothalamus and transported to the posterior pituitary through a portal capillary system

93. Hormones are secreted _____.

   a. directly onto an external or internal surface of the body
   b. directly into the blood
   c. directly into the interstitial fluid from which they diffuse into the blood
   d. directly onto cellular receptors
   e. only by primary endocrine glands

94. Which of the following cell types of the pancreas secretes insulin?

   a. alpha cells   c. delta cells   e. somatostatin cells
   b. beta cells   d. somatomedin cells

95. Which of the following statements is true regarding secondary endocrine organs?

   a. Their primary purpose is to secrete hormones.
   b. In addition to their primary purpose, they also secrete hormones.
   c. They secrete only tropic hormones.
   d. They secrete only androgens and estrogens.
   e. They are present only after puberty.

96. Which of the following hormones is secreted by the kidneys?

   a. atrial natriuretic peptide   c. somatomedins   e. erythropoietin
   b. gastrin   d. secretin

Sequencing

97. List the following in the order in which they occur in a stimulatory tropic hormone pathway.

   a. Hypothalamic tropic hormone travels through the portal vein in the infundibulum.
   b. Anterior pituitary hormone causes a hormone to be released from another endocrine gland.
   c. Hypothalamic hormone is secreted into capillaries within the hypothalamus.
   d. Hypothalamic hormone enters capillary bed in the anterior pituitary gland.
   e. Anterior pituitary hormone is secreted into the blood.

   Sequence: _____

Completion

98. Complete the following table, listing the hormones secreted by the anterior and posterior pituitary glands, the hypothalamic tropic hormones that affect the release of anterior pituitary hormones, whether the effect of the tropic hormone is stimulatory or inhibitory, and the type of stimulus that causes the release of posterior pituitary hormones. Put an * by the anterior pituitary hormones that are tropic hormones.

Anterior Pituitary Hormone	Hypothalamic Tropic Hormone(s)	Stimulatory (+) or Inhibitory (-) Effect
Posterior Pituitary Hormone	**Release Stimulus**	

Challenge Questions

99. Why do hypothalamic tropic hormones have a greater effect than anterior pituitary tropic hormones?

100. Under what circumstances would the placenta be considered an endocrine gland, and why?

101. List all the hormones that come from primary or secondary endocrine organs that influence blood glucose levels, and those that influence blood calcium levels.

Clinical Questions

102. What symptoms would you expect to see in a child with an anterior pituitary lobe tumor resulting in the oversecretion of growth hormone?

103. A friend of yours has been diagnosed as having a tumor in the infundibulum, which is blocking the neuronal pathway between the hypothalamus and pituitary gland but is not affecting the hypothalamic-pituitary portal system. The release of what hormone or hormones will be adversely affected by this situation, and what types of symptoms might your friend experience?

104. What clinical symptoms might you expect to see in a person experiencing hypothyroidism (lower than normal secretion of thyroid hormones)?

Concept Map

105. Fill in the blanks in the following concept map depicting the mechanism by which glucocorticoid secretion is regulated. Use a (+) to indicate steps that are stimulatory and a (−) to indicate steps that are inhibitory. In the boxes, indicate the hormone released and the gland from which it comes. In the final box of the pathway, indicate the target cell responses. Also label the arrows indicating short loop and long loop negative feedback.

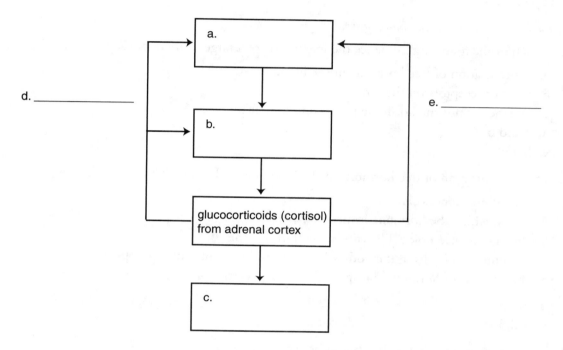

HORMONE ACTIONS AT THE TARGET CELL

Matching

106. Match the following statements to the term to which each best applies: hypersecretion (ER), hyposecretion (O), primary secretion disorder (PSD), secondary secretion disorder (SSD), antagonism (A), additive effect (AE), synergistic effect (SE), and permissiveness (P).

a. _____ Two or more hormones produce a similar response in the body; the net effect equals the sum of the individual effects.

b. _____ The effects of two or more hormones oppose each other.

c. _____ excessive secretion of a hormone

d. _____ insufficient secretion of a hormone

e. _____ abnormal secretion of a hormone that originates in the endocrine gland that secretes the hormone

f. _____ The presence of one hormone is needed in order for another hormone to exert its actions.

g. _____ abnormal secretion of a hormone that originates in the anterior pituitary or hypothalamus

h. _____ two or more hormones produce a similar response in the body; the net effect is greater than the sum of the individual effects

Multiple Choice

Select the best answer from the choices given.

107. Which of the following influence the magnitude of a target cell's response to a hormone?
    a. concentration of free hormone in the blood
    b. types of receptors on the target cell
    c. whether or not the hormone is a second messenger
    d. a and b
    e. b and c

108. The concentration of free hormone in the blood depends on which of the following?
    1. rate of hormone secretion
    2. rate at which the hormone is metabolized
    3. the rate of anaerobic ATP synthesis within the cells
    4. the number of cells in the body with active sodium-potassium pumps
    5. the amount of hormone transported bound to carrier proteins

    a. 1,2,3,4,5   c. 1,2,5   e. 2,4,5
    b. 1,3,5   d. 3,4,5

109. Neural signals directly regulate hormone secretion by the _____.
    a. hypothalamus, anterior pituitary gland, and adrenal cortex
    b. anterior pituitary, posterior pituitary, and adrenal cortex
    c. hypothalamus, anterior pituitary, and adrenal medulla
    d. hypothalamus, posterior pituitary, and adrenal medulla
    e. anterior pituitary, posterior pituitary, and adrenal medulla

110. Humoral signals that regulate hormone secretion include _____.
    a. ions, prostaglandins, and metabolites
    b. prostaglandins, metabolites, and minerals
    c. ions, vitamins, and minerals
    d. vitamins, metabolites, and minerals
    e. ions, hormones, and metabolites

111. The hormones transported in the blood bound to carrier molecules are _____.
    a. epinephrine and norepinephrine
    b. steroid and thyroid hormones
    c. ACTH and prolactin
    d. oxytocin and ADH
    e. peptide hormones and catecholamines

112. Which of the following is **not** true of hormone metabolism?

   a. Hormones that bind to receptors on target cells are often metabolized by the target cell itself.

   b. Hormones bound to membrane receptors can be internalized and degraded by lysosomal enzymes.

   c. Hormones can be metabolized by enzymes in the liver.

   d. Hormones are usually metabolized by enzymes in the kidneys.

   e. Hormones can be metabolized by enzymes in the blood.

113. The release of which of the following hormones is not directly affected by circadian rhythms?

   a. growth hormone releasing hormone

   b. corticotropin releasing hormone

   c. antidiuretic hormone

   d. ACTH

   e. prolactin

True/False

Label the following statements as true (T) *or false* (F). *If false, change the statement to make it true.*

114. _____ Hormones secreted at a relatively steady rate facilitate normal cellular processes, rather than "triggering" a target cell response.

115. _____ Many hormones are secreted according to a circadian rhythm.

116. _____ When hormones are transported in the blood bound to carrier proteins, the hormone binds to the receptor only while it is bound to the carrier protein.

117. _____ Steroids and thyroid hormones have a longer biological half-life than peptides and amines.

118. _____ A single hormone may have receptors on different types of cells.

Short Answer

Answer the following question in 1–4 sentences.

119. Name two hormones that have antagonistic functions to each other.

Completion

Fill in the blanks to complete the following narrative.

120. __(a)__ levels of __(b)__ ions in the blood stimulate cells in the adrenal __(c)__ to secrete aldosterone. Aldosterone stimulates the __(d)__ to secrete potassium ions which lowers the __(e)__ level of potassium.

    a. _____   d. _____

    b. _____   e. _____

    c. _____

Challenge Questions

121. Why can plasma levels of steroid and thyroid hormones remain elevated even when the rate of secretion of these hormones is at its normal resting level?

122. Explain why bronchioles will not dilate in response to epinephrine in the absence of thyroid hormones?

Clinical Questions

123. Explain what would happen to a person's thyroid hormone, TSH, and TRH levels if they were experiencing a thyroid disorder resulting from a primary hyposecretion.

124. Explain what would happen to a person's thyroid hormone, TSH, and TRH levels if they were experiencing a thyroid disorder resulting from a secondary hypersecretion that originated in the anterior pituitary gland.

6 Nerve Cells and Electrical Signaling

Objectives

We recommend that you review the **Objectives** for this chapter, found on page 170 of *Principles of Human Physiology*. The **Objectives** outline what you should know from each chapter.

Key Terms

action potential
activation gate
afferent
afferent neuron
after-hyperpolarization
all-or-none principle
autonomic nervous system
axon
axon hillock
axon terminal
cell body (soma)
central nervous system
collateral
commissure
conductance
convergence
current
dendrite
depolarization
divergence
effector organ
efferent
efferent neuron

electrotonic conduction
equilibrium potential
excitable cell
excitatory
ganglia (ganglion)
glial cell
graded potential
hyperpolarization
inactivation gate
inhibitory
innervate
interneuron
leak channel
ligand-gated channel
motor neuron
myelin
nerve
neuron
neurotransmitter
nodes of Ranvier
nuclei (nucleus)
Ohm's law
oligodendrocyte

pathway
peripheral nervous system
refractory period
    absolute refractory period
    relative refractory period
regenerative
repolarization
resistance
resting membrane potential
saltatory conduction
Schwann cell
sensory information
somatic nervous system
spatial summation
stimulus
sub-threshold
supra-threshold
temporal summation
threshold
tract
trigger zone
visceral information
voltage-gated channel

OVERVIEW OF THE NERVOUS SYSTEM

Matching

1. Match each of the following parts of the nervous system with the appropriate description below: afferent division (AD), central nervous system (CNS), effector organ (EO), efferent division (ED), peripheral nervous system (PNS).

   a. _____ consists of brain and spinal cord

   b. _____ composed of nerve cells that provide communication between the central nervous system and organs of the body

   c. _____ transmits information to the central nervous system

   d. _____ transmits information from the central nervous system

   e. _____ responds to the signals sent by the efferent division

   f. _____ communicates with internal organs, sweat glands, and blood vessels

Completion

Fill in the blanks to complete the following narrative.

2. The nervous system can be divided into two main parts: the **(a)**, composed of the **(b)** and spinal cord, and the peripheral nervous system. The peripheral nervous system consists of two divisions. The **(c)** division is composed of nerve cells that transmit information from the periphery to the **(d)**, while the **(e)** division transmits information from the central nervous system to the periphery. The efferent division is further subdivided into two main branches: the **(f)**, which communicates with skeletal muscles and the **(g)**, which communicates with smooth muscle, cardiac muscle, and **(h)**. The autonomic nervous system is divided into the sympathetic and **(i)** nervous systems.

   a. _____   f. _____

   b. _____   g. _____

   c. _____   h. _____

   d. _____   i. _____

   e. _____

Short Answer

Answer the following questions in 1–4 sentences.

3. Describe the role of motor neurons.

4. Describe the role of effector organs in the somatic and autonomic nervous systems.

Multiple Choice

Select the best answer from the choices given.

5. Which of the following regulates the functioning of the heart?

    a. enteric nervous system
    b. peripheral nervous system
    c. somatic nervous system
    d. afferent division
    e. autonomic nervous system

6. The optic nerve has axons that send information from the retina of the eye to the brain. Axons in the optic nerve are a component of which division of the nervous system?

    a. parasympathetic nervous system
    b. afferent division of the peripheral nervous system
    c. sympathetic nervous system
    d. efferent division of the peripheral nervous system
    e. somatic nervous system

7. Some neurons in the vagus nerve slow down the heart. These neurons are part of which nervous system?

    a. parasympathetic nervous system
    b. somatic nervous system
    c. central nervous system
    d. afferent division of the peripheral nervous system
    e. efferent division of the peripheral nervous system

8. Evan has a condition in which some neurons cannot communicate well with the skeletal muscles on his face and this causes his facial muscles to relax, giving his face a droopy look. Which structure(s) is/are **most likely** affected?

    a. sympathetic nerves
    b. brain
    c. enteric nervous system
    d. spinal cord
    e. somatic motor nerves

9. The body has a network of neurons that innervate the gastrointestinal tract and communicate with the autonomic nervous system. What is the name for this network of neurons?

    a. somatic nervous system
    b. enteric nervous system
    c. sympathetic division
    d. effector organ
    e. central nervous system

True/False

Label the following statements as true (T) *or false* (F). *If false, change the statement to make it true.*

10. _____ Visceral information is sent from internal organs to the brain.

11. _____ Sensory information is sent from the brain to sensory receptors.

12. _____ The peripheral nervous system is directly divided into the parasympathetic and sympathetic nervous systems.

13. _____ The autonomic nervous system is usually under involuntary control.

14. _____ Skeletal muscles are the effector organs of the somatic nervous system.

15. _____ Afferent neurons send signals to the brain and spinal cord.

Clinical Questions

16. Psychotropic drugs ("mood changers") alter the mental state and mood of an individual. Which part of the nervous system is likely affected to produce the psychotropic effect?

17. Dentists may use Lidocaine to block the transmission of pain during some potentially painful dental procedures. On which part of the nervous system does this drug operate to ease pain?

18. A physician diagnoses a 45-year-old man with high blood pressure (hypertension). She has determined that the cause of his disease is that his heart is contracting too forcefully. In addition, his blood vessels are being stimulated by neurons, causing them to constrict. Which subdivision of the nervous system is causing this man's hypertension?

Challenge Questions

19. You accidentally place your hand on a hot stove burner and almost immediately pull your hand away. Trace the neural pathway that led to your quick response.

20. You have just eaten a satisfying meal and feel full. Identify the parts of the nervous system and their roles in this response.

Concept Map

21. Fill in each blank or box of the concept map of the organization of the nervous system.

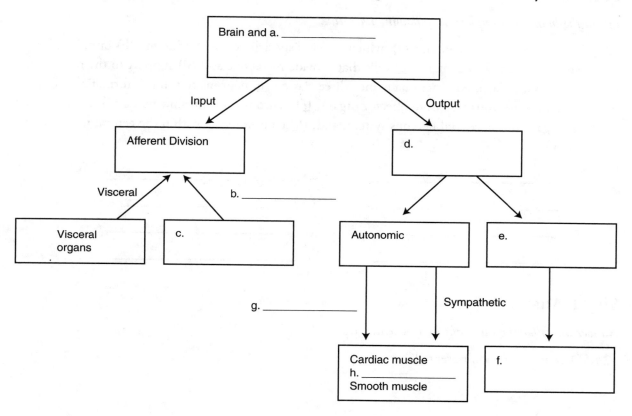

CELLS OF THE NERVOUS SYSTEM

Matching

22. Match the following terms with their descriptions below: axon (A), axon hillock (AH), cell body (CB), collateral (C), dendrite (D), glial cell (GC), oligodendrocyte (O), Schwann cell (SC).

a. _____ general term for a cell that provides support to neurons

b. _____ contains the nucleus and most of the organelles

c. _____ branch of the cell body that receives information

d. _____ forms myelin in the peripheral nervous system

e. _____ a branch of an axon

f. _____ site where the action potential is initiated

g. _____ support cell for neurons in the central nervous system

h. _____ site where neurotransmitter is released

i. _____ specialized support cell that produces myelin and is found only in the central nervous system

j. _____ forms myelin in the peripheral nervous system

Completion

Fill in the blanks to complete the following narrative.

23. The nervous system contains **(a)**, which are cells specialized for conducting **(b)** impulses. The nervous system also contains **(c)** cells that provide metabolic and **(d)** support to the neurons. Neurons are classified functionally into three classes: **(e)** neurons transmit information from the central nervous system to effector organs, **(f)** neurons transmit information from sensory or **(g)** organs to the central nervous system, and, **(h)** communicate within the central nervous system.

a. _____   e. _____

b. _____   f. _____

c. _____   g. _____

d. _____   h. _____

Short Answer

Answer the following questions in 1–4 sentences.

24. Describe an action potential.

25. Where are action potentials initiated within a neuron?

26. Describe the three general types of ion channels present in the plasma membrane of a neuron.

27. What is the function of interneurons?

Multiple Choice

Select the best answer from the choices given.

28. Which part of a neuron releases neurotransmitter?

a. dendrite
b. cell body
c. axon terminal
d. axon hillock
e. axon

29. Which of the following glial cells is **not** present in the CNS?

a. astrocyte
b. ependymal cells
c. microglial cells
d. oligodendrocytes
e. Schwann cells

30. Where are ligand-gated channels principally located in a nerve?

a. axon terminal
b. axon
c. cell body and dendrites
d. Schwann cell
e. glial cell

31. Where are voltage-gated channels most densely located in a nerve?

a. axon terminal
b. axon hillock
c. cell body and dendrites
d. Schwann cell
e. glial cell

32. Which of the following structural classifications of neurons is correctly paired with its description or example?

a. bipolar neuron : typical neuron used in vision
b. bipolar neuron : most common type of neuron in the body
c. multipolar neuron : least common neuron in the body
d. unipolar neuron : has a peripheral axon
e. unipolar neuron : most common neuron type in the body

33. The vagus nerve has axons which slow down the heart rate; the vagus nerve is part of which nervous system?

a. parasympathetic nervous system
b. somatic nervous system
c. central nervous system
d. afferent division of the peripheral nervous system
e. efferent division of the peripheral nervous system

True/False

Label the following statements as true (T) or false (F). If false, change the statement to make it true.

34. _____ Visceral receptors send information from the brain to skeletal muscles.

35. _____ Dendrites receive information and axons send information.

36. _____ A ganglion is a cluster of cell bodies located in the CNS.

Sequencing

37. Place the following in the order in which they receive or send information on a neuron.

a. axon,   b. dendrite,   c. axon hillock,   d. cell body,   e. axon terminal

Sequence: _____

Clinical Question

38. A woman is admitted to the hospital and is diagnosed with Guillain-Barre syndrome. Her symptoms started with weakness in her legs, which spread to the muscles in her trunk and arms. Given her symptoms, which part of her peripheral nervous system is most likely not operating correctly?

Challenge Questions

39. Describe the general arrangement of cell bodies and axons in the central and peripheral nervous systems.

40. Compare and contrast the locations and functions of Schwann cells and oligodendrocytes.

41. What are the advantages of having several dendrites associated with one cell body, as is the case with multipolar neurons?

42. Histological examination of axons shows that, at the nodes of Ranvier, the diameter of the axon increases. What purpose might this increase in diameter serve?

ELECTRICAL SIGNALS IN NEURONS

Matching

43. Match the following types of potentials with their definitions below: action potential (AP), equilibrium potential (EP), graded potential (GP), membrane potential (MP), potential difference (PD), resting membrane potential (RMP), synaptic potential (SP).

a. _____ difference in voltage between two points

b. _____ difference in voltage across a plasma membrane

c. _____ a membrane potential with no threshold or refractory period

d. _____ a potential produced in the postsynaptic cell in response to a neurotransmitter

e. _____ difference in voltage across a plasma membrane when the cell is at rest

f. _____ a large, rapid change in membrane potential

g. _____ the membrane potential that exactly counters the chemical forces acting to move an ion across the membrane

Completion

Fill in the blanks to complete the following narrative.

44. At rest, cells have a membrane potential such that the inside of the cell is **(a)** relative to the outside of the cell. Changes in membrane potential can occur by changing the permeability of the membrane to **(b)**. **(c)** potentials are small changes in membrane potential in response to a stimulus that opens or closes **(d)** channels. If graded potentials result in a depolarization of the neuron above **(e)**, a/n **(f)** is produced. Graded potentials can have an additive effect, either by **(g)** summation or **(h)** summation.

a. _____   e. _____

b. _____   f. _____

c. _____   g. _____

d. _____   h. _____

Short Answer

Answer the following questions in 1–4 sentences.

45. Why is the plasma membrane a good insulator? (Why does it have a high resistance?)

46. What is an inhibitory graded potential?

47. Describe hyperpolarization.

48. Describe the chemical driving forces acting on sodium and potassium in a neuron at rest.

Multiple Choice

Select the best answer from the choices given.

49. Neurons of the autonomic nervous system usually have much thinner myelin than neurons of the somatic nervous system. Which of the following statements is true?

    a. Neurons of the autonomic and somatic nervous systems generally have the same resistance and conductance.

    b. Neurons of the autonomic nervous system have greater resistance and decreased conductance relative to neurons in the somatic nervous system.

    c. Neurons of the autonomic nervous system have greater resistance and a greater conductance relative to neurons in the somatic nervous system.

    d. Neurons of the autonomic nervous system have less resistance and decreased conductance relative to neurons in the somatic nervous system.

    e. Neurons of the autonomic nervous system have less resistance and increased conductance relative to neurons in the somatic nervous system.

50. Which of the following is the critical membrane potential that must be met or exceeded if an action potential is to be generated?

    a. graded potential   d. hyperpolarization

    b. threshold   e. repolarization

    c. equilibrium potential

51. Which of the following is the term for a nerve cell becoming more positive on the inside?

    a. hyperpolarization
    b. repolarization
    c. inhibitory spatial summation
    d. inhibitory temporal summation
    e. depolarization

52. When a neuron is at rest, which of the following best describes the relationship between sodium and potassium?

    a. Net sodium does not move into or out of the cell, but net potassium moves out.
    b. Net sodium leaks into the cell, and net potassium leaks out.
    c. Net sodium leaks out of the cell, and net potassium leaks in.
    d. Potassium does not move into or out of the cell, but net sodium moves in.
    e. Neither sodium nor potassium moves across the cell membrane.

53. What role do the Na^+/K^+ pumps play in maintaining the resting membrane potential?

    a. They pump sodium out of the cell and pump potassium into the cell.
    b. They pump both sodium and potassium into the cell.
    c. They pump both sodium and potassium out of the cell.
    d. They pump sodium into the cell and potassium out of the cell.
    e. They abolish the resting membrane potential.

True/False

Label the following statements as true (T) *or false* (F). *If false, change the statement to make it true.*

54. _____ When a neuron is at rest, sodium and potassium ions are at equilibrium.

55. _____ A nerve cell membrane is more permeable to potassium than it is to sodium.

56. _____ Plasma membranes make good conductors of electricity.

57. _____ In a resting neuron, net potassium leaks out of the cell and net sodium leaks into the cell.

58. _____ The Na^+/K^+ pump moves potassium into the cell and sodium out of the cell.

59. _____ Ligand-gated channels open only in response to changes in the membrane potential.

60. _____ When an axon of one neuron branches to communicate with many other cells it is called divergence.

61. _____ The axon hillock is also called the trigger zone.

Labeling

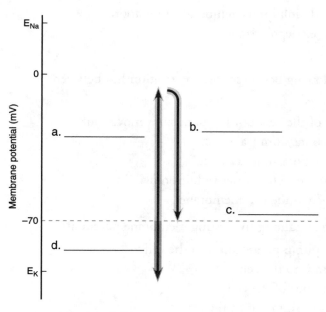

FIGURE 6.1

62. Label the letters in Figure 6.1.

Sequencing

63. Assume that a nerve cell has just been stimulated at a dendrite and an action potential will take place in that neuron. Place in sequence the following locations with their associated potentials.

a. axon hillock : action potential
b. axon terminal : induces a synaptic potential in postsynaptic cell
c. axon : action potential
d. dendrite : graded potential

Sequence: _____

Clinical Questions

64. Some neurotoxins such as tetrodoxin (found in puffer fish) and saxitoxin (found in marine dinoflagellates) act by blocking voltage-gated sodium channels. a) Which type of potential do they interrupt when they exert their effects? b) Which functional groups of nerves are affected if the toxin causes a tingling sensation? c) These neurotoxins can cause death when they interfere with somatic motor neurons. The nerves cannot send impulses to the muscles to tell them to contract, thus causing paralysis. These neurotoxins could cause death by paralysis of which skeletal muscle?

65. A patient is found to be hypokalemic (low levels of potassium) and the physician prescribes potassium supplements. Describe why potassium supplements are important in relation to normal neuron function.

Challenge Questions

66. If a toxin were to inhibit the action of the Na^+/K^+ pumps of a neuron, what would eventually happen to the membrane potential of that neuron?

67. Compare and contrast excitatory and inhibitory graded potentials.

68. Describe what would happen if a neuron were stimulated by excitatory and inhibitory graded potentials that are in an exact balance.

Concept Map

69. Note the resting membrane potential on the graph below, and the dotted line that indicates threshold. Draw two graded potentials: one that is inhibitory and one that is stimulatory.

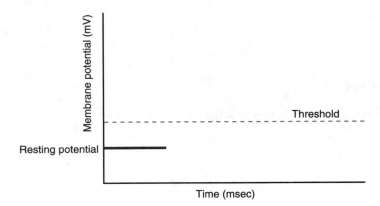

ACTION POTENTIALS AND
THE BASIS OF NEURAL STABILITY

Matching

70. Match each phase of an action in the following list with the appropriate description below: depolarization (D), repolarization (R), after-hyperpolarization (AH). Some statements may have more than one right answer.

    a. _____ fast, inward movement of sodium

    b. _____ membrane potential goes from −70 mV to −80 mV

    c. _____ fast, outward movement of potassium

    d. _____ membrane potential goes from +30 mV to −70 mV

    e. _____ activation and inactivation gates of Na^+ channels are both open

    f. _____ membrane potential goes from −70 mV to +30 mV

    g. _____ potassium gates are open

Completion

Fill in the blanks to complete the following narrative.

71. Action potentials are rapid depolarizations of the plasma membrane that travel from the **(a)** to the **(b)**. The action potential is divided into three phases. Depolarization is caused by the opening of **(c)** channels, which allows this ion to **(d)** the cell. The repolarization phase is caused by the closing of **(e)** channels and the opening of **(f)** channels; this allows potassium to **(g)** the cell. After-hyperpolarization occurs because **(h)** channels are slow in closing, allowing continued movement of potassium **(i)** of the cell for a brief period of time.

    a. _____   f. _____

    b. _____   g. _____

    c. _____   h. _____

    d. _____   i. _____

    e. _____

Short Answer

Answer the following questions in 1–4 sentences.

72. Describe when the two refractory periods occur in relation to an action potential.

73. Define *saltatory conduction*.

74. What is the relationship between the diameter of an axon and the speed of conduction of action potentials?

75. What effect does myelin have on the speed of action potentials?

76. Describe the net movement through voltage-gated channels of the ions responsible for each of the three phases of an action potential.

Multiple Choice

Select the best answer from the choices given.

77. Which of the following has the most resistance longitudinally down the axon?
   a. a myelinated axon with a diameter of 5 μm
   b. a myelinated axon with a diameter of 10 μm
   c. a myelinated axon with a diameter of 20 μm
   d. an unmyelinated axon with a diameter of 5 μm
   e. an unmyelinated axon with a diameter of 10 μm

78. What is the term used to describe the jumping of an action potential from node to node?
   a. absolute refractory period
   b. relative refractory period
   c. after-hyperpolarization
   d. saltatory conduction
   e. repolarization

79. Which of the following statements about the Na^+/K^+ pump is false?
   a. It transports Na^+ out of the cell and K^+ into the cell.
   b. It is present in neurons.
   c. Its activity requires the expenditure of metabolic (cellular) energy.
   d. It transports Na^+ and K^+ in a 1:1 ratio.
   e. It is active during the resting potential.

80. Which of the following statements about the membrane potential is true?

    a. It is normally equal to zero volts.

    b. The inside of the membrane is positively charged compared to the outside.

    c. It results, in part, from the unequal concentrations of Na^+ outside the cell and K^+ inside the cell.

    d. It is due in part to the presence of proteins outside of the cell.

    e. Chloride and calcium ions are the main ions responsible for it.

81. What happens to the conduction rate of a neuron when you increase the amount of myelination around the axon leaving the nodes intact?

    a. The rate increases.

    b. The rate decreases slightly.

    c. The rate is unchanged because all myelinated nerves have the same conduction rate.

    d. The rate oscillates from slow to fast to slow.

    e. The rate slows drastically.

82. In a nerve, what types of channels open at threshold?

    a. voltage-gated Na^+ channels

    b. voltage-gated K^+ channels

    c. ligand-gated channels

    d. voltage-gated Ca^{++} channels

    e. no channels actually open at threshold

83. Which of the following is **not** a property of an action potential?

    a. It has a threshold.

    b. It has a refractory period.

    c. It is graded.

    d. It is all-or-none.

    e. It involves ions.

84. If the sodium channels were closed more slowly than normal, the resulting action potential would _____.

    a. be abolished

    b. decrease in amplitude

    c. be inverted in polarity

    d. be prolonged

    e. not occur at all

85. The relative refractory period occurs when _____.

    a. Na^+ channel gates are open

    b. K^+ channel gates are open

    c. Ca^{++} channel gates are open

    d. Ca^{++} channel gates are closed

    e. ligand-gated channels are open

86. When a nerve cell is initially depolarized, _____.

    a. the inside of the cell becomes more positive

    b. the inside of the cell becomes less positive

    c. the outside of the cell becomes more positive

    d. voltage-gated Na^+ channels close

    e. K^+ leak channels open

True/False

Label the following statements as true (T) *or false* (F). *If false, change the statement to make it true.*

87. _____ During the depolarization phase of an action potential, the membrane potential changes from approximately +30 mV to −70 mV.

88. _____ Saltatory conduction is seen in unmyelinated axons.

89. _____ Myelinated axons conduct nerve impulses faster than unmyelinated axons.

90. _____ The membrane potential during after-hyperpolarization goes from approximately −70 mV to +30 mV.

91. _____ A subthreshold stimulus at the axon hillock initiates an action potential.

92. _____ If given enough of a stimulus, an action potential can be stimulated during the relative refractory period.

93. _____ Action potentials tend to be graded in their response.

94. _____ The positive feedback loop of the opening of sodium activation gates is initiated at threshold.

95. _____ During repolarization, voltage-gated potassium gates are open.

Sequencing

96. Place the following events of an action potential in the correct order.

   a. Sodium permeability decreases rapidly and potassium permeability increases.
   b. Potassium exits the cell rapidly.
   c. After-hyperpolarization occurs.
   d. Potential returns from approximately +30 mV back to −70 mV.
   e. Potassium permeability remains elevated briefly after reaching −70 mV.
   f. Membrane potential changes from approximately −70 mV to +30 mV.
   g. rapid sodium influx into the cell
   h. an increase in sodium permeability

   Sequence: _____

Clinical Question

97. Multiple sclerosis (MS) is characterized by loss of myelin in the white matter of the lateral and posterior columns of the spinal cord or along nerve tracts within the brain. Both efferent and afferent nerves can be affected. Knowing the function of myelin in sensory and motor nerves, can you predict the symptoms of MS? What specific process does the lack of myelination interfere with in the physiology of nerves?

Challenge Questions

98. Some local anesthetics block action potentials generated by sensory neurons. What specific process do anesthetics impair and how does this interfere with nerve transmission?

99. Describe an action potential in a neuron that does not have K⁺ channel pumps compared to a neuron with K⁺ channel pumps.

Concept Map

100. In the graph below, draw the following: a. a subthreshold stimulus, b. a threshold stimulus with an action potential, and c. a suprathreshold stimulus with an action potential.

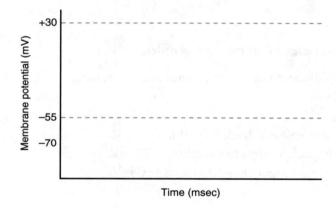

7 Synaptic Transmission and Neural Integration

Objectives

We recommend that you review the **Objectives** for this chapter, found on page 201 of *Principles of Human Physiology*. The **Objectives** outline what you should know from each chapter.

Key Terms

acetylcholine
acetylcholinesterase
adenylate cyclase
adrenergic
alpha adrenergic receptor
amino acid neurotransmitter
aspartate
autoreceptor
axo-axonic synapse
axo-dendritic synapse
axo-somatic synapse
beta adrenergic receptor
biogenic amine
catechol-o-methyltransferase
channel-linked receptor
chemical synapse
choline acetyl transferase
cholinergic
electrical synapse
endogenous opioid
endorphin

enkephalin
EPSP
excitatory postsynaptic
    potential
excitatory synapse
fast response
frequency coding
GABA
glutamate
glycine
inhibitory post-synaptic
    potential
inhibitory synapse
ionotropic receptor
IPSP
metabotropic receptor
monoamine oxidase
muscarinic cholinergic
    receptor
neural integration
neuroactive peptide

neuromodulator
neuropeptide
nicotinic cholinergic receptor
nitric oxide
nitric oxide synthetase
oxytocin
postsynaptic neuron
postsynaptic potential (PSP)
presynaptic facilitation
presynaptic inhibition
presynaptic neuron
reuptake
slow response
spatial summation
substance p
synaptic cleft
synaptic delay
synaptic vesicle
temporal summation
TRH
vasopressin

TYPES OF SYNAPSES AND CHEMICAL SYNAPSES

Matching

1. Match each word in the list with its description below: axoaxonic synapse (AAS), axodendritic synapse (ADS), axosomatic synapse (ASS), chemical synapse (CS), electrical synapse (ES), post-synaptic neuron (PON), presynaptic neuron (PEN), synaptic cleft (SC), synaptic vesicle (SV).

    a. _____ uses gap junctions to communicate between neurons

    b. _____ generalized term for the junction between neurons

c. _____ the neuron that releases neurotransmitters

d. _____ the neuron that has ligand-binding channels on its dendrites and cell body, and receives the neurotransmitter signal

e. _____ the extracellular space between two cells that the neurotransmitter crosses

f. _____ when a presynaptic neuron synapses with a dendrite on the postsynaptic neuron

g. _____ when a presynaptic neuron synapses with a cell body on the postsynaptic neuron

h. _____ when a presynaptic neuron synapses with an axon on the postsynaptic neuron

i. _____ membrane-bound compartment where neurotransmitters are stored

Completion

Fill in the blanks to complete the following narrative.

2. Neurons communicate with other neurons or effector organs at **(a)**. Neurons communicate at either **(b)** or electrical synapses. Electrical synapses are rare in humans and exist where **(c)** occur between cells in the heart. Chemical synapses are much more common and involve the release of a/n **(d)** from the **(e)** neuron. The **(d)** then crosses the **(f)** to communicate with a/n **(g)** neuron. For the neurotransmitter to be released, an action potential travels down the axon of the presynaptic neuron to the **(h)** where it stimulates the opening of voltage-gated **(i)** channels. **(i)** enters the cell, triggering the release of **(j)** by means of **(k)**. The neurotransmitter binds to **(l)** on the postsynaptic neuron.

a. _____   g. _____

b. _____   h. _____

c. _____   i. _____

d. _____   j. _____

e. _____   k. _____

f. _____   l. _____

Short Answer

Answer the following questions in 1–4 sentences.

3. Define *inhibitory synapse* and *excitatory synapse*.

4. What is synaptic delay and what is its likely cause?

5. What is an ionotropic receptor?

6. What are neuromodulators?

7. Acetylcholine is the neurotransmitter that is released from neurons and causes skeletal muscle to contract. Normally, an enzyme (cholinesterase) breaks down acetylcholine after the muscle has contracted. Neostigmine is a drug that prevents acetylcholine from being cleared from the synaptic cleft by cholinesterase, and is given to patients with muscle weakness. How might this drug affect skeletal muscles?

Multiple Choice

Select the best answer from the choices given.

8. The influx of these ions into a nerve cell causes an IPSP.

   a. sodium and potassium   c. sodium and chloride   e. potassium and chloride
   b. sodium and calcium   d. chloride and calcium

9. _____ has the strongest electrochemical gradient during an EPSP, and moves _____ the cell.

   a. Potassium : into   c. Sodium : into   e. Chloride : into
   b. Potassium : out of   d. Sodium : out of

10. Which of the following is the term for a synapse with a cell body?

   a. axosomatic synapse   c. electrical synapse   e. axoaxonic synapse
   b. axodendritic synapse   d. postsynaptic neuron

11. What transport process moves the neurotransmitter out of the cell?

   a. receptor-mediated   b. exocytosis   d. phagocytosis
     active transport   c. endocytosis   e. pinocytosis

12. Which of the following are highly concentrated at the dendrites?

   a. ligand-gated channels   d. voltage-gated sodium channels
   b. voltage-gated potassium channels   e. inhibitory synapses
   c. voltage-gated calcium channels

13. A fast postsynaptic response occurs whenever a neurotransmitter binds to _____.

   a. a metabotropic receptor   c. a G protein   e. an ionotropic receptor
   b. adenylate cyclase   d. cAMP

14. Which of the following is true about G proteins?

   a. They are stimulated by ionotropic receptors.
   b. They are involved in metabotropic receptor transduction.
   c. They occur in fast responses of EPSPs.
   d. They occur in fast responses of IPSPs.
   e. They occur only in the rare electrical synapses.

True/False

Label the following statements as true (T) *or false* (F). *If false, change the statement to make it true.*

15. _____ Electrical synapses occur at gap junctions between neurons.

16. _____ Neurotransmitters usually stay in the synaptic cleft indefinitely.

17. _____ Synaptic vesicles usually contain neurotransmitters.

18. _____ Binding of the neurotransmitter to the postsynaptic membrane is an irreversible process.

19. _____ Slow EPSPs often use a second messenger such as cAMP.

20. _____ Movement of either potassium ions out of the cells or chloride ions into the cell can cause an EPSP.

Sequencing

21. Place the following steps of the mechanism of cAMP mediated slow EPSPs in the correct order.

a. G protein is activated.

b. ATP is converted to cAMP.

c. A phosphate group is added to a potassium channel.

d. G protein activates the enzyme adenylate cyclase.

e. cAMP acts as a second messenger that activates protein kinase A.

f. Phosphorylation of the potassium channel causes it to close.

g. A neurotransmitter from the presynaptic cell binds to the receptor on the postsynaptic cell.

Sequence: _____

Clinical Question

22. A number of drugs affect neurotransmitter activity at their axon terminal synapses. The drugs listed below affect the synapse physiology of somatic motor neurons (neurons that communicate with skeletal muscles). Examine the following list and predict the effect that each drug will have on skeletal muscles.

Drug	Effect on neurotransmitter activity	Predicted effect on skeletal muscle
Succinylcholine	reduces the muscle's sensitivity to the neurotransmitter	(a)
Toxin from *Botulinus* bacterium	blocks the release of the neurotransmitter to the skeletal muscle	(b)
Organophosphates, such as those found in insecticides	prevents acetylcholinesterase from degrading the neurotransmitter	(c)

Challenge Questions

23. Describe how an excitatory synapse produces a fast EPSP.

24. Describe how an inhibitory synapse produces an IPSP using potassium as an example.

25. Describe the three ways in which neurotransmitters are removed from the synaptic cleft.

Concept Map

26. On the graph below, draw an EPSP and an IPSP.

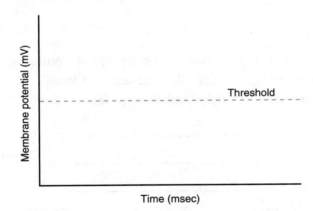

NEURAL INTEGRATION AND PRESYNAPTIC MODULATION

Matching

27. Consider the statements below and mark whether they describe spatial summation (SS) or temporal summation (TS).

    a. _____ Two or more postsynaptic potentials are generated in rapid succession at the same synapse.

    b. _____ Two or more postsynaptic potentials are generated at approximately the same time.

    c. _____ Neuron A triggers an EPSP at the same time as neuron B, and between the two of them, they produce an action potential.

28. Match whether the statements below describe presynaptic facilitation (PF), presynaptic inhibition (PI), or both (B).

    a. _____ occur(s) at axoaxonic synapses

    b. _____ have/has a modulating neuron

    c. _____ cause(s) the enhanced release of a neurotransmitter

    d. _____ presynaptic modulation affects transmission to the postsynaptic neuron at one specific synapse

    e. _____ cause(s) a decreased release of a neurotransmitter

Completion

Fill in the blanks to complete the following narratives.

29. **(a)** is the spatial and/or temporal summation of synaptic potentials at the **(b)** of a postsynaptic membrane. If the axon hillock is depolarized to **(c)**, a/n **(d)** will be generated. Once depolarization reaches threshold, greater **(e)** will elicit higher frequency of **(f)**.

    a. _____   d. _____
    b. _____   e. _____
    c. _____   f. _____

30. Synaptic communication can be modulated. The most common presynaptic modulation occurs at **(a)** synapses. At these synapses, the presynaptic cell modulates the release of **(b)** from the **(c)** cell. In presynaptic **(d)**, communication at the specific synapse is enhanced, whereas in presynaptic **(e)**, communication at a specific synapse is decreased.

    a. _____   d. _____
    b. _____   e. _____
    c. _____

Short Answer

Answer the following questions in 1–4 sentences.

31. Is the amount of neurotransmitter released from the postsynaptic neuron increased or decreased during presynaptic facilitation?

32. Describe the simple rule of summation for neural integration.

Multiple Choice

Select the best answer from the choices given.

33. Where are voltage-gated calcium channels most densely located on a peripheral neuron?

    a. on the cell body

    b. all along the axon near the nodes

    c. at the axon terminals

    d. on the axon hillock

    e. at the dendrite

34. Where do most presynaptic modulating neurons form a synapse with the postsynaptic neuron?

    a. at the dendrites

    b. throughout the cell body

    c. all along the axon

    d. at the dendrites and cell body

    e. at the axon hillock

35. What does frequency coding entail?

    a. a higher action potential

    b. a lower action potential

    c. a longer duration action potential

    d. no action potential

    e. more action potentials per unit time

True/False

Label the following statements as true (T) or false (F). If false, change the statement to make it true.

36. _____ Modulating neurons can regulate the flux of calcium into the postsynaptic neuron.

37. _____ Presynaptic facilitation occurs when the release of a neurotransmitter is reduced.

38. _____ Axodendritic and axosomatic neurons affect transmission at selective synapses.

39. _____ Presynaptic inhibition only occurs at inhibitory synapses.

40. _____ Spatial summation occurs when two or more different postsynaptic potentials are generated at the same time.

41. _____ Only EPSPs can be summed.

42. _____ Frequency coding is a process that affects the size of the action potentials.

Labeling

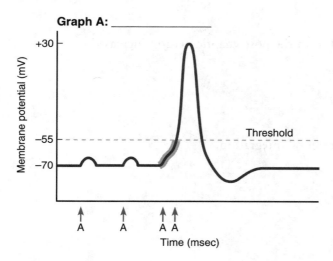

Graph A: _____

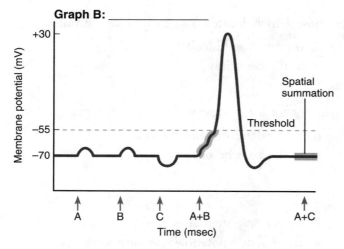

Graph B: _____

FIGURE 7.1

43. Examine Figure 7.1. Which type of neural integration is seen in each of the graphs?

Sequencing

44. Place the following events of presynaptic modulation in the correct order.

   a. The presynaptic neurotransmitter induces a change in the amount of calcium that enters the postsynaptic axon.

   b. The presynaptic neurotransmitter binds with its receptor on the postsynaptic neuron.

   c. The presynaptic neuron synapses with the postsynaptic neuron.

   d. The presynaptic neuron releases a neurotransmitter.

   e. The amount of neurotransmitter released from the postsynaptic neuron is altered.

   Sequence: _____

Challenge Questions

45. Compare and contrast temporal and spatial summation.

46. Explain the concept of frequency coding.

Concept Map

47. Fill in the blanks or boxes with the events of presynaptic modulation.

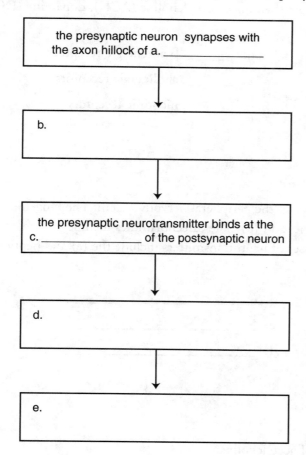

the presynaptic neuron synapses with the axon hillock of a. _____

b.

the presynaptic neurotransmitter binds at the c. _____ of the postsynaptic neuron

d.

e.

NEUROTRANSMITTERS: STRUCTURE, SYNTHESIS, AND DEGRADATION

Matching

48. Match the neurotransmitter or neuropeptide in the list with its description below: acetylcholine (ACH), catecholamines (CAT), endorphin (END), glutamate (GLU), glycine (GLY), histamine (HIS), nitric oxide (NO), serotonin (SER), substance p (P).

    a. _____ not stored in synaptic vesicles

    b. _____ an excitatory amino acid neurotransmitter

    c. _____ an endogenous opioid

    d. _____ commonly found in the brainstem and regulates sleep and emotion

    e. _____ can be degraded by catechol-o-methyltransferase

    f. _____ a biogenic amine found primarily in the hypothalamus

    g. _____ an inhibitory amino acid

    h. _____ derived from choline

    i. _____ a neuroactive peptide that decreases activity of the gastrointestinal tract

49. Match the neurotransmitter in the list with the name of its receptor below. Each neurotransmitter can be used once or more than once: acetylcholine (ACH), dopamine (DOP), epinephrine (EPI).

    a. _____ dopaminergic

    b. _____ α adrenergic receptors

    c. _____ muscarinic receptors

    d. _____ β adrenergic receptors

    e. _____ cholinergic receptors

    f. _____ nicotinic receptors

Completion

Fill in the blanks to complete the following narrative.

50. **(a)** is the most common neurotransmitter in the peripheral nervous system. The biogenic amines include catecholamines, histamine, and **(b)**. The catecholamines include norepinephrine, **(c)**, and **(d)**. Other classes of neurotransmitters include the **(e)** and peptides. ATP and **(f)** are also neurotransmitters.

    a. _____   d. _____

    b. _____   e. _____

    c. _____   f. _____

Short Answer

Answer the following question in 1–4 sentences.

51. Which enzyme catalyzes the synthesis of acetylcholine?

Multiple Choice

Select the best answer from the choices given.

52. Which of the following neurotransmitters, or group of neurotransmitters, are the most abundant in the central nervous system?

    a. ATP
    b. biogenic amines
    c. amino acid neurotransmitters
    d. acetylcholine
    e. catecholamines

53. Which of the following is an inhibitory amino acid neurotransmitter?

    a. serotonin
    b. GABA
    c. acetylcholine
    d. aspartate
    e. glutamate

54. Which of the following neurotransmitters is an endogenous opioid?

    a. enkephalin
    b. GABA
    c. glycine
    d. MAO
    e. norepinephrine

55. Which of the following neurotransmitters stimulates skeletal muscles to contract?

    a. dopamine
    b. serotonin
    c. GABA
    d. nitric oxide
    e. acetylcholine

56. *Procaine* is a drug that reduces a neuron's membrane permeablity to sodium. What is the likely effect it produces at normal doses?

    a. anesthesia
    b. muscle stimulation
    c. increased excitability of nerves
    d. stopping of the heart
    e. increased release of acetylcholine

57. Barbiturates decrease the rate of acetylcholine release. What effect do these drugs have on skeletal muscles?

    a. make them more excitable
    b. make them contract more forcefully
    c. most likely have no significant effect on skeletal muscles
    d. produce muscle weakness
    e. make the muscles larger and stronger

True/False

Label the following statements as true (T) or false (F). If false, change the statement to make it true.

58. _____ Catecholamines can be degraded by MOA or COMT.

59. _____ Nitric oxide does not bind to plasma membrane protein receptors as other neurotransmitters do.

60. _____ Catecholamines are rapidly-acting neurotransmitters.

61. _____ Amino acid neurotransmitters are the most abundant neurotransmitter in the peripheral nervous system.

62. _____ The two classes of adrenergic receptors are muscarinic and nicotinic.

63. _____ Acetylcholinesterase catalyzes the breakdown of acetylcholine.

Clinical Questions

64. A patient comes into the emergency room after an accidental overdose of acetylcholine. An examination of symptoms reveals skeletal muscle stiffness, but an extremely slowed heart rate. How can the same drug have such different effects on these two muscle types?

65. One form of military nerve gas blocks acetylcholinesterase activity, causing asphyxiation in the affected individual. Explain how this happens.

Challenge Question

66. Compare and contrast the two types of cholinergic receptors.

Concept Map

67. Fill in the blanks on the following concept map which shows the release and breakdown of acetylcholine.

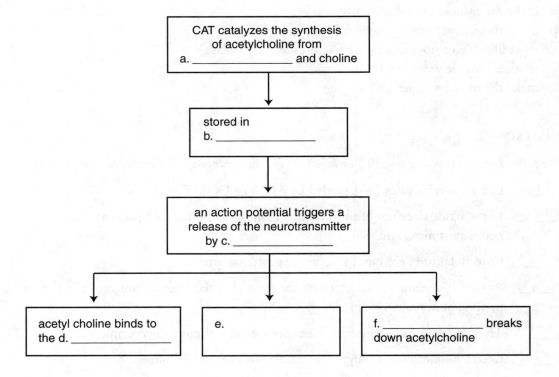

8 The Nervous System: Central Nervous System

Objectives

We recommend that you review the **Objectives** for this chapter, found on p. 223 of *Principles of Human Physiology*. The **Objectives** outline what you should know from each chapter.

Key Terms

arachnoid mater
ascending tract
association area
association fiber
associative learning
astrocyte
basal nuclei
blood-brain barrier
brain
brainstem
Broca's area
central canal
central nervous system (CNS)
cerebellum
cerebral cortex
cerebral hemisphere
cerebral ventricle
cerebrospinal fluid (CSF)
cerebrum
choroid plexus
circadian rhythm
commissural fiber
consolidated
contralateral
corpus callosum
cranial nerve
cranium
crossed-extensor reflex
declarative memory
descending tract

diencephalon
dorsal horn
dorsal root
dorsal root ganglia
dura mater
electroencephalogram
ependymal cell
extrapyramidal tract
forebrain
frontal lobe
gray matter
gyri (gyrus)
hypothalamus
ipsilateral
learning
limbic system
long-term memory
medulla oblongata
memory
meninges
midbrain
mixed nerve
motor homunculus
motor neuron
muscle spindle stretch reflex
nerve fiber
nonassociative learning
nuclei
occipital lobe
parallel processing

parietal lobe
pia mater
plasticity
pons
primary motor cortex
primary somatosensory cortex
procedural memory
projection fiber
pyramidal tract
reflex
reflex arc
REM sleep
reticular formation
sensitization
sensory homunculus
slow-wave sleep
spinal cord
spinal nerves
subarachnoid space
sulci (sulcus)
temporal lobe
thalamus
tract
ventral horn
ventral root
vertebral column
Wernicke's area
white matter
withdrawal reflex

GENERAL ANATOMY OF THE CENTRAL NERVOUS SYSTEM

Matching

1. Match the following list of structures of the central nervous system (CNS) with the descriptions below: blood-brain barrier (BBB), brain (BR), cerebrospinal fluid (CSF), cranium (CR), meninges (MN), vertebral column (VC).

   a. _____ a clear watery liquid that bathes the CNS

   b. _____ bony structure that surrounds the brain

   c. _____ three membranes: dura mater, pia mater, and arachnoid mater

   d. _____ bony structure that surrounds the spinal cord

   e. _____ prevents the movement of hydrophilic molecules across capillary walls in the CNS

   f. _____ composed of neural and glial tissue and protected by the cranium

Completion

Fill in the blanks to complete the following narrative.

2. The central nervous system (CNS) is composed of the **(a)** and **(b)**. The CNS is protected by various structures, including the **(c)** and vertebral column, connective tissues called the **(d)**, and the **(e)**. The **(f)** fluid also cushions the structures in the CNS. CNS tissue is organized into **(g)** and **(h)** matter. **(g)** matter consists primarily of cell **(i)**, **(j)**, and axon **(k)**. **(h)** matter consists of myelinated **(l)**. **(m)** cells are also located throughout the CNS, and serve in a support role for the neurons.

   a. _____   h. _____

   b. _____   i. _____

   c. _____   j. _____

   d. _____   k. _____

   e. _____   l. _____

   f. _____   m. _____

   g. _____

Short Answer

Answer the following questions in 1–4 sentences.

3. Describe the blood-brain barrier.

4. Where are ependymal cells and astrocytes found in the central nervous system and what are their functions?

Multiple Choice

Select the best answer from the choices given.

5. The brain has four _____. These are continuous with the _____, a long thin cavity that runs the length of the spinal cord.
   a. choroid plexi : ventricle
   b. ventricles : central canal
   c. blood-brain barriers : choroid plexus
   d. gyri : sulcus
   e. subarachnoid spaces : central canal

6. Jacob has not eaten in 24 hours and is feeling lightheaded; which biomolecules are his brain cells lacking?
   a. ketone bodies
   b. fats
   c. glucose
   d. proteins
   e. nucleic acids

7. Which of the following cells help to form the blood-brain barrier?
   a. ependymal cells
   b. interneurons
   c. neurons
   d. astrocytes
   e. absorptive cells

8. You are looking at a cross-section of the spinal cord. Which of the following is the outermost portion composed of?
   a. myelinated axons
   b. cell bodies
   c. dendrites of neurons
   d. cerebrospinal fluid
   e. axon terminals only

9. What is another name for the axons in the CNS?
   a. projection fibers
   b. cerebral hemispheres
   c. ganglia
   d. gray matter
   e. nerve fibers

10. Which types of fibers connect one area of the cerebral cortex to another area of the cortex on the same side of the brain?
    a. commissural fibers
    b. association fibers
    c. corpus callosum
    d. cerebral cortex
    e. gray matter

True/False

Label the following statements as true (T) or false (F). If false, change the statement to make it true.

11. _____ The corpus callosum is the largest structure composed of commissural fibers in the brain.

12. _____ Strokes are devastating to central nervous tissue because the CNS cannot store energy reserves.

13. _____ Gases and other hydrophobic molecules enter endothelial cells by active transport.

14. _____ The choroid plexus produces the cerebrospinal fluid.

15. _____ The thin layer of gray matter that covers the cerebrum is called the blood-brain barrier.

16. _____ The pia mater is immediately adjacent to the nervous tissue of the brain.

Sequencing

17. Place the following structures associated with the brain in order from the outermost to the innermost.

   a. pia mater
   b. skull
   c. dura mater
   d. arachnoid mater

   e. white matter
   f. gray matter
   g. subarachnoid space

   Sequence: _____

Clinical Question

18. In treatments for meningitis or other CNS infections, the antibiotic penicillin is not used because it is excluded from the brain by the blood-brain barrier (unless the blood-brain barrier is damaged). What is it about penicillin that keeps it from crossing the endothelial capillaries of the CNS?

Challenge Questions

19. Compare and contrast the structure and function of gray matter and white matter.

20. Why does the CNS receive about 15% of the blood supply from the heart when it makes up only approximately 2% of your body weight?

21. Compare and contrast commissural fibers and association fibers.

THE SPINAL CORD

Matching

22. Match each of the following words with its description or definition below: ascending tracts (AT), descending tracts (DT), dorsal horn (DH), dorsal roots (DR), dorsal root ganglia (DRG), mixed nerves (MN), ventral horn (VH), ventral roots (VR).

    a. _____ a bundle of efferent axons

    b. _____ Cell bodies of afferent fibers are located here

    c. _____ This describes all spinal nerves because they contain both afferent and efferent axons.

    d. _____ a bundle of afferent axons

    e. _____ white matter that transmits information from the spinal cord to the brain

    f. _____ gray matter region of the spinal cord that contains interneurons and axon terminals of sensory receptors

    g. _____ white matter that transmits information from the brain to the spinal cord

    h. _____ gray matter region of the spinal cord that contains cell bodies of efferent axons and interneurons

Completion

Fill in the blanks to complete the following narrative.

23. All spinal cord nerves are mixed nerves because they contain both **(a)** and **(b)** axons. The white matter of the spinal cord contains **(c)** and **(d)** tracts that carry information to and from the **(e)**, respectively. The **(f)** is divided into ventral and **(g)** horns. Cell bodies and **(h)** of **(i)** are located in the ventral horn, **(j)** of **(k)** are located in the **(g)** horns. The gray matter also contains **(l)** scattered throughout.

    a. _____   g. _____

    b. _____   h. _____

    c. _____   i. _____

    d. _____   j. _____

    e. _____   k. _____

    f. _____   l. _____

Short Answer

Answer the following questions in 1–4 sentences.

24. How do descending and ascending tracts differ in conveying information?

25. In neurological examinations, what do dermatomes describe and why are they useful?

26. Describe the various regions of the spinal nerves and the points from which they emerge.

Multiple Choice

Select the best answer from the choices given.

27. Kyle has injured a lumbar spinal nerve. Which of the following areas of the body is probably affected by the nerve damage?

    a. neck   c. head   e. chest
    b. legs   d. arms

28. Which of the following is present in the dorsal root ganglia?

    a. cell bodies of efferent nerves   d. interneurons
    b. axon terminals of efferent nerves   e. axon terminals of afferent nerves
    c. cell bodies of afferent nerves

29. Yolanda places her hand on a hot stove. Which of the following will be the pathway along which information travels to the CNS?

    a. dorsal columns   c. ventral horns   e. dorsal root ganglia
    b. interneurons   d. interneurons

30. Which of the following is the name for the last third of the spinal cord that is composed of individual spinal nerves?

    a. cauda equina   c. ventral root   e. intermediolateral cell column
    b. dorsal root ganglia   d. ascending tract

True/False

Label the following statements as true (T) or false (F). If false, change the statement to make it true.

31. _____ Signals from the brain travel along descending tracts to efferent neurons in the dorsal horn.

32. _____ The lateral horns of the gray matter of the spinal cord are the origins of efferent nerves of the autonomic nervous system.

33. _____ The white matter of the spinal cord consists mainly of interneurons.

34. _____ The only function of descending tracts is to control efferent neurons.

Labeling

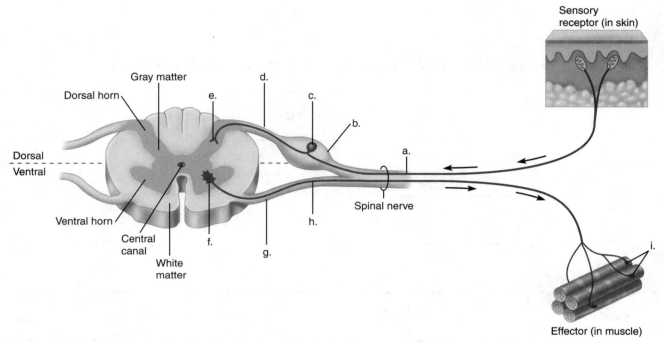

FIGURE 8.1

35. In the space below, identify the structures (a–i) in Figure 8.1 and state whether each area or structure is associated with the afferent division or efferent division of the peripheral nervous system.

Clinical Question

36. Two automobile crash victims, who were not wearing their seat belts, are brought into the emergency room following a near fatal car crash. Both have suffered major trauma to their spinal cords. Julie is paralyzed from the neck down and is receiving artificial respiration. Sven is paralyzed in the legs only. Explain the general area where the spinal cord damage is likely located in each person.

Challenge Question

37. Compare and contrast ipsilateral and contralateral communication between the brain and spinal cord.

Concept Map

38. Fill in the blanks and boxes of the concept map of the organization of the spinal cord.

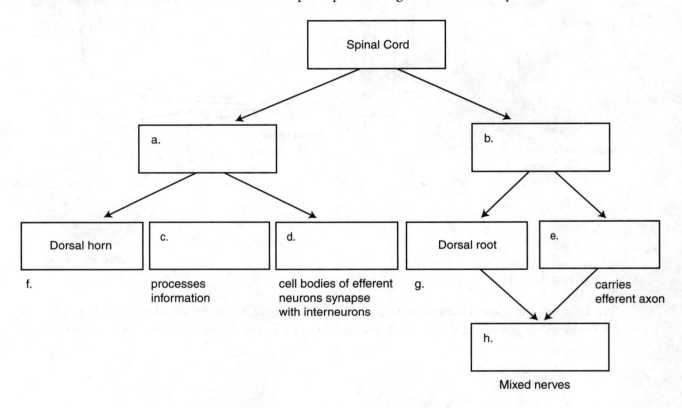

THE BRAIN

Matching

39. Match each of the following areas of the brain with its function below: brainstem (B), cerebellum (C), frontal lobe (FL), hypothalamus (H), limbic system (L), occipital lobe (OL), parietal lobe (PL), temporal lobe (TL), thalamus (T).

a. _____ This part of the brain sorts sensory input.

b. _____ Involuntary functions such as breathing and heart rate are controlled here.

c. _____ This part of the brain processes visual information.

d. _____ This part of the brain processes hearing.

e. _____ The link between the endocrine and nervous system is located here.

f. _____ This area of the brain functions in learning, memory, and emotion.

g. _____ Somatic sensory information associated with touch and pain is located here.

h. _____ Voluntary movement, language, and planning are located here.

Completion

Fill in the blanks to complete the following narrative.

40. The brain has three major parts: forebrain, **(a)**, and cerebellum. The forebrain includes the cerebrum and **(b)**. The **(a)** is composed of the midbrain, pons, and **(c)**. The functions of the **(d)** include motor control, sensory perception, language, emotions, learning, and memory. The subcortical nuclei include the **(e)**, which are important in motor control, and the **(f)**, which is involved in emotions, learning, and memory. The **(g)**, located beneath the cerebrum at the core of the forebrain, includes the **(h)** and the hypothalamus. The function of the **(h)** is to serve as a relay station for information traveling to the **(i)**. The hypothalamus regulates a number of body functions and serves as the link between the **(j)** and **(k)** systems.

a. _____   g. _____

b. _____   h. _____

c. _____   i. _____

d. _____   j. _____

e. _____   k. _____

f. _____

Short Answer

Answer the following questions in 1–4 sentences.

41. Describe the functional specialization of the right and left cerebral cortex.

42. Describe the role of the limbic system.

Multiple Choice

Select the best answer from the choices given.

43. Jean has injured her cerebellum. Which of the following symptoms will she likely have?
    a. unregulated thirst control
    b. problems with coordination and balance
    c. irregular heart rate
    d. irregular breathing
    e. emotional swings

44. Which of the following parts of the body have the most cortical area devoted to it?
    a. hip
    b. shoulder
    c. fingers
    d. toes
    e. ankle

45. Which of the following is a direct relay between sensory information and the cerebral cortex?
    a. thalamus
    b. primary motor cortex
    c. limbic system
    d. hypothalamus
    e. basal nuclei

46. Tim has trouble initiating voluntary motor functions. Which lobe of the cerebrum is most likely affected?
    a. frontal lobe
    b. left parietal lobe
    c. right parietal lobe
    d. occipital lobe
    e. temporal lobe

47. Ann has had a stroke that has left her partially blind. Which part of the brain is most likely affected?
    a. left parietal lobe
    b. right parietal lobe
    c. temporal lobe
    d. occipital lobe
    e. frontal lobe

48. Which of the following is **not** a function of the hypothalamus?
    a. links the endocrine and nervous systems
    b. regulates body temperature
    c. voluntary muscle movements
    d. regulates wake-sleep cycles
    e. thirst center

49. Yuki cannot hear well and seems to have lost her sense of balance. Which cranial nerve is most likely affected?
    a. olfactory
    b. vestibulocochlear
    c. abducens
    d. vagus
    e. optic

50. Which of the following cranial nerves is **not** paired with its proper function(s)?
    a. olfactory : smell
    b. abducens : eye movement
    c. facial : motor control of facial muscles, sensation of taste, secretion from tear glands
    d. vagus : motor and visceral afferent of thoracic and abdominal viscera
    e. hypoglossal : eye movements, pupillary reflex

True/False

Label the following statements as true (T) or false (F). If false, change the statement to make it true.

51. _____ Association areas of the cerebral cortex are directly involved with regulation of some hormones.

52. _____ The auditory cortex is part of the temporal lobe.

53. _____ Circadian rhythms are regulated in the thalamus.

54. _____ Cranial nerve VII is the facial nerve and contains only sensory nerves from the face and tongue.

55. _____ The cerebral cortex is composed of gray matter and is involved with higher level neural processing.

Clinical Questions

56. Simon comes to the emergency room complaining he cannot move his left arm or hand. After a careful examination, it is determined that he has had a cerebrovascular accident (CVA), or a stroke. What can you conclude about the general location of the stroke based on the above information?

57. During a routine physical exam a physician may shine a light in your eye to ascertain whether the pupils will constrict. Which cranial nerve(s) is/are the physician testing?

Challenge Questions

58. Explain the significance of the convolutions of the cerebral cortex.

59. Damage to the hypothalamus might result in what general types of symptoms?

INTEGRATED CNS FUNCTION: REFLEXES

Matching

60. Match the description of the reflexes below with one choice from each pair of reflexes listed here: spinal (SP) or cranial (CR); somatic (SO) or autonomic (AU); innate (IN) or conditioned (CO); monosynaptic (MO) or polysynaptic (PO).

a. _____ You see a person bite into a lemon and you salivate.

b. _____ The patellar tendon is struck and you show a knee-jerk response.

c. _____ You walk out into bright sunlight and your pupils constrict.

d. _____ Your dog begins to salivate when she hears you open the dog food bag.

e. _____ You put your hand on a hot Bunsen burner, but pull it away quickly.

Completion

Fill in the blanks to complete the following narrative.

61. The simplest actions of the nervous system are **(a)**, or automatic responses to a particular stimulus. **(a)** can be mediated either by the brain or **(b)**; they may be either somatic or **(c)**, and they may be either conditioned or **(d)**. Two spinal reflexes discussed in the chapter are the withdrawal-crossed extensor reflex and the **(e)**. The **(f)** reflex is an example of a/n **(g)** cranial reflex that causes constriction of the **(h)** of the eye.

a. _____   e. _____

b. _____   f. _____

c. _____   g. _____

d. _____   h. _____

Short Answer

Answer the following question in 1–4 sentences.

62. Upon standing up from a lying down position your blood pressure drops as blood moves down and away from your heart. The body responds to this drop in blood pressure by increasing the heart rate and constricting the blood vessels. Both of these reflex actions cause the blood pressure to rise. What type of reflex is observed here?

Multiple Choice

Select the best answer from the choices given.

63. Which of the following is not necessary for a reflex arc?

    a. sensor
    b. effector organ
    c. skeletal muscle
    d. integrating center
    e. afferent neuron

64. What are nociceptors?

    a. sensory receptors that act to produce the sensation of pain
    b. specialized cells of the CNS that act as integrators of information
    c. an alternative name for interneurons
    d. photoreceptors present in the eye
    e. a necessary component of reflex arcs

65. Why is the pupillary light reflex considered a cranial reflex?

    a. because it is a learned reflex
    b. because it is automatic
    c. because integration involves the central nervous system
    d. because integration involves cranial nerves that lead directly to and from the brain
    e. because smooth muscles are involved in the reflex

66. During a reflex, the spinal cord sends signals to which of the following by way of efferent neurons?

    a. brain
    b. effector organ
    c. afferent neuron
    d. other areas of the spinal cord
    e. sensory receptors

True/False

Label the following statements as true (T) or false (F). If false, change the statement to make it true.

67. _____ Reflexes are some of the most intricate and complex functions of the nervous system.

68. _____ The withdrawal reflex is a good example of an autonomic reflex.

69. _____ The knee-jerk reflex is an example of the muscle spindle reflex.

70. _____ Some somatic reflexes can be overridden by the brain.

Sequencing

71. Place the following events of a reflex arc into the proper sequence.

    a. The effector produces the appropriate response.
    b. The CNS integrates the information.
    c. The CNS sends signals to the efferent neuron.
    d. A receptor detects a stimulus.
    e. An afferent neuron sends information to the CNS.

    Sequence: _____

Clinical Questions

72. During a routine physical exam the clinician may strike you with a rubber mallet just below your patella, which should cause a knee-jerk reflex. Explain how this reflex operates.

73. During a physical exam you may test for the plantar reflex. To test for this reflex, a blunt object is drawn on the bottom of the foot from the middle of the heel to the great toe. In adults, stimulation of these receptors causes the toes to flex and move closer together. Describe the characteristics of this reflex.

Challenge Questions

74. Compare and contrast spinal and cranial reflexes.

75. Explain the significance of the crossed-extensor reflex.

Concept Map

76. Fill in the blanks and boxes in the concept map of the withdrawal and crossed-extensor reflexes of the leg.

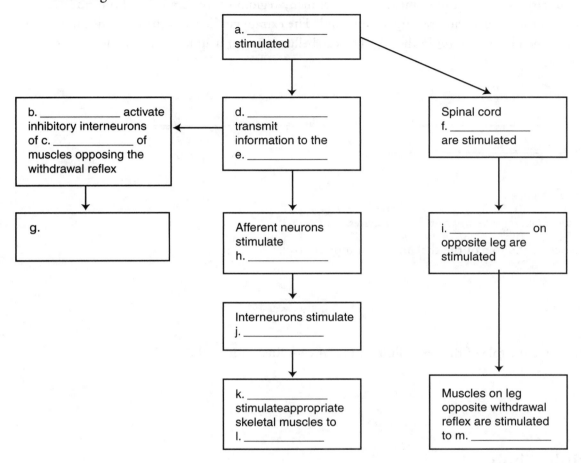

a. _____ stimulated

b. _____ activate inhibitory interneurons of c. _____ of muscles opposing the withdrawal reflex

d. _____ transmit information to the e. _____

Spinal cord f. _____ are stimulated

g.

Afferent neurons stimulate h. _____

i. _____ on opposite leg are stimulated

Interneurons stimulate j. _____

k. _____ stimulateappropriate skeletal muscles to l. _____

Muscles on leg opposite withdrawal reflex are stimulated to m. _____

INTEGRATED CNS FUNCTION: VOLUNTARY MOTOR CONTROL

Matching

77. Match the following structures with their functions below: basal nuclei (BN), extrapyramidal tracts (EPT), reticular formation (RF), upper motor neurons (UMN).

a. _____ This is a direct pathway from the primary motor cortex to the spinal cord; axons in this terminate in the ventral horn of the spinal cord.

b. _____ This area provides feedback to the cortex through the thalamus for smooth muscle movements. In addition, this area is affected by Huntington's chorea and Parkinson's disease.

c. _____ Located in the brainstem, this area is involved in involuntary movements.

d. _____ These are indirect connections from the spinal cord to the brain; neurons from this area do not form synapses on motor neurons.

Completion

Fill in the blanks to complete the following narrative.

78. Voluntary motor control of muscles involves many regions of the CNS. The **(a)** formulates plans for movement and sets up a command. The extrapyramidal and **(b)** transmit information about the plan to the **(c)** in the **(d)**. The cerebellum and **(e)** help to make the movement smooth.

   a. _____   d. _____

   b. _____   e. _____

   c. _____

Short Answer

Answer the following questions in 1–4 sentences.

79. Describe the role of the thalamus in motor control.

80. Describe the role of the cerebellum in motor coordination.

Multiple Choice

Select the best answer from the choices given.

81. Which of the following receives information from the cortex and assists in making corrections to the force and direction of movement of muscles?

   a. brainstem   c. motor neurons   e. red nuclei
   b. reticular formation d. cerebellum

82. A 54-year-old woman has damaged her brainstem. Which of the following general motor functions will likely be affected ?

   a. involuntary control of posture
   b. voluntary movement of legs and toes
   c. formulation of intentions about movement
   d. controlling large groups of muscles in the upper body
   e. assisting in learned repetitive motions

83. Which of the following are direct pathways from the primary motor cortex to the spinal cord?

   a. extrapyramidal tracts   c. pyramidal tracts   e. reticular formation
   b. basal nuclei   d. red nuclei

84. Jill has had some brain damage due to a blow to the base of her skull. She has control of voluntary movements, but she is clumsy and she has trouble telling how much force to use in her movements. Which of the following is most likely damaged?

 a. basal nuclei   c. red nuclei   e. cerebellum
 b. reticular formation   d. cerebral cortex

85. Huntington's chorea disrupts the functioning of which of the following parts of the CNS?

 a. cerebellum   c. red nuclei   e. vestibular nuclei
 b. basal nuclei   d. cerebral cortex

True/False

Label the following statements as true (T) *or false* (F). *If false, change the statement to make it true.*

86. _____ Medullary pyramids are axons that cross over to the opposite side of the CNS.

87. _____ Parallel processing is rare in the nervous system.

88. _____ A characteristic sign of cerebellar damage is initiation tremor.

89. _____ The basal nuclei send output to the cortex through the cerebellum.

90. _____ The pyramidal tracts are also known as the corticospinal tracts.

Clinical Question

91. People who suffer from Tourette's syndrome have an excess of dopamine in the basal nuclei. What might be some symptoms of an individual with Tourette's syndrome?

Challenge Questions

92. Explain parallel processing, including its importance.

93. A surgeon is repairing the delicate nerves and muscles in the hand of a young boy who put his arm through a pane of glass. Describe the role of the pyramidal and extrapyramidal tracts *of the surgeon* as he operates.

Concept Map

94. Fill in the blanks and boxes in the concept map of the parts of the brain involved in voluntary motor control.

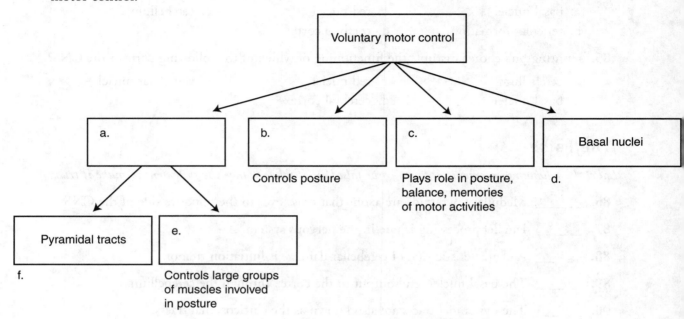

INTEGRATED CNS FUNCTION: LANGUAGE AND SLEEP

Matching

95. Match the brain wave with its characteristic below: slow wave sleep (SWS), rapid eye movement (REM).

a. _____ Postural muscles are paralyzed.

b. _____ Jaw muscles relax.

c. _____ Bursts of involuntary muscle movement may occur every 10–20 minutes.

d. _____ Thoughts tend to be illogical; dreams are elaborate.

e. _____ Multiple stages of low-frequency EEG waves occur.

Completion

Fill in the blanks to complete the following narratives.

96. The areas of the brain important for language include **(a)** in the temporal lobe and **(b)** in the frontal lobe. An abnormality in language skills is called **(c)**. Damage to **(a)** causes **(d)**, while damage to **(b)** results in **(e)**.

a. _____   d. _____

b. _____   e. _____

c. _____

97. The body moves through various stages throughout sleep. The stages of sleep can be monitored using a/n **(a)**. **(b)** is characterized by low-frequency, high-amplitude **(a)** waves, while **(c)** sleep is characterized by high-frequency, low-amplitude **(a)** waves.

a. _____

b. _____

c. _____

Short Answer

Answer the following question in 1–4 sentences.

98. Describe the electrical activities of the brain during alert wakefulness and resting wakefulness.

Multiple Choice

Select the best answer from the choices given.

99. Tim is in deep sleep during a physiology class. Which of the following would be most prominent on an EEG?

   a. alpha waves   c. ARAS   e. REM
   b. beta waves   d. SWS

100. Tim's classmate drops his textbook on the floor, and Tim wakes up. Now he is awake and alert. Which of the following structures is important in *maintaining* alert wakefulness?

   a. reticular formation   c. Broca's area   e. hypothalamus
   b. Wernicke's area   d. cerebellum

101. Which of the following is characteristic of slow-wave sleep?

   a. alpha waves
   b. beta waves
   c. increased parasympathetic nervous system activity
   d. postural muscles paralyzed
   e. elaborate dreams

102. Which of the following neurotransmitters has been implicated in the induction of slow-wave sleep?

   a. glycine   c. acetylcholine   e. adenosine
   b. GABA   d. endorphins

103. Which of the following parts of the brain is important in switching between wakefulness and sleep?

   a. cerebellum   c. Wernicke's area   e. vestibular nuclei
   b. reticular formation   d. Broca's area

True/False

Label the following statements as true (T) or false (F). If false, change the statement to make it true.

104. _____ During REM the EEG waves are fast and high in amplitude.

105. _____ SWS dreams are more likely to be remembered.

106. _____ REM sleep is often referred to as paradoxical sleep.

107. _____ Alpha waves are present while you are awake and alert.

Clinical Questions

108. A 68-year-old woman is admitted to the emergency room following a stroke. When asked questions, she appears to understand, but when the woman answers her words are garbled and do not seem to make sense. What is this condition called? Which lobe of the brain is probably affected and which area of the lobe is damaged?

109. You are a clinician at the college campus health clinic where you see many students just after mid-term exams who have chronic infections and do not seem to get well. After questioning these students the pattern emerges that many of them have also spent many sleepless nights writing papers and attempting to study for tests. What advice might you give these students about the benefits of sleep?

Challenge Question

110. Compare and contrast the location and functions of Wernicke's area and Broca's area.

INTEGRATED CNS FUNCTION: EMOTIONS AND MOTIVATION, LEARNING AND MEMORY

Matching

111. Determine whether each of the statements below is describing associative learning (AL) or nonassociative learning (NL).

a. _____ Your physiology lab partner repeatedly clicks her pen during an exam; in the beginning it annoys you, but by the end of class you do not hear it anymore.

b. _____ A class of fifth graders gets restless as the minute hand on the clock approaches the time for recess.

c. _____ A toad attempts to eat a bee and is stung. After that episode the toad no longer attempts to eat bees.

112. Determine whether each of the statements below is describing procedural memory (PM) or declarative memory (DM).

a. _____ After not playing ice hockey for ten years, you go ice skating in the winter and find that you can ice skate very well.

b. _____ Even though you are 30 years old now, you can still remember the phone number of the first house you lived in.

c. _____ You are able to show your little brother how to jump rope, even though you have not jumped rope for five years.

Completion

Fill in the blanks to complete the following narratives.

113. Emotions are generated by the **(a)** based on **(b)**. The **(a)** then transmits information to the **(c)**, where the emotion is actually perceived. Emotion-related responses also include changes in the **(d)** nervous system. **(e)** directs actions and is closely associated with pleasure.

a. _____   d. _____

b. _____   e. _____

c. _____

114. **(a)** is the acquisition of new information, whereas **(b)** is the retention of knowledge. Both **(a)** and **(b)** require plasticity. One type of plasticity is **(c)**, in which communication across a/n **(d)** is enhanced.

a. _____   c. _____

b. _____   d. _____

Short Answer

Answer the following questions in 1–4 sentences.

115. Describe the difference between emotions and motivation.

116. Distinguish between learning and memory.

Multiple Choice

Select the best answer from the choices given.

117. Which of the following neurotransmitters is the most likely candidate for development of addiction?

    a. choline   c. acetylcholine   e. glycine

    b. dopamine   d. GABA

118. Which of the following is most often tested for on physiology exams?

    a. habituation   c. emotion   e. procedural memory

    b. associative learning   d. declarative memory

119. What is the term for when short-term memories are placed into long-term memory?

    a. consolidation   c. motivation   e. habituation

    b. potentiation   d. sensitization

True/False

Label the following statements as true (T) or false (F). If false, change the statement to make it true.

120. _____ Research suggests that repetition is necessary to form all memories.

121. _____ Long-term potentiation leads to an increase in the strength of the synaptic connection between two neurons.

122. _____ Pleasure is an emotion that can lead to addiction.

123. _____ Habituation is an increase in response to repeated stimulus.

Clinical Question

124. A man is brought into the clinic because he was found walking aimlessly in the streets. Upon examination he seems to be able to remember how to perform memorized motor skills such as taking the cap off of a bottle, how to use a pen, etc. However, he has trouble remembering facts and events such as his birth date or his address. Which part of the brain do you suspect has been damaged?

Challenge Question

125. Ten months after a severe automobile accident you have completely recovered physically, but you have to describe the incident to a jury who will decide monetary damages for your injuries. After you describe the incident, you notice that your heart is racing, you are sweating and breathing deeply. What areas of the brain are involved in these responses?

Concept Map

126. Fill in the boxes of the concept map of the areas of the brain involved in emotions.

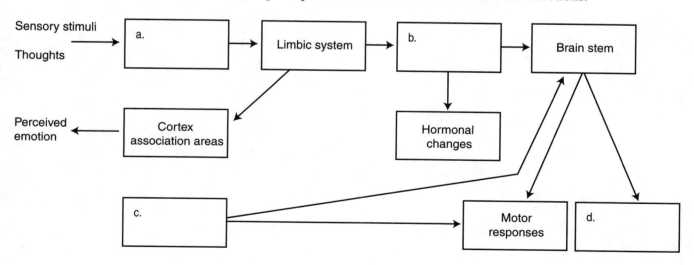

9 The Nervous System: Sensory Systems

Objectives

We recommend that you review the **Objective**s for this chapter, found on p. 260 of *Principles of Human Physiology*. The **Objectives** outline what you should know from each chapter.

Key Terms

accommodation
acuity
adaptation
adequate stimulus
ampulla
analgesia
anterior cavity
aqueous humor
auditory cortex
basal cell
basilar membrane
bipolar cell
blind spot
choroid
ciliary body
ciliary muscle
circular muscle
cochlea
cold receptor
concave
cone
convex
cornea
cranial nerve II
cupula
dorsal column - medial
   lemniscal pathway
emmetropia
endogenous analgesia system
endolymph
eustachian tube

external auditory meatus
fast pain
first-order neuron
fovea
free nerve ending
ganglion cell
gate-control theory
hair cell
helicotrema
hyperopia
iris
kinocilium
labeled line
lateral geniculate body
lateral inhibition
law of specific nerve energies
lens
macula lutea
mechanical nociceptor
mechanoreceptor
medial geniculate body
modality
myopia
nociceptor
odorant
olfactory binding protein
olfactory epithelium
olfactory nerve
olfactory receptor cell
optic chiasm
optic disk

optic nerve
optic radiation
optic tract
organ of Corti
ossicle
otolith
oval window
parallel processing
perception
perilymph
photopigment
photoreceptor
phototransduction
polymodal nociceptor
proprioception
pupil
radial muscle
rapidly-adapting (phasic)
   receptor
receptive field
receptor potential
referred pain
reflection
refraction
retina
rod
round window
saccule
scala media = cochlear duct
scala tympani
scala vestibuli

sclera	spinothalamic tract	two-point discrimination
second-order neuron	stereocilia	threshold
semicircular canal	supporting cell	tympanic membrane
sensory receptor	tastant	utricle
sensory unit	taste bud	vestibular apparatus
slow pain	tectorial membrane	vestibular membrane
slowly-adapting (tonic) receptor	thermal nociceptor	visual cortex
	thermoreceptor	vitreous chamber
somatosensory system	third-order neuron	vitreous humor
somesthetic sensation	tonotopic map	warm receptor
special sensory system	transduction	zonular fiber

GENERAL PRINCIPLES OF SENSORY PHYSIOLOGY

Matching

1. Match the type of receptor with its modality below: chemoreceptor (CR), mechanoreceptor (MR), photoreceptor (PR), thermoreceptor (TR). Each receptor can be used more than once.

   a. _____ sound waves

   b. _____ oxygen dissolved in plasma

   c. _____ photons of light

   d. _____ free hydrogen ions in plasma

   e. _____ stretch of blood vessel wall

   f. _____ increase in temperatures between 37°C and 45°C

   g. _____ substances dissolved in mucus

Completion

Fill in the blanks to complete the following narrative.

2. Our ability to perceive the outside world depends on the presence of **(a)** and specific neural pathways to communicate information to the **(b)**. Sensory systems must code for different qualities of the stimulus. Stimulus type is coded by the **(c)** and the **(d)** activated. Stimulus intensity is coded by **(e)** and **(f)**. The ability to locate a stimulus depends on the size of the **(g)**, the degree of overlap of **(g)**, and **(h)**.

   a. _____   e. _____

   b. _____   f. _____

   c. _____   g. _____

   d. _____   h. _____

Short Answer

Answer the following question in 1–4 sentences.

3. Explain the functional relationship between sensory receptors and receptor potentials.

Multiple Choice

Select the best answer from the choices given.

4. Which of the following senses is not a special sensory system?

a. taste   c. hearing   e. proprioception
b. vision   d. vestibular

5. A physiology classmate sits next to you wearing a strong perfume. You notice it initially, but by the end of class you seem not to smell the perfume any more. Which of the following receptors adapted to the stimulus?

a. rapidly adapting receptors   d. proprioceptors
b. tonic receptors   e. stretch receptors
c. phasic receptors

6. Why can't a photoreceptor respond to small changes in temperature?

a. The stimulus (temperature) is too low to be sensed by the photoreceptor.
b. The body does not have very many photoreceptors.
c. There is not an adequate stimulus for the photoreceptor.
d. Photoreceptors do not produce receptor potentials very easily.
e. Photoreceptors are slowly adapting.

7. Free hydrogen ions are sensed by chemoreceptors on cells that are in contact with the blood, but these same chemoreceptors are normally insensitive to blood pressure. What is the term for this selectivity of receptors to particular modalities?

a. the law of specific nerve energies   d. acuity
b. sensory transduction   e. lateral inhibition
c. frequency coding

True/False

Label the following statements as true (T) or false (F). If false, change the statement to make it true.

8. _____ A sensory unit is a single afferent axon and all of the receptors associated with it.

9. _____ Receptive fields are about the same size for most sensory neurons.

10. _____ All senses use the same labeled line for communication with the cerebral cortex.

Labeling

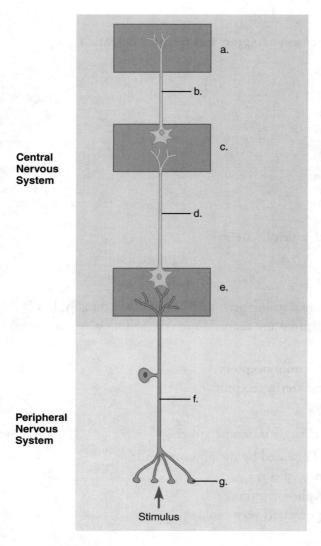

FIGURE 9.1

11. Label a–g in Figure 9.1.

Challenge Questions

12. A small gnat (about 2 mm in size) lands on your index finger and you feel it, but when the same insect lands on your calf you do not notice it. Explain why.

13. Explain how the body increases the acuity of locating a stimulus.

14. Compare and contrast frequency coding and population coding.

THE SOMATOSENSORY SYSTEM

Matching

15. Match each of the following skin receptor types with its description below: free nerve ending (FNE), hair follicle receptor (HFR), Pacinian corpuscle (PC), Ruffini's ending (RE).

a. _____ superficial receptor that senses light touch

b. _____ present in deep, hairy skin, and senses pressure

c. _____ a superficial receptor that senses bending of the hair shaft

d. _____ a rapidly adapting sensor that senses vibrations

Completion

Fill in the blanks to complete the following narrative.

16. The somatosensory system enables perception of stimuli associated with the body surface, also known as **(a)**, or body position, also known as **(b)**. Some receptors in the somatosensory system are specialized nerve endings or **(c)**. Information about touch, pressure, vibration, and proprioception is transmitted to the **(d)** via the **(e)**. Information about **(f)** and temperature is transmitted to the **(g)** via the **(h)**. Information from the **(g)** is then transmitted to the **(i)**.

a. _____   f. _____

b. _____   g. _____

c. _____   h. _____

d. _____   i. _____

e. _____

Short Answer

Answer the following questions in 1–4 sentences.

17. You accidentally slam your index finger in a car door. You notice that there is an initial sharp pain and then a more prolonged aching pain. Describe the two pain responses, including the fiber types involved.

18. What is referred pain?

Multiple Choice

Select the best answer from the choices given.

19. Which of the following skin receptor types has the greatest acuity?
    - a. free nerve ending
    - b. Pacinian corpuscle
    - c. Meissner's corpuscle
    - d. hair follicle receptor
    - e. Merkel's disk

20. You have just placed your hand on a tack—and it hurts! Which receptor was used to sense the pain?
    - a. Ruffini's ending
    - b. thermal nociceptors
    - c. mechanical nociceptors
    - d. Meissner's corpuscle
    - e. Pacinian corpuscle

21. Which of the following is not sensed by polymodal nociceptors?
    - a. vibrations
    - b. intense heat
    - c. intense cold
    - d. chemicals released from damaged tissue
    - e. intense mechanical stimulation

22. Which of the following parts of the body has the most somatosensory cortex devoted to it?
    - a. lips
    - b. calf
    - c. back
    - d. forehead
    - e. thigh

23. Juanita has pain in her upper left chest area. Unbeknownst to her, she is having spasms in her esophagus that is causing her pain. What kind of pain is she experiencing?
    - a. intense
    - b. analgesic
    - c. referred
    - d. second-order
    - e. thermal

24. Which neurotransmitter has been implicated in the blocking of pain on second-order neurons and induces inhibitory postsynaptic potentials?
    - a. acetylcholine
    - b. epinephrine
    - c. oxytocin
    - d. dopamine
    - e. enkephalin

True/False

Label the following statements as true (T) *or false* (F). *If false, change the statement to make it true.*

25. _____ Merkel's disks have large receptive fields in the skin and sense intense hot or cold stimuli in the skin.

26. _____ Nociceptors sense intense stimuli (such as pain) in the skin.

27. _____ Thermoreceptors for warmth in the skin are specialized structures known as Pacinian corpuscles.

28. _____ Polymodal nociceptors in the skin respond to changes in temperature only.

Labeling

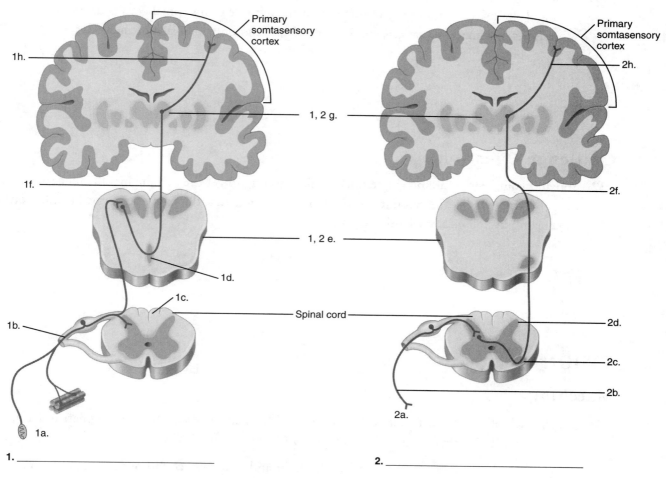

FIGURE 9.2

29. Label the structures (1a–h and 2a–h) in Figure 9.2. Also label which side (**1** or **2**) is the spinothalamic tract or the dorsal column-medial lemniscal pathway.

Sequencing

30. Starting in the periqueductal gray matter, place the following CNS pathway involved in endogenous analgesia in the correct sequence.

    a. lateral reticular formation
    b. second-order neuron is blocked
    c. nociceptive afferent neuron
    d. nucleus raphe magnus

    Sequence: _____

Clinical Question

31. A man washing windows falls two stories and is brought into the emergency room. After an MRI and extensive X rays it is determined that the left side of his spinal cord is damaged. What types of somatic sensations are likely to be lost and on which side of the body?

Challenge Question

32. You and your brother are playing tennis. While running to get the ball, he hits the fence and hurts his right thigh. You tell him to rub it and he notices that the pain goes away. He asks you to explain physiologically why this works.

VISION

Matching

33. Match each of the following clinical conditions with its characteristic below: astigmatism (AS), emmetropia (EO), hyperopia (HO), myopia (MO), presbyopia (PO).

    a. _____ The eye can focus light from both far and near sources without accommodation.

    b. _____ A hardening of the lens that occurs with aging, making accommodation for near vision difficult.

    c. _____ Causes erratic bending of light waves.

    d. _____ The eye can focus on distant objects, but not on near ones.

    e. _____ In this condition, the lens or cornea is too strong for the length of the eyeball.

Completion

Fill in the blanks to complete the following narrative.

34. The axons of ganglion cells make up the **(a)**. Information is transmitted from the **(a)** to the **(b)**, where half of the axons from each eye cross to the opposite side of the CNS such that all input from the **(c)** is now on the left side, and all information from the **(d)** is on the right side. The axons of ganglion cells after the optic chiasm make up the **(e)**. The **(e)** terminates in the **(f)** of the **(g)**, where the ganglion cell axons communicate with neurons that transmit information to the **(h)** in the **(i)** lobe.

a. _____   f. _____

b. _____   g. _____

c. _____   h. _____

d. _____   i. _____

e. _____

Short Answer

Answer the following questions in 1–4 sentences.

35. When you close one eye your depth perception is compromised. Explain why.

36. Define parallel processing.

Multiple Choice

Select the best answer from the choices given.

37. Which of the following would be found in the fovea?

    a. ganglion neurons   c. bipolar neurons   e. aqueous humor
    b. cones   d. rhodopsin

38. While looking in the shallow end of a swimming pool, you notice a coin that someone has dropped in the water. You reach into the water to pick up the coin but you misjudge where the coin was. What happened to the light rays that caused you to misjudge the position of the coin?

    a. The light waves were reflected off of the water's surface.
    b. The light waves were greater than 800 nm.
    c. The light waves were refracted.
    d. The light waves were in your blind spot.
    e. The light waves were less than 300 nm.

39. Refraction can be altered for near or far vision by the _____.

    a. ciliary muscles   c. vitreous humor   e. neural layer of the retina

    b. cornea   d. aqueous humor

40. Joe is focusing his eyes on a distant airplane in the sky. Which of the following statements is true?

    a. The lens is at its thickest width.

    b. The ciliary muscles are contracted.

    c. Accommodation is not occurring in the eyes.

    d. The light rays are nearly parallel.

    e. Only the cornea is involved in focusing.

True/False

Label the following statements as true (T) *or false* (F). *If false, change the statement to make it true.*

41. _____ Rods provide the ability to see color vision.

42. _____ In the fovea, only cones are present and the ratio of rods to cones increases with distance from the fovea.

43. _____ The macula lutea is a depression in the retina that provides a clear path for light to reach the fovea.

44. _____ The inner layer of the retina contains bipolar cells, rods, and cones.

Clinical Questions

45. A 53-year-old woman comes to the eye clinic complaining of blurred side vision. An eye examination reveals a very high intraocular pressure (pressure within the anterior chamber). What is the name for this condition and what causes it?

46. Madison, a 6-year-old girl, attends first grade, but she is not doing well. Her teacher suspects that she may have vision problems. Madison's parents take her to the eye clinic where an eye exam reveals that she is myopic. Will she need concave or convex lenses? Explain.

Challenge Questions

47. When you are frightened your pupils dilate. Explain how and why this happens.

48. Lions often hunt at night. Birds such as eagles, however, feed during the day. Discuss the relative distribution of rods and cones in lions and eagles, including some characteristics of the rods and cones.

Concept Map

49. Fill in the blanks in the following concept map of phototransduction in rods in the dark.

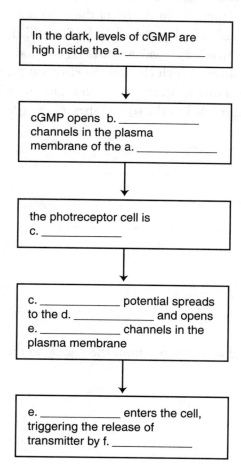

In the dark, levels of cGMP are high inside the a. _____

cGMP opens b. _____ channels in the plasma membrane of the a. _____

the photreceptor cell is c. _____

c. _____ potential spreads to the d. _____ and opens e. _____ channels in the plasma membrane

e. _____ enters the cell, triggering the release of transmitter by f. _____

THE EAR AND HEARING

Matching

50. Match the structure below with its location in the ear: external ear (EA), inner ear (IE), middle ear (ME). Each location can be used more than once.

a. _____ amplifies sound waves

b. _____ fluid filled

c. _____ The eustachian tube connects the pharynx to this part of the ear.

d. _____ The pinna is located here.

e. _____ conducts sound waves to the eardrum

f. _____ contains the cochlea

Completion

Fill in the blanks to complete the following narrative.

51. The ear contains the receptor cells for two sensory systems, **(a)** and equilibrium. Sound waves must enter the **(b)** and then be transduced into neural impulses in the **(c)** of the inner ear. Sound transduction occurs in hair cells of the **(d)**. When sound waves reach the fluid-filled **(e)**, they set up waves that cause movement of the basilar membrane, which causes **(f)** to bend. This bending causes the opening or closing of **(g)** channels, which changes the electrical properties of the cells. When depolarized, a chemical transmitter is released and communicates with afferent neurons in the **(h)**. Sound information is transmitted to the **(i)** and then to the **(j)**.

a. _____   f. _____

b. _____   g. _____

c. _____   h. _____

d. _____   i. _____

e. _____   j. _____

Short Answer

Answer the following question in 1–4 sentences.

52. Describe the two ways that sound waves are amplified as they travel from the middle to the inner ear.

Multiple Choice

Select the best answer from the choices given.

53. Movement of the _____ membrane causes bending of hairs of the hair cells in the organ of Corti.

    a. basilar   c. round window   e. tectorial

    b. tympanic   d. endolymph

54. Which of the following is an ossicle present in the middle ear?

    a. incus   c. oval window   e. auditory meatus

    b. cochlea   d. round window

55. When the ear receives sound waves, which ossicle vibrates first?

    a. incus   c. cochlea   e. round window

    b. tympanic membrane   d. malleus

56. Conduction of sound from the middle ear to the inner ear occurs via vibration of which of the following?

    a. vibration of hairs of the receptor cells

    b. compression of fluids in the cochlea

    c. malleus against the tympanic membrane

    d. stapes against the tympanic membrane

    e. stapes in the oval window

57. When sound waves interact with the stereocilia, which of the following occurs?

    a. Both potassium and calcium channels are open.

    b. Potassium channels are open and calcium channels are closed.

    c. Potassium channels are closed and calcium channels are open.

    d. Both potassium and calcium channels are closed.

    e. Potassium and calcium channels are not involved in sound transmission.

True/False

Label the following statements as true (T) or false (F). If false, change the statement to make it true.

58. _____ The fluid in the scala vestibuli is called endolymph.

59. _____ In the organ of Corti, hair cells bend, causing receptor potentials in the tectorial membrane.

60. _____ The cranial nerve that sends auditory information to the brain is cranial nerve VIII, the vestibulocochlear nerve.

61. _____ Stereocilia code for sound amplitude because the stereocilia bend more when exposed to louder sounds.

Sequencing

62. Place the following structures associated with hearing in the correct sequence.

   a. cochlear nerve
   b. cochlea
   c. stapes
   d. oval window
   e. external auditory meatus
   f. tympanic membrane

   g. incus
   h. malleus
   i. pinna
   j. auditory cortex of the temporal lobe
   k. medial geniculate body

   Sequence: _____

Clinical Question

63. During a physical exam, it was determined that a young boy had difficulty hearing high-pitched sounds in his left ear. The physician sees no blockages, such as wax buildup. Assuming the problem is organic in nature, what is the likely source of his problem?

Challenge Question

64. Elephants can hear low-pitched sounds well and dogs can hear high-pitched sounds well. What might be the structural differences between the ears of these two animals?

THE EAR AND EQUILIBRIUM

Matching

65. Match the structures with their functions below: ampulla (A), cupula (C), kinocilium (K), saccule (S), utricle (U).

   a. _____ the largest stereocilia

   b. _____ contains otoliths with stereocilia extending vertically

   c. _____ an enlarged area at the base of the semicircular canal

   d. _____ a gelatinous area of the ampulla

   e. _____ contains otoliths with stereocilia extending horizontally

Completion

Fill in the blanks to complete the following narrative.

66. The vestibular apparatus of the inner ear includes the **(a)** (for detecting rotation) and the utricle and **(b)** (for detecting linear acceleration). The vestibular apparatus contains hair cells with **(c)** that bend with acceleration of the head. In the **(a)**, the hair cells are located in the **(d)**. Vestibular information is transmitted to the vestibular nuclei of the **(e)**, which communicate to the **(f)** and then to the cortex for perception of equilibrium.

a. _____   d. _____

b. _____   e. _____

c. _____   f. _____

Short Answer

Answer the following question in 1–4 sentences.

67. You are traveling in a roller coaster and gaining speed as you descend the first hill. Which part of the ear senses this change in speed?

Multiple Choice

Select the best answer from the choices given.

68. What happens to the stereocilia in the cupula when the head rotates left?

    a. The stereocilia bend to the left and then to the right.
    b. The stereocilia bend to the right and then to the left.
    c. The stereocilia do not bend much at all when the head is rotated.
    d. The stereocilia bend to the right.
    e. The stereocilia bend to the left.

69. Which of the following is present in the utricle and saccule?

    a. otoliths   c. hemolymph   e. bipolar cells
    b. endolymph   d. perilymph

70. While driving to the local pizza shop you need to slam on the breaks to avoid hitting a pedestrian. Of course you sense the rapid deceleration in speed of the car. Which part of the ear is responsible for detecting changes in this type of movement?

    a. ampulla   c. utricle   e. reticular formation
    b. saccule   d. organ of Corti

True/False

Label the following statements as true (T) *or false* (F). *If false, change the statement to make it true.*

71. _____ Most vestibular afferent nerves terminate in the vestibular nuclei.

72. _____ At rest, hair cells of the vestibular apparatus do not release any neurotransmitters.

Clinical Question

73. Jamilia visits her physician and complains of disturbances in equilibrium, dizziness, and nausea. Assuming the problem is with her ear and not nerves, what part of the ear is probably not operating correctly?

Challenge Question

74. Explain the mechanism of how a person senses rotation of the head.

TASTE AND OLFACTION

Matching

75. Match the following cells involved with olfaction with their description or function below: basal cells (BC), olfactory receptor cells (ORC), supporting cells (SC).

    a. _____ respond to olfactory stimuli

    b. _____ secrete mucus

    c. _____ pass through the cribiform plate

    d. _____ replace the neurons that respond to olfactory stimuli

Completion

Fill in the blanks to complete the following narrative.

76. Taste receptor cells are located within **(a)**. Molecules that bind to taste receptors are called **(b)**. Each of the four primary tastes use a different **(c)**. Sensory information is first transmitted via **(d)** to the gustatory nuclei of the **(e)**, then relayed through the **(f)** to the gustatory cortex.

a. _____   d. _____

b. _____   e. _____

c. _____   f. _____

Short Answer

Answer the following question in 1–4 sentences.

77. Describe the role of olfactory binding proteins.

Multiple Choice

78. Taste receptor cells are stimulated by which of the following?
    a. sodium channels closing
    b. potassium channels closing
    c. calcium channels closing
    d. stretching of the receptor cells
    e. chemicals binding to the receptor cells

79. Which of the following cranial nerves is a neural pathway for taste?
    a. vagus
    b. oculomotor
    c. abducens
    d. optic
    e. olfactory

80. Tastants containing bitter compounds can either block potassium channels or _____.
    a. open sodium channels
    b. open calcium channels
    c. activate transducin
    d. activate gustducin
    e. bind olfactory proteins

True/False

Label the following statements as true (T) or false (F). If false, change the statement to make it true.

81. _____ Sensory impulses transmitted over the facial, glossopharyngeal, and vagus nerves are involved in the sensation of taste.

82. _____ Receptors for bitter flavors are most highly concentrated on the tip of the tongue.

Challenge Question

83. Describe the steps involved in olfactory signal transduction and the neural pathway for olfaction.

Concept Map

84. Fill in the boxes of signal transduction of sour and salty tastes.

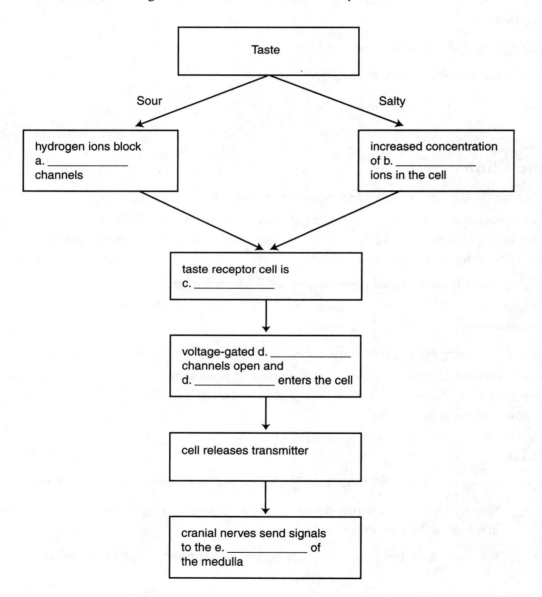

10 The Nervous System: Autonomic and Motor Systems

Objectives

We recommend that you review the **Objectives** for this chapter, found on p. 311 of *Principles of Human Physiology*. The **Objectives** outline what you should know from each chapter.

Key Terms

adrenergic

alpha receptor

autonomic ganglia

beta receptor

cholinergic

collateral ganglia

effector organ

end-plate potential (EPP)

fight-or-flight response

lateral horn

motor end plate

motor neuron

motor unit

neuromuscular junction

postganglionic neuron

preganglionic neuron

sympathetic chain

sympathetic trunk

terminal bouton

vagus nerve (CN X)

varicosity

visceral reflex

THE AUTONOMIC AND SOMATIC NERVOUS SYSTEMS

Matching

1. Match the physiological condition below with whether the parasympathetic (P) or sympathetic (S) branch of the autonomic nervous system is most active.

   a. _____ swimming the first leg of the swim team relay

   b. _____ sleeping

   c. _____ relaxing while reading a novel

   d. _____ running to a class for which you are late

   e. _____ eating a relaxing meal at a fine restaurant

2. Match the sympathetic receptor type with its appropriate effect listed below: α_1, α_2, β_1, β_2.

   a. _____ relaxation of bronchial muscle

   b. _____ inhibition of secretions of the digestive tract

   c. _____ stimulation of secretions of sweat glands

   d. _____ inhibition of endocrine secretions of the pancreas

   e. _____ increased force of contraction of the heart

   f. _____ dilation of the pupils

3. Match the following terms associated with the somatic nervous system with their descriptions below: end-plate potential (EPP), motor end plate (MEP), motor neuron (MN), motor unit (MU), muscle fiber (MF), neuromuscular junction (NJ), terminal bouton (TB).

   a. _____ the synapse of a motor neuron with skeletal muscle fiber at a very specialized location of the fiber

   b. _____ the part of the motor neuron that releases the neurotransmitter

   c. _____ the part of the muscle fiber containing very dense concentrations of cholinergic receptors

   d. _____ the only nerve cell present in the somatic nervous system

   e. _____ a muscle cell

   f. _____ the depolarization caused at the motor end plate

   g. _____ a motor neuron and all of the muscle cells that it innervates

Completion

Fill in the blanks to complete the following narratives.

   4. There are two main branches of the efferent nervous system: the **(a)** and the **(b)**. The **(a)** includes the **(c)** and **(d)** nervous systems, which innervate **(e)** muscle, smooth muscle, **(f)**, and adipose tissue. Effector organs of the **(a)** are usually innervated by both **(c)** and **(d)**, an arrangement called **(g)**.

   a. _____   e. _____

   b. _____   f. _____

   c. _____   g. _____

   d. _____

   5. The somatic nervous system consists of pathways of single **(a)**, which innervate only **(b)**. **(a)** originate in the **(c)** of the spinal cord. A **(d)** is a single motor neuron and the muscle cells it innervates. The synapse between a motor neuron and a skeletal muscle fiber is called a/n **(e)**. The motor neuron contains the neurotransmitter **(f)**, stored in vesicles in the **(g)**. The binding of **(f)** to **(h)** receptors in the motor end plate causes a/n **(i)**.

   a. _____   f. _____

   b. _____   g. _____

   c. _____   h. _____

   d. _____   i. _____

   e. _____

6. State YES or NO as to whether each of the following effector organs receives dual innervation from the autonomic nervous system.

Effector organ	Dual innervation?
Iris muscle of eye	a.
Salivary glands	b.
Arterioles to brain	c.
Pancreatic endocrine glands	d.
Bronchial muscles	e.
Motility of digestive tract	f.
Arterioles to skeletal muscles	g.

Short Answer

Answer the following questions in 1–4 sentences.

7. Describe the parts of neurons that are present in autonomic ganglia.

8. Describe the location and responses of the two types of cholinergic receptors.

9. Define visceral reflex and provide an example.

10. Describe collateral ganglia and their location in the autonomic nervous system.

11. Describe the location and function of varicosities.

12. Describe the role of the following parts of the brain in regulating autonomic function: hypothalamus, pons, and medulla oblongata.

13. Contrast the effects of latroxin and crotoxin on the neuromuscular junction.

Multiple Choice

Select the best answer from the choices given.

14. Where are the cell bodies of somatic neurons and preganglionic neurons of the autonomic nervous system located?

    a. in the ganglia
    b. in the gray matter of the CNS
    c. in the white matter of the PNS
    d. scattered throughout the nervous system
    e. only in the brain

15. Which cells of the adrenal medulla are innervated by some postganglionic neurons of the sympathetic branch of the autonomic nervous system?

    a. gray matter cells
    b. white ramus cells
    c. chromaffin cells
    d. cells in the collateral ganglia
    e. cells in the autonomic ganglia

16. Where do preganglionic neurons of the sympathetic division originate?

    a. scattered in the peripheral nervous system
    b. white matter of the brain
    c. cortex of the brain
    d. autonomic ganglia
    e. lateral horn of the spinal cord

17. The _____ is a gland that releases _____ in response to sympathetic stimulation.

    a. adrenal medulla : catecholamines
    b. hypothalamus : oxytocin
    c. thyroid gland : endorphins
    d. cerebellum : glycine
    e. kidney : GABA

18. In the somatic nervous system, _____ innervate _____.

    a. postganglionic neurons : skeletal muscles
    b. preganglionic neurons : cardiac muscle
    c. motor neurons : skeletal muscles
    d. motor neurons : cardiac and smooth muscle
    e. preganglionic : cardiac and smooth muscle

19. Which of the following cranial nerves does **not** serve a parasympathetic function?

    a. vagus nerve
    b. glossopharyngeal nerve
    c. facial nerve
    d. olfactory nerve
    e. oculomotor nerve

20. Which of the following pairs of neurotransmitters are present in the peripheral nervous system?

    a. acetylcholine and dopamine
    b. dopamine and norepinephrine
    c. epinephrine and acetylcholine
    d. dopamine and epinephrine
    e. dopamine and acetylcholine

21. α_1 adrenergic receptors have the greatest affinity for _____ and generally exert a/n _____ effect in the postsynaptic cell.

    a. acetylcholine : stimulatory
    b. epinephrine : stimulatory
    c. norepinephrine : inhibitory
    d. acetylcholine : inhibitory
    e. GABA : stimulatory

22. β_2 adrenergic receptors have the greatest affinity for _____ and generally exert a/n _____ effect in the postsynaptic cell.

    a. norepinephrine : stimulatory
    b. glycine : stimulatory
    c. norepinephrine : inhibitory
    d. epinephrine : inhibitory
    e. acetylcholine : stimulatory

23. Autonomic postganglionic neurotransmitters are released from which of the following?

    a. axon terminals
    b. varicosities
    c. synaptic bulbs
    d. cell bodies
    e. dendrites

24. Upon standing up, which of the following visceral reflexes would occur?

    a. dilation of blood vessels
    b. increased force of contraction of the heart
    c. slower heart rate
    d. increased parasympathetic activity
    e. decreased sympathetic activity

25. Neural communication at the neuromuscular junction is _____.

    a. always inhibitory
    b. inhibitory if catecholamines are the neurotransmitter
    c. always stimulatory
    d. stimulatory only if EPI or NE is the neurotransmitter
    e. inhibitory only if EPI or NE is the neurotransmitter

26. An example of effects produced by the parasympathetic branch of the autonomic nervous system could be _____.

    a. dilation of bronchioles
    b. increased secretion by digestive glands
    c. increased force of heart contractions
    d. increased heart rate
    e. increased epinephrine production and release

27. Which of the following is the function of the intrinsic neurons of the autonomic nervous system?

    a. entirely stop the flow of information in parasympathetic neurons
    b. synapse with the interneurons of the cortex
    c. modulate the flow of information to the target organs
    d. speed up the transfer of information to the spinal cord and brain
    e. synapse with the gray matter and white matter in the spinal cord

True/False

Label the following statements as true (T) *or false* (F). *If false, change the statement to make it true.*

28. _____ Acetylcholine is the only neurotransmitter released from preganglionic axons of the autonomic nervous system and motor neurons of the somatic nervous system.

29. _____ Neurons that release norepinephrine are referred to as cholinergic.

30. _____ Skeletal muscle cells contain muscarinic cholinergic receptors.

31. _____ Monamine oxidase degrades catecholamines at adrenergic neuroeffector junctions.

32. _____ Nerves of the autonomic nervous system contain only efferent fibers.

33. _____ Nicotinic cholinergic receptors have an excitatory effect on the postsynaptic cell.

34. _____ The autonomic nervous system is sometimes called the voluntary nervous system.

35. _____ Innervation by a motor neuron controls skeletal muscle contraction.

Labeling

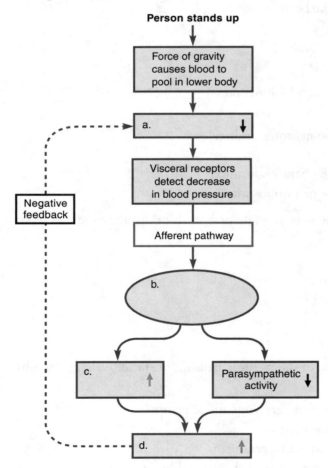

FIGURE 10.1

36. Label a–d in Figure 10.1.

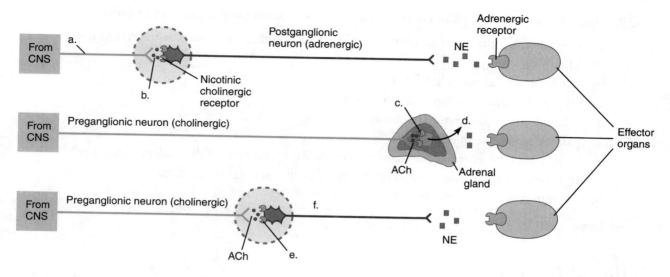

Sympathetic nervous system

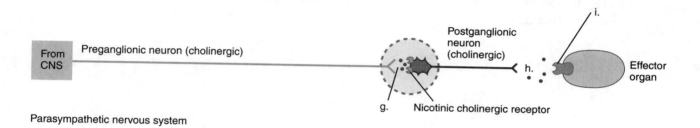

Parasympathetic nervous system

FIGURE 10.2

37. In the space below, identify the structures (a–h) in Figure 10.2.

Sequencing

38. Place the following events of the mechanism of action of α_2 adrenergic receptors in the proper sequence.

   a. inhibitory G protein activated
   b. cAMP synthesis reduced
   c. adenylate cyclase activity decreased
   d. NE or EPI bind to the α_2 receptor

   Sequence: _____

39. Place the following events in communication at the neuromuscular junction in order.

   a. Acetylcholine diffuses to and binds to nicotinic cholinergic receptors at the motor end plate.
   b. Voltage-gated calcium channels open.
   c. Small conductance cation channels open.
   d. Calcium enters the terminal bouton of the motor neuron.
   e. Sodium enters the muscle cell.
   f. An end-plate potential is generated in the plasma membrane of the skeletal muscle cell.
   g. An action potential is generated in the muscle cell, causing contraction.
   h. Calcium triggers the release of acetylcholine by exocytosis.

   Sequence: _____

Clinical Questions

40. Explain why people who take asthma medication containing epinephrine feel better because they can breathe easier, but may experience the undesirable side effects of a fast heart rate or increased sweating.

41. Some antihypertensive drugs are in the class of drugs called beta-blockers. These drugs help to lower blood pressure. How do you suppose these drugs may exert their effects?

Challenge Questions

42. Drugs that have effects similar to those of norepinephrine and epinephrine are called sympathomimetic drugs. What might be some symptoms of an overdose of sympathomimetic drugs?

43. In the visceral reflex, blood pressure increases when you stand up. A number of effector organs are stimulated during this reflex. For example, the heart beats faster and more forcefully, and the arterioles to most of the body constrict. For each of these three effects, list the receptor involved in the response.

44. During the pupillary light reflex, the pupils constrict when a light is shined in the eye. On the other hand, when entering a darkened room, the pupils dilate. Describe which neurotransmitters and receptors regulate pupil diameter in each situation.

Concept Maps

45. The following concept map shows the most common arrangement of neurons in the sympathetic division of the nervous system. Fill in the boxes and blanks.

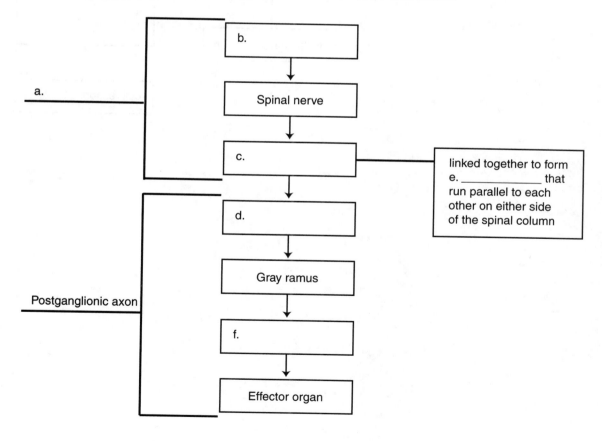

46. The following concept map that shows the mechanism of action of α_1 adrenergic receptors. Fill in the blanks.

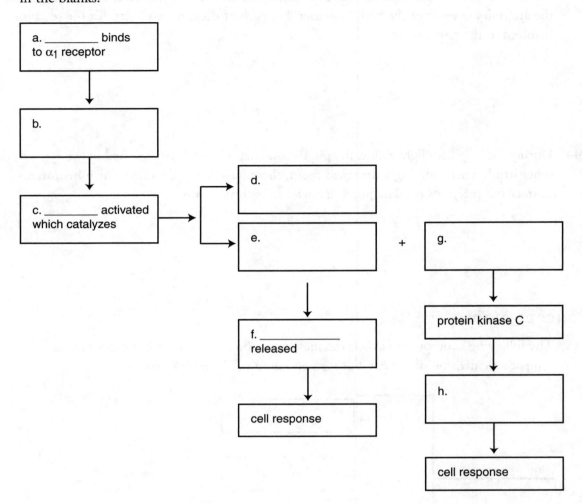

a. _____ binds to α_1 receptor

b.

c. _____ activated which catalyzes

d.

e.

\+

g.

f. _____ released

protein kinase C

cell response

h.

cell response

11 Muscle Physiology

Objectives

We recommend that you review the **Objectives** for this chapter, found on p. 333 of *Principles of Human Physiology*. The **Objectives** outline what you should know from each chapter.

Key Terms

A band
actin
cardiac muscle
contractile component
contractile protein
contraction phase
creatine
creatine phosphate
crossbridge
crossbridge cycle
excitation-contraction
    coupling
fast-twitch fiber
fatigue
glycolytic fiber
H zone
I band
insertion
isometric twitch
isotonic twitch

latent period
length-tension curve
M line
maximum tetanic tension
motor unit
multi-unit smooth muscle
muscle fiber
myofibril
myoglobin
myosin
myosin kinase
neuromuscular junction
origin
oxidative fiber
pacemaker cell
pacemaker potential
recruitment
regulatory protein
relaxation phase
sarcolemma

sarcomere
sarcoplasmic reticulum
series elastic component
single-unit smooth muscle
size principle
skeletal muscle
sliding-filament model
slow-twitch fiber
smooth muscle
striated muscle
summation
tendon
tetanus
thick filament
thin filament
transverse tubule
tropomyosin
troponin
twitch
Z line

SKELETAL MUSCLE STRUCTURE

Matching

1. Match each term in the following list with its anatomical or physiological role below: actin (A), fascicle (F), muscle fiber (MF), myofibril (M), myosin (MY), sarcolemma (S), sarcoplasmic reticulum (SR), transverse tubules (TT), tropomyosin (TM), troponin (T).

   a. _____ the plasma membrane of a muscle cell

   b. _____ Calcium ions bind to this regulatory protein.

   c. _____ also known as a muscle cell

   d. _____ blocks the myosin binding sites

   e. _____ forms crossbridges to actin filaments

   f. _____ Surrounded by connective tissue, this bundle contains many individual muscle cells.

   g. _____ This net-like sac acts as a storage site for calcium ions.

   h. _____ connected to the sarcolemma and extends into the interior of the muscle cell

   i. _____ a bundle of overlapping actin and myosin filaments

   j. _____ The I band contains only this contractile protein.

Completion

Fill in the blanks to complete the following narrative.

2. The fundamental unit of a muscle cell is the **(a)**. This unit is bordered on each side by **(b)**, composed only of actin. The darkest portion of the sarcomere is composed of the **(c)** that spans the entire length of the thick filaments. Adjacent to the A bands is the **(d)**, which is the lightest region because it contains only thin filaments. In the middle of the A band is the **(e)**, which is bordered on either side by the **(f)**.

   a. _____   d. _____

   b. _____   e. _____

   c. _____   f. _____

Short Answer

Answer the following questions in 1–4 sentences.

3. Define crossbridge.

4. Describe the two important roles of the "head groups" of myosin molecules.

Multiple Choice

Select the best answer from the choices given.

5. I bands are composed of which of the following?

a. actin only
b. myosin only
c. both actin and myosin
d. one M line and myosin
e. an I band and actin

6. When a muscle contracts, all of the following are true **except**:

a. Z lines move farther apart from each other.
b. The A band does not change in length.
c. The I bands shorten.
d. The H zone shortens.
e. The M line remains stationary.

7. Which of the following pairs of words are the contractile proteins of skeletal muscles?

a. actin and tropomyosin
b. actin and troponin
c. actin and myosin
d. myosin and the tropomyosin
e. myosin and troponin

8. Which of the following pairs of words are the regulatory proteins of skeletal muscles?

a. actin and tropomyosin
b. tropomyosin and troponin
c. actin and myosin
d. myosin and tropomyosin
e. myosin and troponin

True/False

Label the following statements as true (T) *or false* (F). *If false, change the statement to make it true.*

9. _____ The muscle cell membrane is known as the sarcomere.

10. _____ The sarcoplasmic reticulum covers only the surface of the muscle cell.

11. _____ The actin-binding site of myosin is located on the head of the myosin filament.

12. _____ Regulatory proteins function to begin and end muscle contractions.

13. _____ Each sarcomere extends from M line to M line.

Labeling

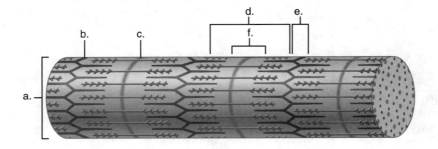

FIGURE 11.1

14. In the space below, identify the structures (a–f) in Figure 11.1 and then describe how each of the following areas of a sarcomere change when a muscle contracts: I bands, A band, M line, Z lines, H zones.

Clinical Question

15. Muscular dystrophies are inherited diseases that affect the normal functioning of skeletal muscle cells. Duchenne's muscular dystrophy (DMD) appears commonly between the ages of 3 and 7, and usually affects males. The incidence of DMD is 3 per 10,000 male births. Males with DMD have abnormal skeletal muscle fibers. They lack the protein dystrophin that is thought to play a role in the regulation of calcium ion channels in the sarcolemma. This condition results in calcium ion channels remaining open too long, giving rise to elevated calcium levels in the sarcoplasmic reticulum, thus causing the muscle fiber itself to degenerate. Based on the above, what symptoms would you expect to find in an individual with DMD?

Challenge Questions

16. Describe the structure of actin and its two regulatory proteins.

17. Compare and contrast the physiological roles of troponin and tropomyosin.

THE MECHANISM OF FORCE GENERATION IN MUSCLE

Matching

18. Match each of the items in the following list of crossbridge cycle events with its description below: binding (B), cocking (C), power stroke (PS), rigor (R), unbinding (U).

a. _____ The myosin head pivots, pulling the actin filament with it.

b. _____ Myosin and actin are tightly bound.

c. _____ P_i is released from the ATPase site.

d. _____ ATP is hydrolyzed; myosin is in its high energy form.

e. _____ The myosin head detaches from the actin.

Completion

Fill in the blanks to complete the following narrative.

19. The crossbridge cycle begins when **(a)** binds to the myosin head. This binding causes the myosin to detach from the **(b)**. Soon after binding to myosin, **(c)** is hydrolyzed, which releases **(d)**. Some of this energy is captured by the **(e)**. The myosin head binds to the active site of actin, which causes the release of **(f)** from the **(g)** site on the myosin. The release of **(h)** allows the myosin molecule to return to its **(i)** form. As it does, the myosin head pivots, pulling the **(j)** along. Now the **(k)** and **(l)** are tightly bound to each other, but the binding of another **(m)** molecule allows the myosin head to detach from the **(n)** filament.

a. _____   h. _____

b. _____   i. _____

c. _____   j. _____

d. _____   k. _____

e. _____   l. _____

f. _____   m. _____

g. _____   n. _____

Short Answer

Answer the following questions in 1–4 sentences.

20. Describe the mechanism of action of acetylcholine and calcium in generating a muscle twitch.

21. Describe the role of creatine phosphate in synthesizing ATP in muscle cells.

Multiple Choice

Select the best answer from the choices given.

22. This ion is responsible for interacting with troponin to expose the active site on the actin.

   a. K^+ c. Na^+ e. Cl^-
   b. Ca^{2+} d. Fe^{2+}

23. Which of the following are highly concentrated at the motor end plate?

   a. voltage-gated calcium channels   d. calcium ions
   b. voltage-gated potassium channels   e. troponin
   c. acetylcholine receptors

24. Which part of the thin filament covers the myosin binding sites?

   a. troponin   c. T tubule   e. crossbridge
   b. titin   d. tropomyosin

True/False

Label the following statements as true (T) or false (F). If false, change the statement to make it true.

25. _____ Titin is an important protein closely associated with the thin filaments.

26. _____ Creatine phosphate is the primary energy source for muscles over long periods of time under anaerobic conditions.

Sequencing

27. Put the following list of statements in the correct sequence.

   a. The myosin head binds to the active site on the actin.
   b. ATP is split and the myosin head cocks.
   c. The myosin head unbinds from actin.
   d. The myosin head has a power stroke, pulling the actin filament.

   Sequence: _____

Challenge Questions

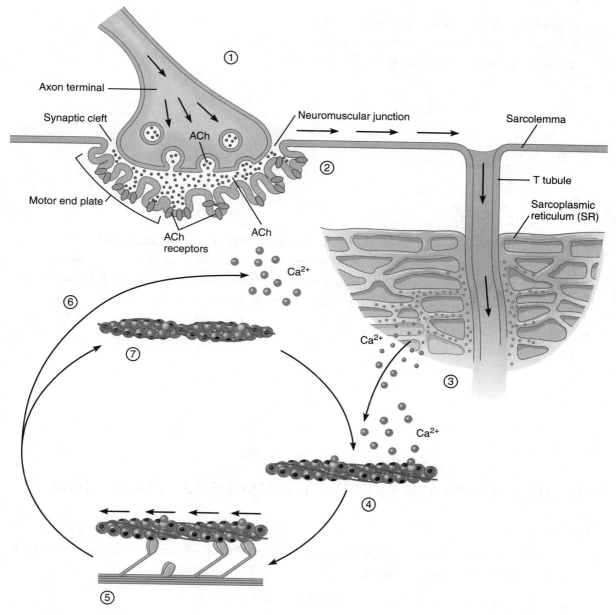

FIGURE 11.2

28. In the space below, describe in detail Steps 1–7 in Figure 11.2. Be sure to include the end result (net effect) of each step that "triggers" the next step.

29. Describe the fuel sources and primary pathway of ATP synthesis used for each of the following activities:

  a. the first ten seconds of a 100-meter sprint

  b. bench pressing 250 pounds over a sustained period of time

  c. the second mile of a light jog around the block

Clinical Questions

30. In one form of myasthenia gravis, there is a decrease in the number of acetylcholine receptors on the motor end plate. Symptoms of myasthenia gravis include general muscle weakness, which tends to be most pronounced in the muscles of the arms, head, and chest. Facial muscles are often involved as well. Given the description above, explain why the weakness occurs.

THE MECHANICS OF SKELETAL MUSCLE CONTRACTION

Matching

31. For each event listed below, indicate the phase during which it occurs: contraction phase (CP), latent period (LP), or relaxation phase (RP).

  a. _____ Calcium returns to the sarcoplasmic reticulum.

  b. _____ The actin site is exposed and myosin attaches to it.

  c. _____ The power stroke of the myosin is occurring.

  d. _____ Acetylcholine has just depolarized the motor end plate.

  e. _____ Troponin and tropomyosin have reverted back to their original position.

  f. _____ The action potential is traveling down the T-tubules.

Completion

Fill in the blanks to complete the following narrative.

32. The force of a muscle contraction is related to the number of **(a)**. This activity requires that **(b)** bind to **(c)**. If you start with a muscle fiber already at optimum length, the tension generated by a muscle fiber **(d)** as the length increases. This is because the amount of overlap between **(e)** and **(f)** decreases as the sarcomeres **(g)**. Thus any crossbridges that do not overlap with **(h)** cannot interact and generate force.

a. _____   e. _____

b. _____   f. _____

c. _____   g. _____

d. _____   h. _____

Short Answer

Answer the following questions in 1–4 sentences.

33. Define muscle twitch.

34. Describe the concept of recruitment.

Multiple Choice

Select the best answer from the choices given.

35. When a muscle creates tension, but does not shorten, it is known as _____.

a. tetanus
b. incomplete summation
c. isotonic contraction
d. isometric contraction
e. fatigue

36. When a skeletal muscle cell is stimulated continuously, but the force does not increase or decrease, it is called _____.

a summation
b. tetanus
c. treppe
d. fatigue
e. twitch

37. What ultimate factor determines a muscle cell's force-generating capacity?

a. the number of sarcomeres
b. the number of actin filaments/unit area
c. the number of myosin filaments/unit area
d. the fiber's diameter
e. the number of tropomyosin molecules/unit area

38. The stepwise increase in muscle tension is known as _____.

    a. treppe   c. tetanus   e. isometric twitch

    b. fatigue   d. incomplete tetanus

39. Which of the following muscles is likely to have the fastest velocity of shortening?

    a. gastrocnemius   c. latissimus dorsi   e. lateral rectus

    b. quadriceps   d. gracilis

True/False

Label the following statements as true (T) *or false* (F). *If false, change the statement to make it true.*

40. _____ The size principle states that there is a correspondence between the size of the motor units recruited and the order in which they are recruited.

41. _____ A motor unit is all of the nerves that innervate a single muscle.

42. _____ The difference between fast- and slow-twitch fibers is related to the different types of myosin each fiber type contains.

43. _____ Summation occurs when action potentials stimulate a muscle before individual twitches can be completed, thus creating a force greater than a single muscle twitch.

Sequencing

44. Place the following in the correct sequence:

    a. contraction phase,   b. latent period,   c. relaxation phase,   d. initiation of stimulus

    Sequence: _____

Clinical Question

45. A patient comes to the emergency room having overdosed on barbiturates. Barbiturates have a number of effects, including a decrease in the rate of release of acetylcholine from motor neurons. What symptoms might this person have?

Challenge Questions

46. Explain how it is possible to use the same muscles to thread a needle and lift 20 pounds.

47. Explain why muscles contract weakly when they are excessively stretched or are already strongly contracted.

Concept Map

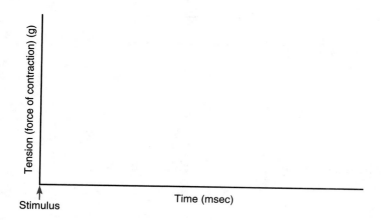

FIGURE 11.3

48. Draw a single muscle twitch. Label the latent period, the contraction phase, and the relaxation phase. Briefly describe what happens during each of these three events.

TYPES OF SKELETAL MUSCLE FIBERS

Matching

49. In the list below, indicate whether the statement describes glycolytic fibers (GF) or oxidative fibers (OF).

a. _____ can quickly generate ATP by glycolysis

b. _____ contain relatively few mitochondria

c. _____ tend to be smaller muscle fibers

d. _____ capillary supply sparse

Completion

Fill in the blanks to complete the following narrative.

50. There are three major classes of skeletal muscle fibers: 1) fast glycolytic fibers, 2) the rare **(a)** fibers, and 3) **(b)** fibers. Fast glycolytic fibers contain fast myosin and can produce **(c)** quickly through **(d)**. **(a)** fibers can generate ATP quickly through **(e)** and contain fast **(f)**. Slow oxidative fibers contain **(g)** myosin and produce most of their ATP through **(e)**.

a. _____   e. _____

b. _____   f. _____

c. _____   g. _____

d. _____

Short Answer

Answer the following question in 1–4 sentences.

51. Explain the physiological difference between glycolytic fibers and oxidative fibers.

Multiple Choice

Select the best answer from the choices given.

52. Slow oxidative fibers generally have all of the following characteristics **except** which?
    a. high oxidative capacity
    b. contain slow myosin
    c. can generate large forces
    d. contain thin fibers
    e. tend to be recruited first

53. All of the following would be expected to occur as a result of aerobic training **except** which?
    a. Some fast glycolytic fibers are converted to fast oxidative fibers.
    b. Some slow-twitch fibers are converted to fast-twitch fibers.
    c. The muscle fiber oxidative capacity has increased.
    d. The muscle fibers are more resistant to fatigue.
    e. The number of mitochondria increase.

54. High-intensity exercise would result in which of the following adaptations of skeletal muscle?
    a. an increase in oxidative capacity
    b. Some fast glycolytic fibers are converted into fast oxidative fibers.
    c. fiber diameter decreases
    d. new fibers are synthesized
    e. reduced muscle resistance to fatigue

True/False

Label the following statements as true (T) *or false* (F). *If false, change the statement to make it true.*

55. _____ High-intensity aerobic training would most likely result in an increased number of capillaries surrounding the muscle fibers.

56. _____ When high-intensity exercise is stressed in a muscle the aerobic performance of the muscle is enhanced.

Sequencing

57. Put the following list of muscle fiber types in the correct sequence in which they are recruited.

a. fast glycolytic,   b. slow oxidative,   c. fast oxidative

Sequence: _____

Clinical Question

58. Scientists have observed many physiological changes in astronauts during and after space travel. Current research into the effects of space travel on changes in muscle physiology has revealed that, when humans are in space for extended periods of time, slow-twitch muscle takes on the characteristics of fast-twitch muscle. This change causes astronauts to experience difficulty in walking once back on Earth. Explain these findings.

Challenge Question

59. Explain why weight lifters can only lift heavy loads for short periods of time, but a marathon runner can run for three hours. Include the reasons for muscle fatigue.

SKELETAL MUSCLES AT WORK AND OTHER MUSCLE TYPES

Matching

60. In the list below, indicate if the statement refers to cardiac muscle (C), skeletal muscle (SK), smooth muscle (SM). Each statement in the list can have one or more right answers.

a. _____ striations present

b. _____ gap junctions present

c. _____ many nuclei per cell

d. _____ involuntary control

e. _____ found in walls of blood vessels

f. _____ nervous stimulation by autonomic nervous system

g. _____ branched cells

h. _____ no sarcomeres present

i. _____ of the three muscle types, can contract the fastest

Completion

Fill in the blanks to complete the following narratives.

61. Skeletal muscles are attached and connected to at least two points in the body. When a skeletal muscle contracts, it usually **(a)** a bone. A skeletal muscle's point of attachment to the bone that does not move is the **(b)**. The place of attachment on the bone that *does* move is called the **(c)**. When muscles exert movement in opposite directions to each other the muscles are said to be **(d)**.

a. _____   c. _____

b. _____   d. _____

62. Smooth muscles are so named because they lack **(a)**. In smooth muscles, contractions are triggered when calcium binds to **(b)**, forming a complex that then binds to **(c)**, causing the phosphorylation of the myosin **(d)**. Termination of the crossbridge cycle requires the action of **(e)** enzymes, which remove the **(f)** groups.

a. _____   d. _____

b. _____   e. _____

c. _____   f. _____

63. Unlike smooth muscle, cardiac muscle has sarcomeres. Cardiac muscle cells, however, are connected by **(a)** junctions, which allow the cardiac cells to act in unison. Cardiac action potentials are **(b)** and act longer than skeletal muscle cell action potentials. This long action potential period of cardiac muscle cells prevents **(c)**. Cardiac muscle cells also exhibit pacemaker activity, which is concentrated in the **(d)** and **(e)** nodes.

a. _____   d. _____

b. _____   e. _____

c. _____

Short Answer

Answer the following questions in 1–4 sentences.

64. The brachioradialis muscles allow for elbow flexion. When the brachioradialis contracts, the radius moves toward the humerus. Based on the above description, what are the origin and insertion of the brachioradialis muscle?

65. Describe the role of calmodulin in smooth muscle contractions.

66. Define pacemaker potentials. Where can they be found?

67. The heart has the ability to beat on its own, but the heart is also controlled by autonomic nerves that regulate the rate at which the heart beats. Which of these is neurogenic control and which is myogenic? Explain.

Multiple Choice

Select the best answer from the choices given.

68. Which of the following muscle types has striations?

I. cardiac   II. smooth   III. skeletal

a. I only
b. II only
c. III only
d. I and II
e. I and III

69. Which of the following muscle types does not use calmodulin?

I. cardiac   II. smooth   III. skeletal

a. I only
b. II only
c. III only
d. I and II
e. I and III

70. Which of the following muscle types contain gap junctions?

I. cardiac   II. smooth   III. skeletal

a. I only
b. II only
c. III only
d. I and II
e. I and III

True/False

Label the following statements as true (T) *or false* (F). *If false, change the statement to make it true.*

71. _____ Smooth muscles are under voluntary control.

72. _____ Smooth muscles can be regulated by autonomic neurons.

73. _____ Gap junctions allow adjacent cells to quickly communicate with each other.

Sequencing

74. Put the following list of steps of the crossbridge cycle regulation in smooth muscle in the correct sequence.

   a. Calcium binds to calmodulin.
   b. Calcium-calmodulin complex activates myosin kinase.
   c. Crossbridge cycle begins.
   d. Activated myosin kinase phosphorylates myosin head groups.
   e. Phosphorylated myosin head groups bind to actin.
   f. increased calcium concentration in cytoplasm

Sequence: _____

Clinical Question

75. Calcium channel blockers are drugs used to dilate coronary arteries. They act by interfering with the movement of calcium ions. How does the mechanism of action of this drug cause dilation of coronary blood vessels?

Challenge Question

76. What is the advantage of having muscles grouped as antagonists?

12 The Cardiovascular System: Cardiac Function

Objectives

We recommend that you review the **Objectives** for this chapter, found on p. 369 of *Principles of Human Physiology*. The **Objectives** outline what you should know from each chapter.

Key Terms

afterload	electrocardiogram (ECG)	pulmonary artery
aorta	end-diastolic volume (EDV)	pulmonary circuit
aortic pressure	end-systolic volume (ESV)	pulmonary semilunar valve
aortic semilunar valve	erythrocyte	pulmonary vein
arteriole	extrinsic control	pulse pressure (PP)
artery	filling time	Purkinje fiber
atrioventricular (AV) node	formed element	QRS complex
atrioventricular bundle	heart	right heart
atrioventricular valve	heart rate (HR)	semilunar valve
atrium	heart sounds	septum
autoregulation	hematocrit	sinoatrial (SA) node
autorhythmicity	hemoglobin	Starling's Law
bicuspid valve	internodal pathway	stroke volume (SV)
blood	intrinsic control	systemic circuit
blood vessel	isovolumetric contraction	systole
bundle branch	isovolumetric relaxation	systolic pressure (SP)
capillary	left heart	T wave
cardiac cycle	leukocyte	tricuspid valve
cardiac output (CO)	mean arterial pressure (MAP)	vein
conduction system	myocardium	vena cava
contractility	P wave	venous return
diastole	pacemaker cell	ventricle
diastolic pressure (DP)	plasma	venule
ejection	platelet	
ejection fraction (EF)	preload	

AN OVERVIEW OF THE MAJOR COMPONENTS OF THE CARDIOVASCULAR SYSTEM AND THEIR FUNCTIONS

Completion

1. Fill in the name of the structure(s) that correspond(s) to the listed definition.

Definition	Structure
Fibrous structures that prevent the AV valves from prolapsing.	a.
Structure that prevents the backflow of blood from the right ventricle into the right atrium.	b.
System of blood vessels that carries blood from the heart to the tissues and back to the heart.	c.
Structure that prevents blood in the left ventricle from mixing with blood in the right ventricle.	d.
Larger vessels that carry blood toward the heart.	e.
Structure that prevents the backflow of blood from the aorta into the left ventricle.	f.

Matching

2. Match each of the following blood components to its function and/or common name: erythrocytes (E), leukocytes (L), platelets (PLAT), plasma (PLAS), hemoglobin (H).

a. _____ fluid component of blood

b. _____ cell fragments involved in blood clotting

c. _____ white blood cells

d. _____ protein found in certain blood cells to which oxygen and carbon dioxide binds

e. _____ formed elements that carry oxygen and carbon dioxide in the blood

Sequencing

3. List the following blood vessels in the order in which blood passes through them as it flows from the heart to the tissues of the body and back to the heart.

a. capillaries, b. venules, c. arterioles, d. arteries, e. veins

Sequence: _____

Multiple Choice

Select the best answer from the choices given.

4. What is the **primary** function of the cardiovascular system?
   a. to carry oxygen from the tissues and organs to the lungs
   b. to carry carbon dioxide from the lungs to the tissues and organs
   c. to provide adequate blood flow to all the organs and tissues of the body
   d. to cause blood clotting following an injury
   e. to directly assist oxygen in diffusing from the interstitial fluid into cells

5. The chambers of the heart that pump blood out of the heart and through the vasculature are the _____.

   a. atria
   b. interatrial septa
   c. interventricular septa
   d. pulmonary trunks
   e. ventricles

6. What is the term for the whole cardiac muscle mass?

   a. myocardium
   b. pericardium
   c. septum
   d. chordae tendineae
   e. papillary muscle

7. The blood vessels that allow for the exchange of substances between the blood and the interstitial fluid are the _____.

   a. arteries
   b. arterioles
   c. capillaries
   d. venules
   e. veins

True/False

Label the following statements as true (T) or false (F). If false, change the statement to make it true.

8. _____ The atria receive blood from the ventricles.

9. _____ During a heart beat, the atria contract before the ventricles contract.

10. _____ The structure to which atrial and ventricular muscle is anchored is the fibrous skeleton of the heart.

11. _____ The left atrioventricular valve of the heart is also known as the tricuspid valve.

12. _____ The pericardium is the membranous sac that surrounds the heart.

Short Answer

Answer the following question in 1–4 sentences.

13. List the three components of the cardiovascular system and the functions of each.

Challenge Questions

14. The cardiovascular system transports molecules through the body by bulk flow. Define bulk flow.

15. Why are capillary walls very thin, while the walls of arteries are thick?

16. Why is the muscle in the walls of the ventricles thicker than that of the atria?

17. Why is the wall of the left ventricle thicker than the wall of the right ventricle?

Clinical Questions

18. A person is born with chordae tendineae that are longer than normal. Which heart valves might this affect? What might happen to these valves during a heart beat, and how would this affect the flow of blood through the heart?

19. What effect would a ventricular septal defect (hole in the interventricular septum) have on the oxygenation of blood?

Matching

20. Match the structure to the type of blood that flows through it. Use (O) for oxygenated blood and (D) for deoxygenated blood.

    a. _____ pulmonary arteries

    b. _____ right ventricle

    c. _____ left atrium

    d. _____ pulmonary veins

    e. _____ aorta

    f. _____ venae cavae

Multiple Choice

Select the best answer from the choices given.

21. Which chamber of the heart pumps blood into the pulmonary circuit?

    a. right atrium   c. left atrium   e. aorta
    b. right ventricle   d. left ventricle

22. Which of the following statements is true of blood flowing through systemic capillary beds?

    a. Oxygen enters the blood and carbon dioxide leaves the blood.
    b. Oxygen and carbon dioxide leave the blood.
    c. Oxygen leaves the blood and carbon dioxide enters the blood.
    d. Oxygen and carbon dioxide enter the blood.
    e. The direction in which oxygen and carbon dioxide move depends on a person's blood pressure.

23. The pulmonary trunk branches into the _____.

    a. pulmonary arteries   d. right and left atrium
    b. pulmonary veins   e. thoracic and abdominal aortas
    c. superior and inferior vena cavae

True/False

Label the following statements as true (T) *or false* (F). *If false, change the statement to make it true.*

24. _____ The right and left sides of the heart are two separate pumps within a single organ.

25. _____ Arteries branching off the aorta are part of the pulmonary circuit.

26. _____ Pulmonary veins carry blood toward the heart.

27. _____ Blood leaving the pulmonary capillaries is deoxygenated.

28. _____ The left side of the heart supplies blood to the systemic circuit.

29. _____ All arteries carry oxygenated blood.

Completion

Fill in the blanks to complete the following sentences.

30. The chamber of the heart that receives blood from the pulmonary circuit is the
   _____.

31. All arteries carry blood _____ the heart.

32. In terms of oxygen content, blood leaving the systemic capillaries is
   _____.

Short Answer

Answer the following questions in 1–4 sentences.

33. Is oxygen completely absent in deoxygenated blood? Explain.

34. Define the terms pulmonary circuit and systemic circuit.

Challenge Question

35. Why is oxygenated blood usually designated in red on diagrams and deoxygenated blood is designated in blue?

Clinical Questions

Mitral valve stenosis is a clinical condition in which the mitral valve becomes scarred and doesn't open normally. Questions 36 and 37 are based on this condition.

36. Blood flow through which side of the heart would be directly affected by mitral valve stenosis?

37. What impact might this condition have on blood flow through the pulmonary circuit?

Sequencing

38. List the following structures in the order in which blood flows through them, beginning with the pulmonary capillaries. Use capital letters for structures containing oxygenated blood, and lowercase letters for structures containing deoxygenated blood. If deoxygenated blood gains a significant amount of oxygen while passing through a structure and leaves it oxygenated, or oxygenated blood loses a significant amount of oxygen while passing through a structure and leaves it deoxygenated, use a combination of lowercase and capital letters for that structure (e.g., if blood enters the structure deoxygenated and leaves it oxygenated, use lowercase letters for the first half of the term and uppercase letters for the second half).

superior vena cava, aorta, systemic veins, pulmonary veins, left ventricle, right ventricle, systemic arterioles, systemic venules, pulmonary capillaries, aortic semilunar valve, pulmonary semilunar valve, systemic capillaries, pulmonary arteries, right atrium, left atrium, inferior vena cava, left AV valve, right AV valve, systemic arteries

Sequence: _____

_____

_____

_____

_____

_____

_____

ELECTRICAL ACTIVITY OF THE HEART

Multiple Choice

Select the best answer from the choices given.

39. What does the term myogenic mean in reference to the contractile activity of cardiac muscle?

    a. Contraction of cardiac muscle is triggered by signals originating in nerves.

    b. Contraction of cardiac muscle is triggered by signals originating in cardiac muscle fibers.

    c. Contraction of cardiac muscle is regulated by the somatic division of the nervous system.

    d. Contraction of cardiac muscle is triggered by myopic action potentials.

    e. The term myogenic applies only to skeletal muscle.

40. Internodal pathways are systems of conduction fibers through which action potentials travel from the _____ to the _____, and are located in the _____.

    a. SA node : AV node : ventricles

    b. SA node : AV node : atria

    c. AV node : AV bundle : atria

    d. AV node : AV bundle : ventricles

    e. AV bundle : Purkinje fibers : ventricles

41. Which of the following is **not** true of intercalated discs?

    a. They contain gap junctions that connect adjacent cardiac muscle cells and allow direct communication between cells.

    b. They contain desmosomes that form physical bonds between adjacent cardiac muscle cells that help the myocardium resist mechanical stress.

    c. They allow an action potential to be rapidly transmitted across the entire myocardium.

    d. They provide important structural stabilization to the interventricular septum.

    e. They are necessary to the coordinated pumping action of the heart.

42. Contraction of the ventricles begins _____.

    a. at the top of the ventricles and moves down to the apex of the heart

    b. in the interventricular septum and spreads laterally through both ventricles

    c. at the apex of the heart and spreads upward through both ventricles

    d. in the right ventricle and proceeds to the left ventricle

    e. in the left ventricle and proceeds to the right ventricle

43. The **initial** phase of slow depolarization that occurs during a pacemaker potential is primarily the result of _____.

    a. opening of potassium channels   d. closure of calcium channels

    b. closure of potassium channels   e. closure of sodium channels

    c. opening of calcium channels

44. During a pacemaker potential, rapid depolarization occurs as the result of _____.

    a. opening of T-type voltage-gated calcium channels

    b. closure of T-type voltage-gated calcium channels

    c. opening of L-type voltage-gated calcium channels

    d. closure of L-type voltage-gated calcium channels

    e. opening of voltage-gated potassium channels

True/False

Label the following statements as true (T) *or false* (F). *If false, change the statement to make it true.*

45. _____ The resting membrane potential of a typical cardiac muscle cell is about –80 mV.

46. _____ The threshold potential of a cardiac pacemaker cell is about –40 mV.

47. _____ Cells of the conduction system of the heart are specialized to generate forceful contractions.

48. _____ When the heart beats, the atria contract as a unit and the ventricles contract as a unit.

49. _____ Conduction fibers transmit action potentials at a slower rate than other cardiac muscle fibers.

50. _____ The SA (sinoatrial) node is the pacemaker of the heart under normal circumstances.

51. _____ After an action potential, cardiac pacemaker cells immediately begin a slow depolarization.

52. _____ The flow of calcium ions into the cardiac muscle fiber during phase 2 of the action potential has an effect on the membrane potential and participates in activating the crossbridge cycle.

53. _____ An electrocardiogram reflects the patterns of action potentials occurring throughout the heart muscle.

Short Answer

Answer the following questions in 1–4 sentences.

54. Before moving from the atria to the ventricles, cardiac impulses are delayed about 0.1 second. Why is this delay essential to cardiac function?

55. Define *pacemaker potential.*

56. Draw a typical ECG pattern, and label the three phases.

Completion

Fill in the blanks to complete the following sentences.

57. Cells that can spontaneously generate their own action potentials are called _____ cells.

58. Cardiac muscle is able to trigger contractions on a periodic basis, a property known as _____.

59. The area of the heart that serves as the only electrical connection between the atria and the ventricles is the _____.

Matching

60. Match the event to the phase of the cardiac action potential during which it occurs: phase 0 (0), phase 1 (1), phase 2 (2), phase 3 (3), phase 4 (4).

a. _____ L-type voltage-gated calcium channels open.

b. _____ Voltage-gated sodium channels open.

c. _____ Most of the calcium channels close.

d. _____ Sodium and calcium channels are closed, potassium channels are open.

e. _____ Some calcium channels close, most remain open.

Sequencing

61. Put the following events in the correct order.

a. Action potentials travel from the AV bundle to the bundle branches.
b. Action potentials spread across the atria.
c. Action potentials travel from the bundle branches to the Purkinje fibers.
d. Action potentials are generated in the SA node.
e. Action potentials are temporarily slowed in the AV node.
f. Action potentials travel from the AV node to the AV bundle.
g. Action potentials travel through internodal pathways to the AV node.

Sequence: _____

Labeling

62. Using the table on page 211, label the phases of the cardiac action potential indicated on Figure 12.1. Specify whether each represents depolarization, repolarization, or a plateau, and indicate the primary ion movements (e.g., sodium influx, potassium efflux, etc.), if any, responsible for generating each phase.

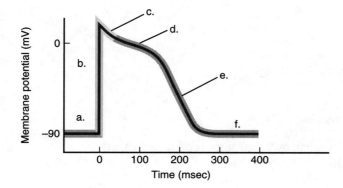

FIGURE 12.1

Phase	Depolarization/repolarization/ plateau/rest	Primary ion movement(s)
a.		
b.		
c.		
d.		
e.		
f.		

Challenge Questions

63. Why will increased sympathetic stimulation of the pacemaker cells of the heart increase the frequency of action potentials in these cells?

64. Both the SA node and the AV node contain numerous pacemaker cells. Why does the AV node rarely initiate cardiac contractions?

65. Why is repolarization of the atria not visible on an ECG?

Clinical Questions

66. If the SA node is damaged and fails to initiate action potentials, but the rest of the cardiac conduction system and the myocardium continue to work normally, will the affected person immediately die? Why or why not? If the person's heart continues to beat, will its rate be altered?

67. While analyzing a patient's ECG, you notice that the length of time between the P wave and the QRS complex is abnormally long. What might this indicate about the functioning of the patient's cardiac conduction system?

THE CARDIAC CYCLE

Matching

68. Match the following events to the phase of the cardiac cycle in which they occur: isovolumetric relaxation (phase 4) (IR), isovolumetric contraction (phase 2) (IC), ventricular filling (phase 1) (VF), ventricular ejection (phase 3) (VE).

a. _____ Atrial systole occurs.

b. _____ Blood leaves the ventricles and enters the aorta and pulmonary trunk/arteries.

c. _____ The atria fill with blood (more than one phase may apply).

d. _____ Blood flows from the atria into the ventricles.

e. _____ The pulmonary and aortic semilunar valves close at the beginning of this phase.

f. _____ Occurs at the beginning of ventricular systole.

g. _____ All valves are closed (more than one phase may apply).

Completion

69. Fill in the term that corresponds to each of the following definitions.

Definition	Term
the volume of blood in the ventricle at the end of ventricular systole	a.
the maximum volume of blood present in each ventricle during the cardiac cycle	b.
the amount of blood ejected from a ventricle during one heart beat	c.
the fraction of blood present in a ventricle at the end of ventricular diastole that is ejected during a heart beat	d.

70. Fill in the name of the ECG phase/wave that corresponds to each of the following cardiac events, and indicate the phase of the cardiac cycle with which it corresponds.

Cardiac event	ECG phase/wave	Corresponding cardiac cycle phase
Ventricles depolarize.	a.	b.
Ventricles repolarize.	c.	d.
Atria depolarize.	e.	f.

Multiple Choice

Select the best answer from the choices given.

71. The opening of the right and left AV valves marks the beginning of _____.

   a. isovolumetric contraction
   b. isovolumetric relaxation
   c. ventricular ejection
   d. ventricular filling
   e. ventricular systole

72. Which of the following statements is true regarding blood flow during isovolumetric relaxation?

   a. Blood flows from the atria to the ventricles.
   b. Blood flows from the ventricles to the atria.
   c. Blood flows from the ventricles into the aorta and pulmonary trunk.
   d. Blood flows from the superior and inferior vena cavae into the left atrium.
   e. Blood does not flow into or out of the ventricles.

73. Which of the following events produces heart sound S1?

   a. closure of the aortic and pulmonary semilunar valves
   b. closure of the AV valves
   c. opening of the aortic and pulmonary semilunar valves
   d. opening of the AV valves
   e. ventricular diastole

74. The semilunar valves close when pressure in the _____ exceeds pressure in the _____.

   a. atria : ventricles
   b. aorta and pulmonary trunk : atria
   c. aorta and pulmonary trunk : ventricles
   d. ventricles : aorta and pulmonary trunk
   e. ventricles : atria

75. A typical stroke volume is _____.

   a. 135 ml
   b. 100 ml
   c. 65 ml
   d. 30 ml
   e. 70 ml

76. All the events associated with the flow of blood through the heart during a single heart beat are collectively known as _____.

    a. the cardiac cycle   c. heart sounds   e. diastolic events

    b. an electrocardiogram   d. systolic events

77. The minimum pressure that occurs in the aorta during relaxation of the ventricles is called _____.

    a. systolic pressure   c. mean arterial pressure   e. cardiac pressure

    b. diastolic pressure   d. pulse pressure

78. What generates the small, abrupt rise in ventricular pressure that occurs near the end of ventricular filling?

    a. closure of the AV valves

    b. opening of the semilunar valves

    c. contraction of the ventricles resulting in blood flow into the aorta and pulmonary trunk

    d. contraction of the atria resulting in blood flow into the ventricles

    e. the flow of blood into the atria from the vena cavae

79. Contraction of the ventricles is also known as _____.

    a. ventricular diastole   d. ventricular symbiosis

    b. ventricular diaphoresis   e. ventricular repolarization

    c. ventricular systole

80. The average pressure that occurs in the aorta during the cardiac cycle is called _____.

    a. ventricular pressure   c. pulse pressure   e. systemic pressure

    b. cyclic pressure   d. mean arterial pressure

True/False

Label the following statements as true (T) *or false* (F). *If false, change the statement to make it true.*

81. _____ One complete cardiac cycle involves the systole and diastole of the chambers of the heart.

82. _____ The maximum pressure generated in the aorta during ventricular contraction is called the systolic pressure.

83. _____ Pulse pressure is the difference between systolic pressure and diastolic pressure.

84. _____ Stroke volume is equivalent to the difference between end-diastolic volume and end-systolic volume.

85. _____ When a ventricle contracts, it ejects all the blood contained within it.

Short Answer

Answer the following questions in 1–4 sentences.

86. At what point in the cardiac cycle does aortic pressure begin to rise?

87. Which is longer at rest, ventricular systole or diastole, and why?

Sequencing

88. List the following events in the order in which they occur during the cardiac cycle, beginning with letter "e."

    a. AV valves close.
    b. Ventricular relaxation begins.
    c. Ventricles contract.
    d. Atria contract.
    e. AV valves open.
    f. Semilunar valves open.
    g. Blood is ejected from the ventricles.
    h. Blood begins traveling from the atria to the ventricles.
    i. Semilunar valves close.

Sequence: _____

Challenge Questions

89. Why does blood flow through the vasculature fairly continuously when it exits the heart in spurts?

90. What generates the dicrotic notch in the aortic pressure curve during a cardiac cycle?

91. Why are all four valves of the heart closed during isovolumetric relaxation?

Clinical Question

92. Why is it recommended that blood pressure readings be taken with the patient in a sitting position with his/her arm resting on a table or other elevated surface?

CARDIAC OUTPUT AND ITS CONTROL

Completion

Fill in the blanks to complete the following sentences and narrative.

93. Another term for end-diastolic pressure is _____.

94. The force of ventricular contraction at any given end-diastolic volume is referred to as
_____.

95. The pressure in the aorta against which blood is ejected generates
_____.

96. Fill in the blanks in the following description of the major autonomic inputs to the heart.

Parasympathetic stimulation reaches the heart via preganglionic fibers traveling through the **(a)** nerves, and is received by the **(b)** and **(c)** nodes of the heart. Sympathetic input travels to the heart along nerve fibers located in **(d)** nerves. It reaches the **(e)** and **(f)** nodes of the heart, as well as the ventricular **(g)**. An increase in sympathetic stimulation to the heart will increase cardiac contractility and will increase **(h)**. In contrast, an increase in parasympathetic stimulation to the heart will have virtually no effect on cardiac contractility, and will **(i)** the heart rate.

a. _____   f. _____

b. _____   g. _____

c. _____   h. _____

d. _____   i. _____

e. _____

Matching

97. Match the causative factor listed to whether it increases (I) stroke volume or decreases (D) stroke volume. Also choose a reason explaining why it has the effect it does on stroke volume from the following list: increases the afterload (AF), increases ventricular contractility (VC), decreases filling time which decreases preload (DFT), decreases atrial pressure which decreases preload (DAP), increases the length of the cardiac muscle fibers which increases force of contraction (IL).

Effect on stroke volume	Causative factor	Explanation
a. _____	increased heart rate	_____
b. _____	increased end-diastolic volume	_____
c. _____	increased systemic blood pressure	_____
d. _____	decreased venous return	_____
e. _____	increased secretion of epinephrine	_____

Multiple Choice

Select the best answer from the choices given.

98. An increase in which of the following would **not** increase the heart rate?

   a. glucagon
   b. parasympathetic stimulation
   c. sympathetic stimulation
   d. epinephrine
   e. norepinephrine

99. The amount of blood ejected from each ventricle per minute is the _____.

   a. heart rate
   b. stroke volume
   c. end-diastolic volume
   d. cardiac output
   e. preload

100. An average heart rate for an average adult at rest is _____.

   a. 100 beats per minute
   b. 85 beats per minute
   c. 70 beats per minute
   d. 55 beats per minute
   e. 25 beats per minute

101. Which of the following is **not** true of cardiac function under normal circumstances?

   a. Cardiac output is equal on both sides of the heart.
   b. The amount of blood pumped into the pulmonary circuit is equal to the amount of blood pumped into the systemic circuit.
   c. The heart rate of the right ventricle is the same as the heart rate of the left ventricle.
   d. Cardiac output can be altered to meet changing metabolic needs of the body.
   e. The left ventricle generates a greater stroke volume than the right ventricle.

102. In order to maintain a constant cardiac output, if stroke volume decreases _____.

   a. heart rate will increase
   b. heart rate will decrease
   c. parasympathetic stimulation to the heart will increase
   d. epinephrine secretion will decrease
   e. sympathetic stimulation of the myocardium will decrease

103. As heart rate decreases, filling time _____ because _____.

   a. increases : systole decreases in duration
   b. increases : diastole decreases in duration
   c. decreases : diastole increases in duration
   d. increases : diastole increases in duration
   e. is unaffected : the durations of systole and diastole are unaffected

104. Which of the following would **not** accompany an increase in sympathetic stimulation of the heart?

   a. an increase in heart rate
   b. an increase in stroke volume
   c. an increase in ventricular contractility
   d. an increase in cardiac output
   e. an increase in filling time

True/False

Label the following statements as true (T) and false (F). If false, change the statement to make it true.

105. _____ As mean arterial pressure rises, afterload decreases.

106. _____ Cardiac output will increase as the result of an increase in heart rate or a decrease in stroke volume.

107. _____ Starling's Law of the Heart demonstrates intrinsic control of cardiac function.

108. _____ An increase in heart rate is often the result of a concurrent increase in sympathetic stimulation and decrease in parasympathetic stimulation.

109. _____ The regulation of heart rate is extrinsically controlled.

110. _____ Ventricular contractility is influenced only by sympathetic stimulation.

111. _____ The total volume of blood in the body is circulated about once per minute.

Short Answer

Answer the following questions in 1–4 sentences.

112. The "natural" frequency of the SA node is about 100 action potentials per minute, but the average adult's heart rate is usually much lower than that. Explain this phenomenon.

113. List the three primary factors that affect stroke volume.

Challenge Questions

114. Explain Starling's Law of the Heart, the Starling effect, and how these phenomena help the heart regulate its size.

115. What impact will an increase in sympathetic stimulation of the SA node have on the duration of systole, and why?

116. Compare and contrast extrinsic control of cardiac function with intrinsic control. Be sure to include the basic definitions of each type of control, and list the specific physiologic mechanisms that fall into each category.

Clinical Questions

A 48-year-old male was admitted to the ER with difficulty breathing. His heart rate was 132 beats per minute, he was pale, and his respiratory rate was 24 breaths per minute. He was diagnosed with left-sided heart failure with associated pulmonary congestion.

117. Define what is meant by "heart failure."

118. Explain why this patient would be experiencing pulmonary congestion.

119. What would explain this patient's elevated heart rate?

Labeling

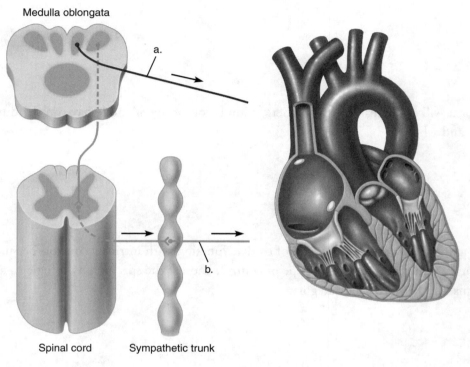

Medulla oblongata

a.

Spinal cord   Sympathetic trunk

b.

FIGURE 12.2

120. Label the vagus nerve and sympathetic cardiac nerve on Figure 12.2. Draw extensions from the nerves to their sites of innervation. Indicate the neurotransmitter each nerve releases at target cells.

Concept Map

121. You are taking care of a patient who is experiencing a decreased cardiac output. Fill in the blanks in the following concept map indicating all of the possible cause and effect relationships that could contribute to a decrease in cardiac output. Indicate whether each of these phenomena would be increased (↑) or decreased (↓) as compared to normal.

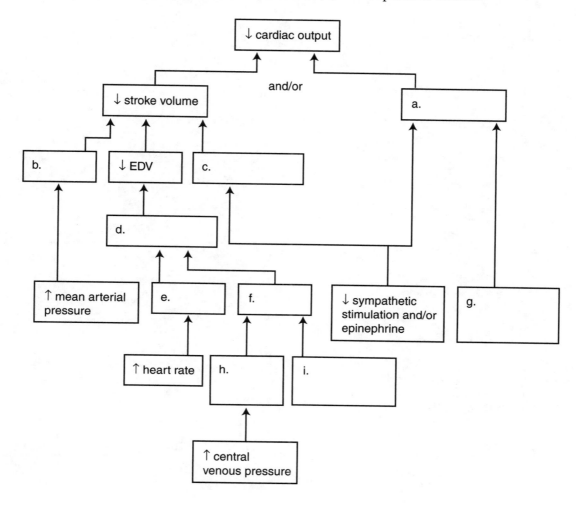

13 The Cardiovascular System: Blood, Blood Flow, and Blood Pressure

Objectives

We recommend that you review the **Objectives** for this chapter, found on p. 403 of *Principles of Human Physiology*. The **Objectives** outline what you should know from each chapter.

Key Terms

absorption
blood flow
bone marrow
central venous pressure
compliance
distending pressure
endothelium
filtration
formed element
hemodynamic
laminar flow

lymphatic fluid
lymphatic system
macrophage
mean arterial pressure
net filtration pressure
oncotic pressure
plasma
pressure drop
pressure gradient
resistance
respiratory pump

skeletal muscle pump
total peripheral resistance
turbulent flow
vasoconstriction
vasodilation
venomotor tone
venous pooling
venous pressure
viscosity

THE COMPOSITION OF BLOOD

Matching

1. Match the following: globulins (G), erythropoietin (E), fibrinogen (F), albumin (A), bilirubin (B). Use each answer once.

   a. _____ plasma protein synthesized by the liver that is integral to the formation of blood clots

   b. _____ breakdown product of hemoglobin that gives a yellowish color to urine and plasma

   c. _____ plasma protein that is a major contributor to the osmotic pressure of the plasma

   d. _____ plasma proteins that help defend the body against pathogens and transport steroid hormones and other lipids

   e. _____ hormone that stimulates the proliferation and maturation of red blood cells

Multiple Choice

Select the best answer from the choices given.

2. The composition of blood can be subdivided into two main categories. These are the _____.

   a. plasma proteins and erythrocytes
   b. plasma and formed elements
   c. platelets and leukocytes
   d. water and electrolytes
   e. erythrocytes and platelets

3. Which of the following is **not** a normal component of blood plasma?

   a. water
   b. albumin
   c. carbon dioxide
   d. deoxyribonucleic acid
   e. nitrogenous waste products

4. Most capillary walls are quite permeable to all of the following substances **except** _____.

   a. sodium ions
   b. glucose
   c. proteins
   d. bicarbonate ions
   e. oxygen

5. Which of the following is **not** a primary location in which formed-element-producing bone marrow would be found in adults?

   a. bones of the chest
   b. skull
   c. pelvic bones
   d. upper long bones of the limbs
   e. bones of the hands and feet

6. The formed element that contains hemoglobin is the _____.

   a. erythrocyte
   b. leukocyte
   c. platelet
   d. megakaryocyte
   e. lymphocyte

True/False

Label the following statements as true (T) or false (F). If false, change the statement to make it true.

7. _____ The concentration of proteins in the plasma is equal to the concentration of proteins in the interstitial fluid.

8. _____ Platelets are cell fragments, not true cells.

9. _____ Oxygen binds to the iron atom associated with the heme groups of hemoglobin.

10. _____ Each hemoglobin molecule binds a maximum of two molecules of oxygen.

11. _____ When hemoglobin is broken down, the iron is reused in the synthesis of new hemoglobin molecules.

12. _____ Leukocytes are not only found in the blood, but in other tissues of the body as well.

13. _____ Erythrocytes are mobile and can migrate through tissues.

Completion

Fill in the blanks to complete the following sentences.

14. Platelets arise when portions of _____ break off.

15. The formed element that is biconcave and lacks a nucleus is the

_____.

16. All blood cells are produced in a tissue called _____.

17. The synthesis of hemoglobin requires adequate dietary supplies of iron, folic acid, and vitamin

_____.

18. Average human blood volume is about _____.

Short Answer

Answer the following question in 1–4 sentences.

19. List the formed elements of the blood and specify the function of each.

Challenge Question

20. Define the term hematocrit. What would be the hematocrit of a 100-ml blood sample of which 52 ml are red blood cells? Would this hematocrit be normal for a male or a female?

Clinical Questions

21. A runner training for a marathon is brought into the emergency room on a very hot day when he collapsed after running steadily for two hours without breaking for fluids or rest. Would you expect his hematocrit to be higher or lower than his normal value? Why?

22. Define anemia. What are the typical symptoms of this disorder? Describe the various causes/types of anemia.

PLATELETS AND HEMOSTASIS

Multiple Choice

Select the best answer from the choices given.

23. Which of the following is the first step in the process of hemostasis?

    a. vascular spasm   d. formation of a blood clot
    b. platelet adhesion   e. synthesis of thromboxane A
    c. platelet aggregation

24. During platelet adhesion, platelets bind to, and are activated by _____.

    a. thrombin   c. fibrin   e. prostacyclin
    b. fibrinogen   d. von Willebrand factor

25. Platelet aggregation is inhibited by _____.

    a. ADP   c. prostacyclin   e. prothrombin
    b. fibrinogen   d. thromboxane A

26. The last step in the coagulation cascade that produces a blood clot is the conversion of _____.

    a. factor XIII to factor X   d. prothrombin to thrombin
    b. plasminogen to plasmin   e. fibrinogen to fibrin
    c. arachadonic acid to thromboxane A

True/False

Label the following statements as true (T) or false (F). If false, change the statement to make it true.

27. _____ The process of platelet aggregation involves a positive feedback loop.

28. _____ The first step in platelet plug formation is platelet adhesion.

29. _____ The conversion of fibrinogen to fibrin is catalyzed by thrombin.

Short Answer

Answer the following question in 1–4 sentences.

30. Describe the mechanisms by which the intrinsic and extrinsic coagulation pathways are activated.

Challenge/Clinical Questions

31. Why would someone in the early stages of a heart attack be administered TPA (tissue plasminogen activator) in the emergency room?

32. Hemophilia is a genetic bleeding disorder that is often the result of a deficiency of coagulation factor VIII in the blood. Why would the deficiency of just one coagulation factor inhibit a hemophiliac's ability to form blood clots?

THE STRUCTURE AND FUNCTION OF BLOOD VESSELS

Completion

Fill in the blanks to complete the following sentences.

33. The largest vessels that carry blood away from the heart are the

_____.

34. The vessels at which substances are exchanged between the blood and the interstitial fluid are the _____.

35. The vessels that directly connect arterioles to venules, bypassing the capillaries, are the

_____.

36. Veins located outside the thoracic cavity are called the _____ veins, while veins within the thoracic cavity are referred to as the _____ veins.

Multiple Choice

Select the best answer from the choices given.

37. Which of the following vessels have internal valves?

    a. venules

    b. peripheral veins

    c. central veins

    d. arteries

    e. arterioles

38. The lumen of all blood vessels is lined by a layer of tissue called the _____, which is composed of _____.

    a. internal fenestrae : connective tissue

    b. basement membrane : connective tissue

    c. basement membrane : smooth muscle

    d. endothelium : connective tissue

    e. endothelium : epithelial tissue

39. Which of the following is the component of the outer layer of vessel walls that provides tensile strength to the vessel?

    a. elastin   c. collagen   e. calcium

    b. smooth muscle   d. skeletal muscle

40. The ability of a vessel to expand when the pressure inside it rises is called _____.

    a. distention   c. transcytosis   e. contractility

    b. distribution   d. compliance

41. The two primary functions of arterioles are to _____.

    a. regulate the amount of blood leaving capillary beds and regulate the venous pressure of the body

    b. regulate the amount of blood flowing into capillary beds and regulate mean arterial pressure

    c. directly connect arteries to veins and return oxygenated blood to the heart

    d. regulate the amount of blood flowing into the heart and regulate the venous pressure of the body

    e. regulate the amount of blood flowing from the intestines to the liver and regulate mean arterial pressure

42. Which of the following is **not** true regarding mechanisms of transport across capillary walls?

    a. Lipid soluble molecules and molecules having very small molecular sizes easily diffuse across the capillary membrane.

    b. Water-soluble substances often cross the capillary membrane by moving through water-filled gaps between the endothelial cells.

    c. Exchangeable proteins are transported by transcytosis, which involves endocytosis on one side of the endothelial cell and exocytosis on the other side.

    d. Carbon dioxide is often transported across the capillary membrane by transcytosis.

    e. Oxygen is often transported across the capillary membrane by diffusion.

True/False

Label the following statements as true (T) *or false* (F). *If false, change the statement to make it true.*

43. _____ At a given point in time, the veins in the body usually contain a greater volume of blood than the arteries.

44. _____ Arteries have a low compliance, while veins have a high compliance.

45. _____ Arteries carry blood toward the heart, while veins carry blood away from the heart.

46. _____ Venules conduct blood from capillaries to veins.

47. _____ Substances that can easily cross continuous capillaries include oxygen, steroid hormones, and proteins.

Matching

48. Match the vessel to the characteristic listed that best describes it: arteries (AR), arterioles (AS), capillaries (C), metarterioles (M), venules (VL), veins (VN). Use each answer once.

    a. _____ Walls contain rings of smooth muscle.

    b. _____ Relative to their wall thickness, these vessels contain more smooth muscle in their walls than any other.

    c. _____ Walls are relatively thin and contain little to no smooth muscle.

    d. _____ Walls are composed of one layer of endothelial cells plus a basement membrane.

    e. _____ Walls are the thickest of all vessel types, contain a lot of smooth muscle, and are highly elastic.

    f. _____ Walls are thinner than are those of the vessels specified in Question e, have a fair amount of smooth muscle, and are highly distensible.

Short Answer

Answer the following questions in 1–4 sentences.

49. What is the structural difference between continuous and fenestrated capillaries?

50. Are continuous or fenestrated capillaries more permeable to large molecules?

Challenge Questions

51. Would fenestrated capillaries be abundant in the brain vasculature? Why or why not?

52. What is meant by the terms *pressure reservoir* and *volume reservoir* as they apply to arteries and veins? What structural properties of arteries and veins allow them to serve as pressure and volume reservoirs, respectively?

Clinical Questions

53. What role would the veins play in maintaining an adequate cardiac output in a person experiencing a slow hemorrhage following surgery?

54. If veins had a lower compliance than they do, would they be able to serve the role described in your answer to Question 53?

PATTERNS OF BLOOD FLOW WITHIN THE CARDIOVASCULAR SYSTEM

Short Answer

Answer the following questions in 1–4 sentences.

55. Define the terms *series flow* and *parallel flow* as they relate to blood flow within the cardiovascular system.

56. Describe the two advantages to the use of parallel flow to organs supplied by the systemic circuit.

Labeling

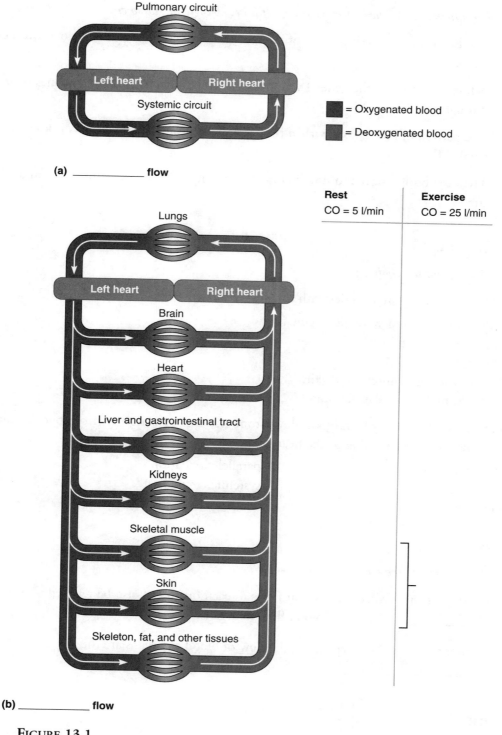

(a) _____ flow

| Rest
CO = 5 l/min | Exercise
CO = 25 l/min |

(b) _____ flow

FIGURE 13.1

57. Label each diagram on Figure 13.1 as to whether it illustrates series flow or parallel flow. Indicate whether blood flow to the organs indicated would increase or decrease during exercise as compared to rest.

True/False

Label the following statements as true (T) or false (F). If false, change the statement to make it true.

58. _____ The heart muscle receives most of its nourishment via the blood that flows through its chambers.

59. _____ Before returning to the general venous circulation, blood from the intestines flows through the liver.

60. _____ The pattern of blood flow **within** the systemic and pulmonary circuits is known as parallel flow.

61. _____ The distribution of blood flow to organs and within organs remains constant at all times.

Multiple Choice

Select the best answer from the choices given.

62. Which of the following are in series with each other in terms of blood flow?
    a. pulmonary circuit and systemic circuit
    b. left heart, brain, and liver
    c. left heart, liver, and kidneys
    d. right heart, skeletal muscle, and skin
    e. right heart, brain, and skeletal muscle

63. A pattern of blood flow in which blood flows from one organ to another (from one vascular bed to another) before returning to the heart is called _____.
    a. portal circulation   d. parallel circulation
    b. visceral circulation   e. systemic circulation
    c. coronary circulation

Completion

Fill in the blanks to complete the following sentences.

64. The proportion of the cardiac output that flows to each organ can also be referred to as the _____ of blood flow to organs.

65. The most important vessels in regulating the flow of blood to organs are the _____.

Sequencing

66. Put the following vessels and associated organs in the order in which blood flows through them. Begin and end with the heart. Vessels may be used more than once.

    a. heart, b. inferior vena cava, c. liver capillaries, d. arterioles, e. venules, f. hepatic portal vein, g. intestinal capillaries, h. arteries, i. hepatic vein

    Sequence: _____

Challenge Question

67. Why does blood flow to the liver and gastrointestinal tract decrease during exercise, while blood flow to the skin and skeletal muscles increases during exercise?

PHYSICAL LAWS GOVERNING BLOOD FLOW AND BLOOD PRESSURE

Multiple Choice

Select the best answer from the choices given.

68. Which of the following statements is **not** true of pressure gradients?
- a. A pressure gradient in the vasculature is equivalent to the difference between the pressures at either end of a vessel or network of vessels.
- b. Pressure gradients push the flow of liquids through pipes, and push blood through the blood vessels.
- c. Pressure gradients drive the flow of a liquid from an area of higher to lower pressure.
- d. The pressure gradient that drives blood flow through the systemic circuit is the difference between the mean arterial pressure and the central venous pressure.
- e. A pressure gradient will increase as the absolute pressure values at either end of the tube increase proportionally to each other.

69. How does the action of the heart relate to the flow of blood through the vasculature?
- a. The force of contraction of the heart directly drives the flow of blood through the vasculature.
- b. When the heart pumps blood into the arteries, the force raises the mean arterial pressure, which creates the pressure gradient that drives the flow of blood through the vasculature.
- c. When the heart pumps blood into the arteries, the force raises the central venous pressure, which creates the pressure gradient that drives the flow of blood through the vasculature.
- d. Heart rate is inversely proportional to total peripheral resistance, so the faster the heart beats, the slower the rate of blood flow through the vasculature.
- e. Heart rate is inversely proportional to the pressure gradient in the vasculature, so the faster the heart beats, the slower the rate of blood flow through the vasculature.

70. The pressure in the superior and inferior vena cavae is known as the _____.
- a. mean arterial pressure
- b. pulse pressure
- c. central venous pressure
- d. systemic blood pressure
- e. diastolic blood pressure

71. Vascular resistance is **primarily** controlled by _____.
    a. increasing or decreasing the number of capillary networks through which blood flows
    b. relaxing or contracting vascular smooth muscle in the walls of venules and veins
    c. increasing or decreasing the number of red blood cells present in the blood
    d. relaxing or contracting the vascular smooth muscle in the walls of arterioles and small arteries
    e. increasing or decreasing the fluid content of the blood

72. Which of the following statements is true?
    a. Longer vessels have less resistance than shorter ones.
    b. Changes in vascular resistance are rarely due to changes in vessel length.
    c. Vessels continually increase or decrease in length in response to sympathetic stimulation.
    d. Vasoconstriction refers to an increase in vessel length.
    e. The greater the vessel length, the greater the pressure gradient.

Completion

Fill in the blanks to complete the following sentences.

73. Mean arterial pressure is generally about _____ mm Hg, while central venous pressure is usually about _____ mm Hg.

74. The pressure gradient in the pulmonary circuit is equal to the difference between the pressures in the _____ and _____, and is usually about _____ mm Hg.

75. An increase in the vessel radius of a small artery or arteriole is termed _____, while a decrease in vessel radius is called _____.

76. The combined resistances of the vessels in all the organs of the systemic circuit, including the vessels leading toward and away from them, is called the _____.

77. _____ anywhere within a network of blood vessels will increase the resistance of the network.

True/False

Label the following statements as true (T) or false (F). If false, change the statement to make it true.

78. _____ Vasodilation decreases vessel resistance, and is the result of relaxation of the smooth muscle in the vessel wall.

79. _____ As vessel radius decreases, resistance decreases.

80. _____ In general, resistance is a measure of the various factors that hinder the flow of liquid through a pipe.

81. _____ The largest pressure drop in the cardiovascular system occurs along the arteries.

82. _____ For any network of blood vessels, the total flow of blood through that network will increase in proportion to the pressure gradient and decrease in proportion to the resistance within the network.

Matching

83. Indicate whether each of the following phenomena will increase (I) or decrease (D) the resistance of a vessel.

a. _____ vasoconstriction

b. _____ decreased hematocrit

c. _____ decreased vessel length

d. _____ change from turbulent to laminar flow

Short Answer

Answer the following questions in 1–4 sentences.

84. List the four factors that affect resistance within the vasculature. Of these, which has the most impact on minute-to-minute, day-to-day changes in vascular resistance?

85. Write the equation that designates the relationships among pressure, resistance, and flow in the systemic circuit. Which of the variables is equivalent to flow?

Challenge Questions

86. From your answers to Questions 73 and 74, you know that the pressure gradient in the systemic circuit is greater than the pressure gradient in the pulmonary circuit. Yet, in chapter 12, you learned that the amount of blood flow through each circuit is identical. How is this possible?

87. If two vessels have the same length and diameter, but blood enters vessel A at a pressure of 50 mm Hg and leaves it at 25 mm Hg, while blood enters vessel B at 200 mm Hg and leaves at 175 mm Hg, would the rate of blood flow differ between the vessels, and if so, how?

Clinical Questions

88. People who are obese often experience high blood pressure. One cause of high blood pressure is increased peripheral resistance. Based on what you know about factors that influence peripheral resistance, why might obesity lead to the development of hypertension?

89. Arteriosclerosis involves the buildup of plaque deposits on the inside of arteries and arterioles and stiffening of these vessels. List all of the possible ways this disorder might interfere with the flow of blood to organs.

90. Blood doping is a process in which athletes infuse their own blood (which has been previously stored) prior to competition to gain a competitive advantage by increasing the oxygen-carrying capacity of their blood. However, this can be a very dangerous practice because it can greatly increase the workload on the heart. What effect might this practice have on peripheral resistance, and how would this impact cardiac function?

Concept Map

91. The following concept map depicts some of the physiologic effects a double amputation above the knee may have on the patient following surgery. Fill in the blanks in the concept map. Assume no change in blood viscosity has occurred, and that the person is experiencing increased stress related to the surgery. Notice that some of the effects will increase blood flow to organs, while others will decrease blood flow, so any overall change in blood flow through the vasculature will be the result of a combination of effects.

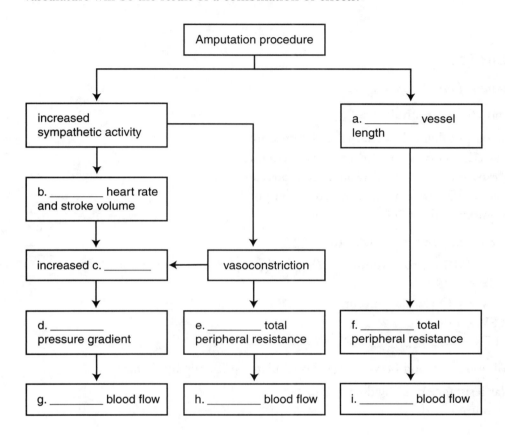

FACTORS AFFECTING FLOW AND DISTRIBUTION OF BLOOD TO ORGANS

Sequencing

Use the following flow rates to answer Questions 92 and 93.

Organ A = 1.25 liters/min.   **Organ B = 5.00 liters/min.**   **Organ C = 0.30 liters/min.**

92. List the organs in order of decreasing resistance.

Sequence: _____

Short Answer

Answer the following question in 1–4 sentences.

93. In the example on page 237, if the resistance in organ B increased but the resistance in organ A and organ C remained the same, what would happen to the distribution of blood flow to each of the organs?

Multiple Choice

Select the best answers from the choices given.

94. Organ blood flow is equivalent to _____.
    a. cardiac output divided by mean arterial pressure
    b. mean arterial pressure divided by organ resistance
    c. organ resistance divided by mean arterial pressure
    d. mean arterial pressure divided by cardiac output
    e. organ resistance divided by cardiac output

95. Mean arterial pressure is equivalent to _____.
    a. heart rate (HR) + stroke volume (SV) + total peripheral resistance (TPR)
    b. $HR \times SV + TPR$
    c. $HR \times SV \times CO$ (cardiac output)
    d. $HR \times SV \times TPR$
    e. $SV \times TPR - HR$

96. The distribution of blood flow to organs is regulated primarily by changes in _____.
    a. vascular resistance of individual organs
    b. cardiac output
    c. stroke volume
    d. heart rate
    e. contraction and relaxation of smooth muscle in venules and veins

True/False

Label the following statements as true (T) or false (F). If false, change the statement to make it true.

97. _____ Differences in blood flow rates between organs are primarily due to differences in organ resistance.

98. _____ If the resistance in individual organs remains constant but mean arterial pressure increases, the blood flow to those organs closest to the heart will increase, while the blood flow to organs further from the heart will remain unchanged.

99. _____ Mean arterial pressure can be expressed as cardiac output divided by organ resistance.

100. _____ The vascular resistance of an organ is altered primarily by the opening and closing of valves in the small arteries and arterioles that supply that organ with blood.

Matching

101. Indicate whether each of the following would increase (I) or decrease (D) mean arterial pressure.

   a. _____ increased heart rate

   b. _____ increased total peripheral resistance

   c. _____ decreased parasympathetic stimulation of the heart

   d. _____ decreased cardiac output

   e. _____ decreased stroke volume

   f. _____ vasodilation of systemic arterioles

HOW CHANGES IN CENTRAL VENOUS PRESSURE AFFECT BLOOD FLOW TO ORGANS

Completion

Fill in the blanks to complete the following sentences.

102. Alternate contraction and relaxation of the leg muscles during exercise _____ venous return by a mechanism known as the _____.

103. The respiratory movements that occur during inhalation create a _____ that promotes the movement of blood from veins in the _____ to veins in the _____.

104. Contraction of the smooth muscle in the walls of veins produces an increase in the tension of the veins, which is referred to as _____.

105. The accumulation of blood in the veins is known as _____.

Multiple Choice

Select the best answer from the choices given.

106. Which of the following is **not** a physiologic factor that affects central venous pressure?
   a. the skeletal muscle pump
   b. the respiratory pump
   c. blood volume
   d. venomotor tone
   e. the amount of bilirubin in the blood

107. Which of the following would **not** be true of the effects of exercise on the cardiovascular system?
   a. It increases venous return.
   b. It increases end-diastolic volume.
   c. It increases venous pooling.
   d. It increases central venous pressure.
   e. It increases cardiac output.

108. Which of the following is **not** an effect of increased venomotor tone?

a. Veins constrict.

b. Pressure within the veins increases.

c. Venous compliance is reduced.

d. Central venous pressure decreases.

e. Stroke volume increases.

109. An increase in blood volume _____.

a. increases central venous pressure

b. decreases central venous pressure

c. decreases mean arterial pressure

d. increases venomotor tone

e. increases venous pooling

True/False

Label the following statements as true (T) *or false* (F). *If false, change the statement to make it true.*

110. _____ Venous pooling lowers mean arterial pressure.

111. _____ Neurons that generate venomotor tone are called vasoconstrictor neurons.

112. _____ The term "respiratory pump" refers to the mechanism by which respiratory movements facilitate the flow of blood to veins within the thoracic cavity.

113. _____ An increase in central venous pressure will increase stroke volume and cardiac output.

Matching

114. Indicate whether each of the following factors will increase (I) or decrease (D) central venous pressure.

a. _____ decrease in blood volume

b. _____ increased rate and depth of breathing

c. _____ running

d. _____ decrease in venomotor tone

e. _____ prolonged bed rest

Short Answer

Answer the following question in 1–4 sentences.

115. Explain the mechanism(s) by which the skeletal muscle pump exerts its effects.

Challenge/Clinical Questions

116. Use a process diagram/concept map to explain why prolonged dehydration would lead to a decrease in mean arterial pressure.

117. How might having a couple of cracked ribs affect a person's central venous pressure and cardiac output?

118. While on clinical rotation one day, you are taking care of a patient who has congestive (left-sided) heart failure. While your back is turned the patient gets out of bed and immediately falls to the floor in a faint. You rush over to him but, before you can take any action, he regains consciousness. In relation to central venous pressure, why, most likely, did the patient faint when he stood up? Why did he regain consciousness soon after falling to the floor?

MOVEMENT OF FLUID ACROSS CAPILLARY WALLS

Completion

Fill in the blanks to complete the following sentences.

119. The movement of fluid from the capillaries into the interstitial space (interstitium) is called _____.

120. The movement of fluid from the interstitial space into the capillaries is called _____.

121. The pressure created by the protein content of the blood is specifically referred to as _____ pressure.

122. Excess fluid in the interstitial space would produce a condition known as _____.

Multiple Choice

Select the best answer from the choices given.

123. Lymph (lymphatic fluid) is _____.

    a. a highly proteinaceous fluid formed by the lymph nodes
    b. excess interstitial fluid absorbed by lymphatic capillaries
    c. an antibody-filled fluid produced by macrophages
    d. excess blood plasma secreted by lymphatic capillaries
    e. a special pathogen-fighting fluid produced by cells of the immune system

124. Which of the following statements is **not** true?

    a. Some immune responses occur within lymph nodes.
    b. Lymph nodes contain macrophages.
    c. Lymph nodes contain lymphocytes.
    d. Lymph nodes filter foreign particles from lymph.
    e. Lymph nodes synthesize lymph.

125. Filtration occurs across capillaries in locations in which _____.

    a. the oncotic pressure gradient is greater than the hydrostatic pressure gradient
    b. the oncotic pressure gradient is equal to the hydrostatic pressure gradient
    c. the hydrostatic pressure gradient is greater than the oncotic pressure gradient
    d. the hydrostatic pressure gradient is equal to atmospheric pressure
    e. the hydrostatic pressure gradient is less than the osmotic pressure gradient

126. The oncotic pressure gradient is a force directing fluid _____ the capillaries, while the hydrostatic pressure gradient directs fluid _____ the capillaries.

    a. behind : in front of   c. out of : into   e. away from : toward
    b. in front of : behind   d. into : out of

127. The concentration of which of the following substances is the most important determinant of the osmotic pressure gradient between the capillary blood and the interstitial fluid?

    a. glucose   c. sodium   e. protein
    b. water   d. potassium

True/False

Label the following statements as true (T) *or false* (F). *If false, change the statement to make it true.*

128. _____ Fluid moves across the capillary wall from the side where hydrostatic pressure is greater to the side where hydrostatic pressure is lower.

129. _____ Fluid moves across the capillary wall from the side where the osmotic pressure is lower to the side where the osmotic pressure is greater.

130. _____ Filtration and absorption never occur in the same capillary.

131. _____ When the sign of the net filtration pressure at a location along a capillary is positive, absorption will occur.

132. _____ For purposes of explaining the pressure gradients that generate filtration and absorption, it is assumed that the oncotic pressure of the plasma remains constant from one end of a capillary to the other.

133. _____ The hydrostatic pressure within a capillary is higher at the arteriolar end than at the venular end, but there is little to no variation in the hydrostatic pressure of the interstitial fluid from one end of a capillary to the other.

134. _____ Fluid within the lymphatic system is returned to the urinary bladder.

135. _____ The lymphatic system removes fluid from the interstitium that was filtered from systemic capillaries but was not absorbed.

136. _____ Fluid enters the lymphatic system via lymph nodes.

Matching

137. Indicate the effect(s) each of the following events would have on filtration or absorption: increase filtration (IF), decrease filtration (DF), increase absorption (IA), decrease absorption (DA). More than one answer may apply to each question.

    a. _____ decreased plasma protein content

    b. _____ increased venous pressure

    c. _____ hemorrhage

    d. _____ increased hydrostatic pressure in the capillaries

Short Answer

Answer the following questions in 1–4 sentences.

138. What drives the flow of lymphatic fluid through the lymphatic system?

139. How do lymphatic capillaries differ structurally from blood capillaries?

Challenge Question

140. In relation to capillary filtration/absorption, explain why bridesmaids or groomsmen sometimes faint during long weddings.

Clinical Questions

141. What causes the peripheral edema and liver enlargement often associated with congestive heart failure?

142. Using a concept map, illustrate two ways in which kidney disease or damage could result in the development of edema.

14 The Cardiovascular System: Regulation of Function

Objectives

We recommend that you review the **Objectives** for this chapter, found on p. 442 of *Principles of Human Physiology*. The **Objectives** outline what you should know from each chapter.

Key Terms

active hyperemia
angiotensin II
baroreceptor
baroreceptor reflex
chemoreceptor

epinephrine
flow autoregulation
hypertension
hypotension
ischemia

myogenic
perfusion pressure
reactive hyperemia
vasopressin

EXTRINSIC CONTROL OF CARDIOVASCULAR FUNCTION: REGULATION OF MEAN ARTERIAL PRESSURE

Completion

Fill in the blanks to complete the following sentences.

1. The part of the brain primarily responsible for coordinating the neural control of mean arterial pressure is the _____.

2. When arterial baroreceptors detect an increase in mean arterial pressure, the response that is produced will increase the activity of the _____ division of the autonomic nervous system and decrease the activity of the _____ division of the autonomic nervous system.

3. When mean arterial pressure falls or rises, the body automatically generates a sequence of physiological responses that will counteract the change in mean arterial pressure. One process by which this occurs is called the _____ reflex.

4. The clinical term for chronically high arterial blood pressure is _____.

5. The adrenergic receptors that promote vasodilation of vascular smooth muscle are _____ receptors.

6. Effects of stimuli such as hormones that *raise* blood pressure are called _____ effects.

7. The name of the substance that converts angiotensin I into angiotensin II is _____.

Matching

8. Indicate whether each of the following phenomena would increase (I) or decrease (D) in response to an increase in mean arterial pressure.

a. _____ heart rate

b. _____ frequency of action potentials conducted to the CNS by arterial baroreceptors

c. _____ venomotor tone

d. _____ stroke volume

e. _____ sympathetic stimulation of the heart and blood vessels

f. _____ parasympathetic stimulation of the heart

g. _____ total peripheral resistance

9. Many of the physiologic responses to hemorrhage are listed below. Indicate whether each response is triggered by arterial baroreceptors (A), volume receptors (cardiac and venous baroreceptors) (V), or both (B).

a. _____ increased secretion of vasopressin (ADH)

b. _____ increased heart rate

c. _____ increased myocardial contractility

d. _____ increased secretion of renin

e. _____ increased secretion of epinephrine

f. _____ increased vasoconstriction

g. _____ increased venoconstriction

10. Match the following hormones to the effects they produce (more than one hormone may apply to each effect): epinephrine (low levels) (EL), epinephrine (high levels) (EH), angiotensin II (AII), vasopressin (ADH).

a. _____ causes vasoconstriction of most arterioles

b. _____ increases heart rate

c. _____ stimulates the secretion of aldosterone, which reduces urine output in conjunction with other mechanisms

d. _____ causes vasodilation of many arterioles

e. _____ directly acts on the kidney distal convoluted tubules and collecting ducts to reduce urine output

f. _____ causes vasodilation of arterioles in cardiac and skeletal muscle

g. _____ increases myocardial contractility

Multiple Choice

Select the best answer from the choices given.

11. Which of the following is **not** true of arterial baroreceptors?

    a. They are sensory receptors that respond to changes in mean arterial pressure.

    b. They are located in the aortic arch and arterioles.

    c. They are stimulated by stretching of the walls of the vessels in which they are located.

    d. They send input to the central nervous system.

    e. Their sensory nerve endings are embedded in the walls of the blood vessels in which they are located.

12. Under most circumstances, the medulla oblongata directly regulates cardiovascular functioning by _____.

    a. sending nerve impulses to the heart and blood vessels by way of somatic nerves

    b. sending nerve impulses to the heart and blood vessels by way of autonomic nerves

    c. altering respiratory rate to change the local oxygen content of tissues

    d. altering respiratory rate to change the local carbon dioxide content of tissues

    e. sending nerve impulses to the cerebral cortex, which will then generate the appropriate cardiovascular responses

13. Which of the following is **not** a role of the cerebral cortex in the regulation of cardiovascular function?

    a. It is involved in cardiovascular changes occurring in response to pain.

    b. It is involved in cardiovascular changes occurring in response to anxiety.

    c It is involved in cardiovascular changes occurring in response to certain emotional states.

    d. It modulates the response of the medulla oblongata to sensory inputs from receptors associated with the cardiovascular system.

    e. It receives input from the medulla oblongata and then directly generates the appropriate cardiovascular response.

14. Which of the following is **not** a receptor that would send input about the status of the cardiovascular system to the medulla oblongata?

    a. arterial baroreceptors

    b. baroreceptors that monitor venous pressure

    c. arterial photoreceptors

    d. chemoreceptors located in the aorta

    e. chemoreceptors located in the carotid arteries

15. Which of the following is **not** correct regarding the neural input received by the cardiovascular system?

    a. Sympathetic and parasympathetic stimulation of the sinoatrial node affects heart rate.

    b. Sympathetic stimulation of the ventricular myocardium affects contractility.

    c. Sympathetic stimulation of arterioles and small arteries affects vascular resistance.

    d. Parasympathetic stimulation of capillaries affects capillary permeability.

    e. Sympathetic stimulation of veins affects venomotor tone.

16. If mean arterial pressure falls, the baroreceptor reflex is triggered when _____.

    a. chemoreceptors increase the frequency of action potentials sent to the cerebral cortex

    b. volume receptors increase the frequency of action potentials sent to the medulla oblongata

    c. arterial baroreceptors decrease the frequency of action potentials sent to the medulla oblongata

    d. arterial baroreceptors increase the frequency of action potentials sent to the medulla oblongata

    e. arterial baroreceptors increase the frequency of action potentials sent to the hypothalamus

17. If mean arterial pressure falls, the baroreceptor reflex will result in _____.

    a. increased parasympathetic activity   d. decreased sympathetic activity

    b. decreased parasympathetic activity   e. b and c are correct

    c. increased sympathetic activity   f. a and d are correct

18. Which of the following is **not** a result of the change in sympathetic activity you indicated in Question 17?

    a. increased action potential frequency in the SA node

    b. increased compliance of veins

    c. increased venous pressure

    d. increased contractility of the myocardium

    e. increased vasoconstriction of arterioles

19. Long-term regulation of arterial pressure is accomplished by _____.

    a. the baroreceptor reflex   d. regulating total peripheral resistance

    b. regulating heart rate   e. regulating blood volume

    c. regulating stroke volume

20. Which of the following is **not** a hormone whose release/production is directly or indirectly stimulated by the activity of arterial baroreceptors following a decrease in mean arterial pressure?

    a. epinephrine   c. angiotensin II   e. angiotensinogen

    b. vasopressin   d. renin

21. Epinephrine is secreted predominately by the _____.

    a. kidney   d. adrenal gland (adrenal medulla)

    b. anterior pituitary gland   e. thyroid gland

    c. posterior pituitary gland

22. The release of epinephrine from the gland indicated in Question 21 is regulated by _____.

    a. parasympathetic stimulation of the gland

    b. sympathetic stimulation of the gland

    c. stimulation of the gland by renin

    d. stimulation of the gland by angiotensin I

    e. stimulation of the gland by aldosterone

23. The primary receptors to which epinephrine binds in cardiac muscle are _____.

    a. cholinergic receptors

    b. adrenergic beta receptors

    c. adrenergic alpha receptors

    d. muscarinic receptors

    e. nicotinic receptors

24. At **low** concentrations, epinephrine generally promotes _____ because it has a greater affinity for _____.

    a. a decrease in heart rate : beta than for alpha receptors

    b. an increase in heart rate : alpha than for beta receptors

    c. vasodilation : beta than for alpha receptors

    d. vasoconstriction : alpha than for beta receptors

    e. decreased urine output : alpha than for beta receptors

25. Vasopressin (ADH) is secreted by the _____.

    a. posterior pituitary gland

    b. anterior pituitary gland

    c. adrenal gland

    d. kidney

    e. lungs

26. Vasopressin (ADH) is released in direct response to _____.

    a. an increased heart rate

    b. a decreased stroke volume

    c. an increased pulse pressure

    d. an increase in mean arterial pressure

    e. a decrease in mean arterial pressure

27. Which of the following are the effects of vasopressin on the body?

    a. causes vasodilation of arterioles and increased urine output

    b. causes vasoconstriction of arterioles and decreased urine output

    c. converts angiotensin I to angiotensin II

    d. converts renin to epinephrine

    e. stimulates the release of aldosterone from the adrenal gland

28. Vasopressin is also known as _____.

    a. renin

    b. angiotensinogen

    c. aldosterone

    d. antidiuretic hormone

    e. angiotensin I

29. Volume receptors are baroreceptors located in the _____.

    a. aortic arch and carotid sinuses

    b. venules and capillaries

    c. walls of the heart and walls of large systemic veins

    d. walls of the pulmonary trunk and pulmonary veins

    e. kidney and liver

Labeling

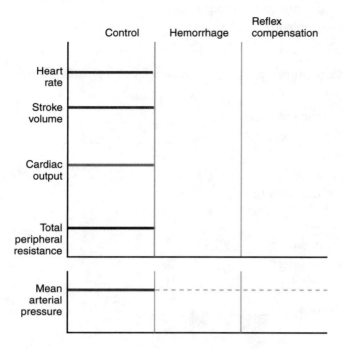

FIGURE 14.1

30. On Figure 14.1, draw in lines representing the changes in the cardiovascular variables indicated that would occur in response to hemorrhage, and that would occur once the baroreceptor reflex generated compensatory responses.

True/False

Label the following statements as true (T) *or false* (F). *If false, change the statement to make it true.*

31. _____ The primary function of the baroreceptor reflex is to maintain adequate organ blood flow.

32. _____ In order to keep mean arterial pressure fairly constant, the baroreceptor reflex is regulated by negative feedback.

33. _____ In response to a decrease in mean arterial pressure, the baroreceptor reflex produces physiologic responses that increase heart rate and stroke volume and decrease total peripheral resistance.

34. _____ A baroreceptor reflex is triggered only in response to a decrease in mean arterial pressure.

35. _____ Increased parasympathetic stimulation will decrease the heart rate and will directly cause vasodilation of the arterioles.

36. _____ As mean arterial pressure increases, the pressure in the aortic arch and carotid sinuses increases, causing the vessel walls to stretch more, which results in greater depolarization of arterial baroreceptors, which increases the frequency of action potentials sent to the medulla oblongata.

37. _____ The regulation of mean arterial pressure is an example of intrinsic control.

38. _____ When arterial baroreceptors notify the central nervous system of a decrease in mean arterial pressure, the responses produced include a decrease in sympathetic nervous system activity and an increase in parasympathetic nervous system activity.

39. _____ When venous pressure increases, mean arterial pressure tends to increase.

40. _____ Arterial baroreceptors and volume receptors (cardiac and venous baroreceptors) produce effects that are antagonistic toward one another.

41. _____ In addition to arterial, cardiac, and venous baroreceptors, baroreceptors are also located in the pulmonary vasculature.

42. _____ Baroreceptors known as volume receptors monitor venous pressure.

43. _____ Angiotensin-converting enzyme is located primarily on the outer surface of blood vessels in the stomach.

44. _____ The increased secretion of vasopressin will increase mean arterial pressure and venous pressure.

45. _____ Increased sympathetic stimulation of the adrenal gland will decrease the secretion of epinephrine.

46. _____ Vascular smooth muscle contains both alpha and beta adrenergic receptors.

47. _____ Stimulation of alpha adrenergic receptors promotes vasoconstriction.

48. _____ Sympathetic nervous activity stimulates alpha adrenergic receptors.

Short Answer

Answer the following questions in 1–4 sentences.

49. Why is it advantageous to the body that arterial baroreceptors are located in the structures that they are?

50. Why do high and low concentrations of epinephrine typically have opposite effects on most vascular beds in the body?

51. Why are venous and cardiac baroreceptors often referred to as volume receptors?

Sequencing

52. List the following events in the order in which they occur.

   a. Angiotensin I is converted to angiotensin II.

   b. Renin secretion from the kidneys increases.

   c. Mean arterial pressure decreases.

   d. Mean arterial pressure increases.

   e. Frequency of action potentials conducted from the baroreceptors to the CNS decreases.

   f. Angiotensinogen is converted to angiotensin I.

   g. Activity of the sympathetic division of the nervous system increases.

   h. Vasoconstriction of arterioles occurs and aldosterone is secreted from the adrenal glands.

   i. Arterial baroreceptors are stimulated by decreased vessel stretch.

Sequence: _____

Challenge Questions

53. When vasodilation occurs in the body, do all the arterioles dilate at once? Why or why not?

54. Following a drop in mean arterial pressure that occurs in response to hemorrhage, the baroreceptor reflex generates responses that bring the MAP almost back to its original value, but the MAP is maintained at a slightly lower pressure than it was before the hemorrhage. Why does this occur?

55. When a baroreceptor reflex is triggered in response to a low mean arterial pressure, the resistance of most, but not all, organs increases. Which organs do not experience an increase in resistance, and why?

56. Why is it advantageous to the body for arterioles in the cardiac and skeletal muscle to have more beta than alpha adrenergic receptors, while arterioles elsewhere usually have more alpha than beta receptors?

Clinical Questions

57. You are walking in the woods with a friend when he slips and falls over the edge of an embankment. During the fall, his leg is impaled by a tree branch and he begins to rapidly lose blood. You manage to slow the bleeding and call the ranger station on your cell phone for help. Based on your location they say it will be about an hour before they can reach you. Using the sphygmomanometer in your medical kit, you periodically monitor your friend's blood pressure while you wait. It remains somewhat low but fairly stable for about 45 minutes, but starts to drop quite rapidly shortly before help arrives, and your friend becomes unconscious. (Help does arrive in time and your friend survives.) Why did his blood pressure remain fairly stable for the first 45 minutes and then begin to rapidly decrease?

58. Why isn't the baroreceptor reflex able to keep the blood pressure within "normal limits" in people who have hypertension?

59. You notice that one of your co-workers is wearing a shirt that looks awfully tight around the collar. In the middle of a meeting she suddenly faints. You loosen her collar to help her breathe, and she soon regains consciousness. Based on what you know about the baroreceptor reflex, why do you think your co-worker fainted? Why did loosening her collar help her regain consciousness?

60. There is a hormonal imbalance known as the Syndrome of Inappropriate Antidiuretic Hormone Secretion, in which ADH is secreted almost continually at higher than normal levels. What impact might this have on a person's blood pressure initially (before compensatory events take place), and why?

Concept Maps

61. In the concept map below, indicate whether each of the variables will increase (I) or decrease (D) in response to an increase in mean arterial pressure, and fill in the names of the missing variables.

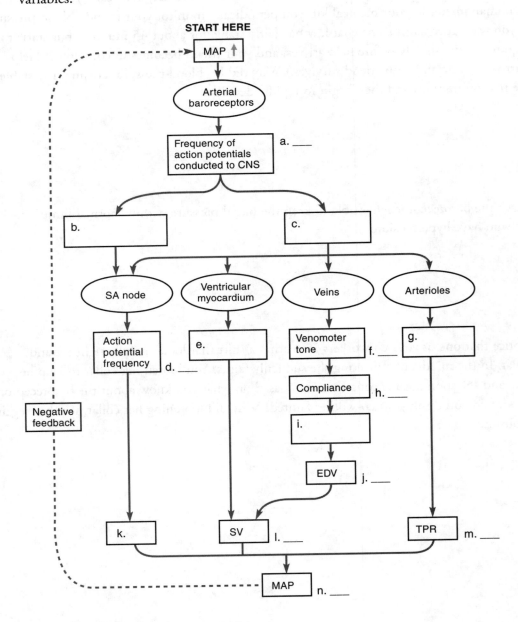

62. Fill in the blanks in the concept map below, indicating whether each of the variables will increase or decrease in response to blood loss resulting from hemorrhage.

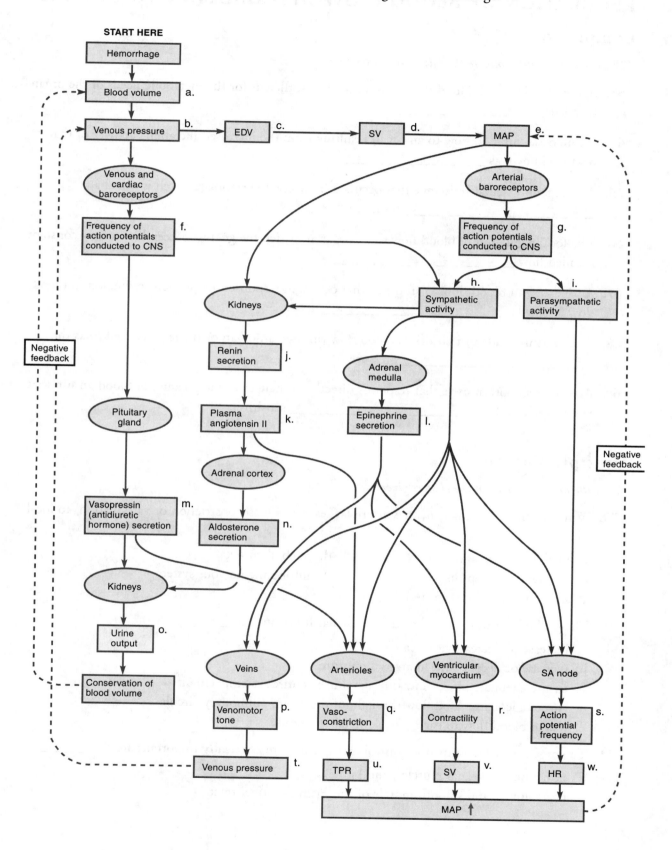

INTRINSIC CONTROL OF CARDIOVASCULAR FUNCTION: REGULATION OF BLOOD FLOW DISTRIBUTION TO ORGANS

Completion

Fill in the blanks to complete the following sentences.

63. A situation in which blood flow to an organ is insufficient for the metabolic needs of the organ is called _____.

64. An increase in blood flow to an organ resulting from the increased metabolic activity of that organ is known as _____.

65. A change in vascular resistance that occurs in response to arteriolar stretch is called a _____ response.

66. The local regulation of blood flow to an organ in which the goal is to keep blood flow constant is called flow _____.

67. An increase in blood flow to an organ that occurs in response to a previous reduction in blood flow is called _____.

68. The pressure gradient that drives blood flow through an organ or tissue is referred to as the _____ pressure.

69. Arteriolar smooth muscle that responds directly to changes in the pressure of blood within that vessel is said to be _____ sensitive.

Multiple Choice

Select the best answer from the choices given.

70. Which of the following generates arteriolar responses (vasoconstriction or vasodilation) to local stimuli?
    a. medulla oblongata
    b. arterial baroreceptors
    c. smooth muscle of the arterioles
    d. cerebral cortex
    e. autonomic nervous system

71. The goal of intrinsic control of cardiovascular function is to _____.
    a. increase or decrease heart rate
    b. increase or decrease mean arterial pressure
    c. ensure adequate blood flow throughout the entire systemic circuit
    d. ensure adequate blood flow throughout the entire pulmonary circuit
    e. match blood flow to each organ's metabolic needs

72. The organs to which intrinsic control mechanisms are **especially** important are the _____.
    a. heart, brain, skeletal muscles, and kidneys
    b. heart, lungs, and smooth muscle of the gastrointestinal tract

c. skeletal muscles, smooth muscle of the gastrointestinal tract, and lungs

d. liver, ovaries, and testes

e. ovaries, testes, and bones

73. Which of the following is **not** true of local control of organ resistance?

    a. It is accomplished through vasodilation or vasoconstriction of arterioles.

    b. It responds to changes in parasympathetic stimulation of the blood vessels.

    c. It regulates the distribution of blood flow among organs.

    d. It regulates the distribution of blood flow within organs.

    e. It responds to changes in the metabolic activity of organs.

74. Which of the following is **not** a local stimulus that would generate changes in the blood flow to an organ (either during or following the stimulus)?

    a. change in the metabolic activity of the organ

    b. change from the normal amount of blood flow to the organ

    c. change in the pressure within the arterioles supplying the organ

    d. change in the amount of vasoactive hormones secreted by endocrine glands into the blood

    e. change in the amount of local vasoactive chemical messengers secreted by endothelial or tissue cells

75. Local control mechanisms are generally regulated by _____.

    a. activity of the medulla oblongata

    b. activity of the sympathetic nervous system

    c. activity of the parasympathetic nervous system

    d. positive feedback mechanisms

    e. negative feedback mechanisms

76. An increase in blood flow to an organ will initially _____.

    a. increase the carbon dioxide and decrease the oxygen content of the tissues

    b. increase the mean arterial pressure and decrease the venous pressure of the systemic circuit

    c. decrease the carbon dioxide and increase the oxygen content of the tissues

    d. decrease the mean arterial pressure and increase the venous pressure of the systemic circuit

    e. decrease the metabolic activity of the organ and increase carbon dioxide production in the tissues

77. In flow autoregulation, the variable that remains constant is _____.

    a. the amount of sympathetic stimulation received by the organ

    b. the amount of parasympathetic stimulation received by the organ

    c. blood flow to the organ

    d. the amount of oxygen being used by the organ

    e. the amount of carbon dioxide being produced by the organ

78. Locally secreted chemical messengers that cause the vasodilation of arterioles include all of the following **except** _____.

    a. endothelin-1   c. bradykinin   e. adenosine

    b. nitric oxide   d. prostacyclin

79. Locally secreted chemical messengers that regulate organ resistance are usually secreted by
_____.

    a. endocrine glands

    b. the liver

    c. the kidney

    d. endothelial cells of blood vessels or cells of surrounding tissues

    e. sympathetic and/or parasympathetic nerves

Matching

80. Indicate whether each of the following local stimuli would cause vasodilation (D) or
vasoconstriction (C) of arterioles in the vascular beds of organs.

    a. _____ decreased tissue oxygen concentration

    b. _____ increased tissue carbon dioxide concentration

    c. _____ increased tissue hydrogen ion concentration

    d. _____ increased perfusion pressure within arterioles

    e. _____ decreased stretch of arteriolar smooth muscle

    f. _____ increased blood flow to the organ

    g. _____ increased tissue potassium ion concentration

    h. _____ increased nitric oxide concentration

    i. _____ decreased metabolic activity of the organ

True/False

Label the following statements as true (T) *or false* (F). *If false, change the statement to make it true.*

81. _____ Vasodilation of organ arterioles will lower the organ resistance, which will decrease
blood flow to the organ.

82. _____ Intrinsic control of blood flow within the brain is important as metabolic activity in
different regions of the brain varies frequently, depending on the type of mental
activities being performed at the time.

83. _____ Changes in tissue chemical levels associated with changes in metabolic activity will
usually cause vasodilation when metabolic activity increases and vasoconstriction
when metabolic activity decreases.

84. _____ An increase in the metabolic activity of an organ will result in a decrease in the tissue
carbon dioxide concentration.

85. _____ A decrease in tissue oxygen concentration will cause arteriolar smooth muscle to relax.

86. _____ A falling metabolic rate usually leads to a falling tissue oxygen concentration.

87. _____ Blood flow to an organ will increase as the tissue concentration of carbon dioxide
decreases.

88. _____ Tissue oxygen and carbon dioxide concentrations can change as a result of a change in metabolic activity or as a result of a change in blood flow.

89. _____ When certain types of arteriolar smooth muscle fibers are stretched, they respond by contracting, resulting in vasoconstriction.

90. _____ In systemic organs, perfusion pressure is equivalent to pulse pressure.

91. _____ A decrease in blood flow to an organ will decrease the perfusion pressure, resulting in the generation of a myogenic response, producing vasodilation and an increase in organ blood flow.

92. _____ In active hyperemia, blood flow to the organ remains constant.

93. _____ Endothelin-1 is a local chemical messenger that causes vasoconstriction.

Sequencing

List the following events in the order in which they occur during each of the following responses.

94. List the changes producing in/resulting from a reactive hyperemia in response to decreased organ blood flow.

   a. decreased organ resistance
   b. increased removal of carbon dioxide from tissues
   c. increased tissue carbon dioxide concentration
   d. increased organ blood flow
   e. vasodilation
   f. decreased tissue carbon dioxide concentration
   g. decreased organ blood flow

   Sequence: _____

95. List the changes involved in the myogenic response occurring as a result of increased perfusion pressure.

   a. increased perfusion pressure
   b. decreased organ blood flow
   c. vasoconstriction
   d. increased stretch of arteriolar smooth muscle
   e. increased organ resistance

   Sequence: _____

Challenge Questions

96. Why is it difficult to tell whether local changes in organ blood flow occur in response to a change in pressure within the arterioles or a change in the metabolic activity of the organ?

97. Are extrinsic and intrinsic controls of organ resistance equally important in all organs? Why or why not?

Clinical Question

98. Why are inflamed tissues red?

OTHER CARDIOVASCULAR REGULATORY PROCESSES

Short Answer

Answer the following questions in 1–4 sentences.

99. Define sinus arrhythmia and explain why it occurs.

100. What roles do sweat glands play in regulating body temperature?

Multiple Choice

Select the best answer from the choices given.

101. The type of receptors that monitor oxygen and carbon dioxide levels in the blood and that, when stimulated, can produce effects on both the respiratory and cardiovascular systems are _____.

    a. thermoreceptors   d. chemoreceptors
    b. volume receptors   e. pulmonary baroreceptors
    c. arterial baroreceptors

102. The thermoregulatory center is located in the _____.

    a. medulla oblongata   d. cerebral cortex
    b. hypothalamus   e. pons
    c. thalamus

103. The thermoregulatory center regulates _____.

    a. body temperature   d. blood oxygen level

    b. mean arterial pressure   e. blood carbon dioxide level

    c. venous pressure

104. Which of the following responses does **not** occur when body temperature increases?

    a. Sympathetic stimulation of the skin decreases.

    b. Vascular smooth muscle in the arterioles of the skin relaxes.

    c. Vasodilation of arterioles in the skin occurs.

    d. Blood flow to the skin increases.

    e. The skin's vascular resistance increases.

105. Which of the following does **not** occur during exercise?

    a. Blood flow to the skin increases.

    b. Blood flow to the heart increases.

    c. Total peripheral resistance increases.

    d. Blood flow to the skeletal muscles increases.

    e. Cardiac output increases.

106. The increase in stroke volume that occurs during exercise is primarily the result of _____.

    a. increased ventricular contractility, resulting from increased sympathetic stimulation of the heart and an increased level of circulating epinephrine

    b. increased ventricular contractility, resulting only from increased sympathetic stimulation of the heart

    c. increased heart rate due to increased sympathetic stimulation of the heart and an increased level of circulating epinephrine

    d. greatly increased end-diastolic volume

    e. greatly increased total peripheral resistance

107. The regions of the brain primarily responsible for triggering the cardiovascular changes that occur during exercise are the _____.

    a. hypothalamus and thalamus

    b. pons and limbic system

    c. cerebral cortex and limbic system

    d. thalamus and pons

    e. mid brain and pons

108. Which of the following does **not** occur in response to exercise?

    a. increased sympathetic stimulation of the heart

    b. decreased parasympathetic stimulation of the heart

    c. increased sympathetic stimulation of the digestive tract

    d. increased sympathetic stimulation of the skin

    e. increased bradykinin secretion by sweat glands

True/False

Label the following statements as true (T) *or false* (F). *If false, change the statement to make it true.*

109. _____ Neurons located throughout the body that monitor changes in body temperature are known as thermoreceptors.

110. _____ During exercise, blood flow to cardiac and skeletal muscle and the skin can increase to about 40% of cardiac output.

111. _____ When body temperature falls, increased sympathetic stimulation of the skin triggers vasoconstriction of the arterioles, which decreases blood flow to the skin and conserves body heat.

112. _____ Increased blood flow to cardiac muscle during exercise is primarily the result of intrinsic control.

Challenge Questions

113. Does venous return increase, decrease, or remain unchanged during exercise? Why?

114. Why is it advantageous for blood flow to certain organs to increase during exercise while blood flow to other organs decreases?

115. Why do competitive marksmen pull the trigger during an exhalation?

116. What are the primary cardiovascular effects produced when chemoreceptors are stimulated by a low arterial oxygen level? How do these responses help the body maintain homeostasis?

Clinical Question

117. Why might the baroreceptor reflex be ineffective in compensating for a severe blood loss suffered on a very hot day?

15 The Respiratory System: Breathing Mechanics

Objectives

We recommend that you review the **Objectives** for this chapter, found on page 469 of *Princicples of Human Physiology*. The **Objectives** outline what you should know from each chapter.

Key Terms

alveolar ventilation
alveoli
bronchi
bronchiole
conducting zone
diaphragm
epiglottis
esophagus
expiration
expiratory reserve volume
external intercostals
external respiration
forced expiratory volume
forced vital capacity
functional residual capacity
   (FRC)

glottis
goblet cell
inspiration
inspiratory capacity
inspiratory reserve
   volume
internal respiration
intra-alveolar pressure
intrapleural pressure
intrapleural space
larynx
minute ventilation
pharynx
pleura
pneumothorax
pulmonary surfactant

pulmonary ventilation
residual volume (RV)
respiration
respiratory bronchiole
respiratory membrane
respiratory zone
secondary bronchi
terminal bronchiole
tidal volume
total lung capacity (TLC)
trachea
transpulmonary pressure
upper airway
vital capacity (VC)

OVERVIEW OF RESPIRATORY FUNCTION AND ANATOMY OF THE RESPIRATORY SYSTEM

Matching

1. Match whether each of the following structures is a part of the conducting zone (CZ) or the respiratory zone (RZ).

    a. _____ alveolar ducts

    b. _____ respiratory membrane

    c. _____ secondary bronchi

    d. _____ bronchioles

    e. _____ alveoli

    f. _____ trachea

Completion

Fill in the blanks to complete the following narrative.

2. Respiration is the process of gas exchange and includes **(a)** and external respiration. Functions of the respiratory system include supplying **(b)** to the tissues and eliminating **(c)**, **(d)** balance of the blood, vocalization, and protection against **(e)** and irritants in the air.

   a. _____   d. _____

   b. _____   e. _____

   c. _____

Short Answer

Answer the following question in 1–4 sentences.

3. Compare and contrast internal and external respiration.

Multiple Choice

Select the best answer from the choices given.

4. Dale has paralyzed two of his respiratory muscles. Which of the following two muscles are likely affected?

   a. diaphragm and psoas major   d. gracilis and deltoid
   b. external intercostals and diaphragm   e. deltoid and diaphragm
   c. internal intercostals and gracilis

5. Which of the following structures has the most surface area exposed to air?

   a. nasal cavity   c. larynx   e. secondary bronchi
   b. trachea   d. alveolar sacs

True/False

Label the following statements as true (T) *or false* (F). *If false, change the statement to make it true.*

6. _____ The surface of the pleural sac attached to the lung tissue is called the visceral pleura.

7. _____ There are three secondary bronchi in the right lung and two secondary bronchi in the left lung.

8. _____ Each alveolus is completely separate from all other alveoli.

9. _____ Cartilage is plentiful in the bronchioles.

Sequencing

10. Place in order the following structures associated with the respiratory tract beginning with the nose.

a. larynx
b. glottis
c. bronchi
d. terminal bronchioles
e. secondary bronchi
f. alveolar ducts
g. respiratory bronchioles
h. tertiary bronchi
i. pharynx
j. alveoli
k. trachea
l. epiglottis

Sequence: _____

Clinical Question

11. Anita has a stabbing pain every time she breathes. Her physician has diagnosed her with pleurisy, which is an inflammation of the pleura. What could be the cause of her irritation?

Challenge Question

12. Describe the locations and functions of each of the specialized cells of the respiratory tract.

FORCES FOR PULMONARY VENTILATION

Matching

13. Match whether each of the conditions below would lead to inspiration (I) or expiration (E).

a. _____ contraction of external intercostal muscles

b. _____ passive process not requiring any muscle contraction

c. _____ contraction of the diaphragm

d. _____ an increase in intra-alveolar pressure

e. _____ a decrease in lung volume

f. _____ contraction of abdominal muscles

g. _____ lungs just beginning to expand

Completion

Fill in the blanks to complete the following narrative.

14. Inspiration and expiration are driven by differences in **(a)** and intra-alveolar pressures. These pressure gradients are created when the volume of the **(b)** is changed. Inspiration is caused by **(c)** of the diaphragm and **(d)** muscles; this causes the volume of the thoracic cavity to **(e)**. As the thoracic cavity expands, the intrapleural pressure **(f)**, creating a force that **(g)** the lungs as the chest wall **(g)**. Intra-alveolar pressure decreases below **(h)** pressure, and inspiration occurs. During quiet breathing, expiration occurs when the **(i)** and lungs return passively to their original positions. Active expiration involves contraction of the **(j)** and abdominal muscles.

a. _____   f. _____

b. _____   g. _____

c. _____   h. _____

d. _____   i. _____

e. _____   j. _____

Short Answer

Answer the following questions in 1–4 sentences.

15. Describe the two factors that determine intra-alveolar pressure.

16. What determines transpulmonary pressure?

Multiple Choice

Select the best answer from the choices given.

17. As air enters the lungs, which of the following pressures is highest?

    a. expiratory pressure
    b. atmospheric pressure
    c. intrapleural pressure
    d. transpulmonary pressure
    e. intra-alveolar pressure

18. At rest, which of the following terms is correctly matched with its pressure?

    a. atmospheric pressure: −4 mm Hg
    b. intrapleural pressure: 760 mm Hg
    c. intra-alveolar pressure: 760 mm Hg
    d. atmospheric pressure: 0 mm Hg
    e. intrapleural pressure: −4 mm Hg

19. At rest, which of the following statements is true about the respiratory system?

    a. Air is rushing into the lungs.

    b. The chest wall is compressed and recoils outward.

    c. The intrapleural pressure rises to near 760 mm Hg.

    d. The pressure in the alveoli is less than atmospheric pressure.

    e. Boyle's law does not apply.

True/False

Label the following statements as true (T) *or false* (F). *If false, change the statement to make it true.*

20. _____ During inspiration, the diaphragm contracts and moves upward.

21. _____ Boyle's law states that, as the volume of a container increases, the pressure exerted by the gas in that container increases as well.

22. _____ During expiration the lungs recoil, decreasing the volume of the alveoli.

Labeling

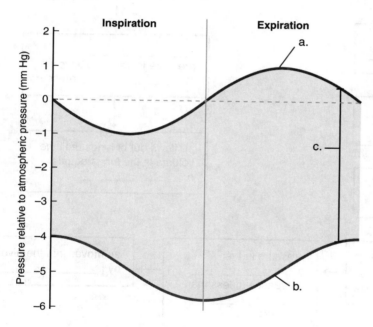

FIGURE 15.1

23. In the space below, identify the pressures in Figure 15.1 and define each.

Concept Map

24. Fill in the boxes of the events of quiet inspiration and expiration.

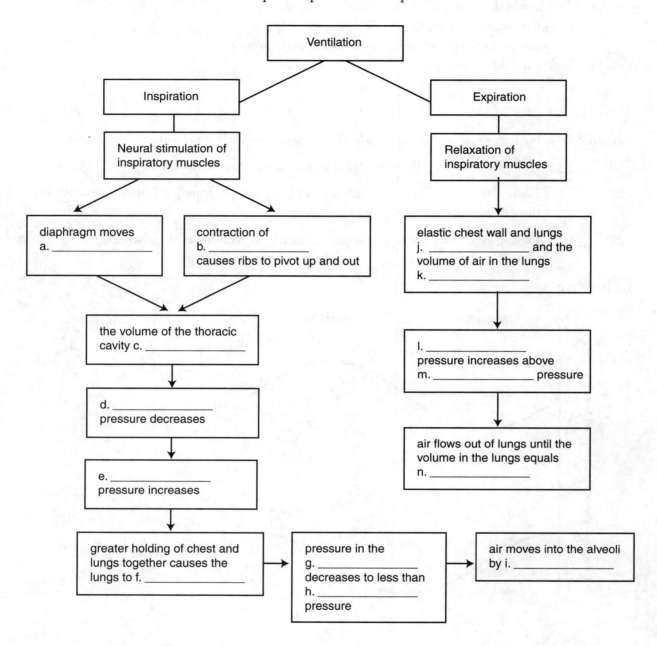

Clinical Question

25. A gunshot victim with a pneumothorax in his left side is brought into the emergency room. Explain the relationship of the intrapleural, atmospheric, and intra-alveolar pressures.

Challenge Question

26. Explain why only one lung collapses when pneumothorax on one side of the body occurs.

FACTORS AFFECTING PULMONARY VENTILATION

Matching

27. Indicate whether each condition below would cause airway resistance to be increased (I) or decreased (D).

    a. _____ a severe case of asthma

    b. _____ release of histamine

    c. _____ relaxation of bronchioles

    d. _____ high levels of carbon dioxide

    e. _____ chronic obstructive pulmonary diseases

    f. _____ increases in mucus lining the airways

    g. _____ increased sympathetic stimulation to the bronchioles

Completion

Fill in the blanks to complete the following narrative.

28. The rate of airflow into or out of the lungs is determined by the magnitude of the pressure gradient driving the flow and **(a)**. Lungs have a high **(b)**, that is, they are easily stretched to increase lung **(c)** for **(d)**. Airway resistance depends primarily on the **(e)** of the tubules of the respiratory tract. Airway resistance is usually low, but can be affected by breathing mechanics, the **(f)** nervous system, chemical factors, and pathological states.

    a. _____   d. _____

    b. _____   e. _____

    c. _____   f. _____

Short Answer

Answer the following questions in 1–4 sentences.

29. Define lung compliance.

30. Describe the two factors that determine the rate of airflow into and out of the lungs.

Multiple Choice

Select the best answer from the choices given.

31. Which of the following statements is true about surfactant?

a. It is involved in bronchoconstriction.
b. It increases lung compliance.
c. It prevents lung recoil.
d. It increases airway resistance.
e. It decreases airway resistance.

32. Which of the following would be true in a person with asthma?

a. Airway resistance would likely not change much.
b. The respiratory membrane surface area would be increased.
c. Airway resistance would be increased.
d. The person would have bronchodilation.
e. Airway diameter would be increased.

True/False

Label the following statements as true (T) or false (F). If false, change the statement to make it true.

33. _____ As carbon dioxide increases, airway resistance is increased.

34. _____ A woman has an allergic reaction to a bee sting. Histamine will be released and cause her airway diameter to decrease, thus increasing airway resistance.

35. _____ Removal of tractive forces during expiration reduces airway diameter and decreases airway resistance.

Clinical Questions

36. A mother gives birth to a baby girl nine weeks early. Describe the respiratory challenges that the infant will face.

37. Jennifer is an 8-year-old girl who has trouble breathing on a hot, humid day. Her mother takes her to the emergency room where the physician notices that she has difficulty breathing and she is wheezing. The physician administers epinephrine through an inhaler, and Jennifer's symptoms diminish almost immediately. Explain how and where epinephrine exerts its effects in the respiratory system.

Challenge Question

38. Compare and contrast asthma and chronic obstructive pulmonary diseases (COPDs) in terms of their effects on airway resistance and duration of effect on breathing.

CLINICAL SIGNIFICANCE OF RESPIRATORY VOLUMES AND AIRFLOWS

Matching

39. Match the lung volume or capacity with its appropriate definition and average volume for a healthy 70-kg male below. Expiratory Reserve Volume (ERV), Functional Residual Capacity (FRC), Inspiratory Reserve Volume (IRV), Residual Volume (RV), Tidal Volume (V_T), Total lung capacity (TLC), and Vital Capacity (VC).

a. _____ The volume of air that moves into and out of the lungs during a normal, unforced breath. Averages 500 mL.

b. _____ The maximum volume of air that can be expired from the end of a normal expiration. Averages 1,000 mL.

c. _____ The volume of air remaining in the lungs after a maximal expiration. Averages 1,200 mL.

d. _____ The volume of air remaining in the lungs at the end of a tidal expiration. Averages 2,200 mL.

e. _____ The maximum volume of air that can be inspired from the end of a normal inspiration. Averages 3,000 mL.

f. _____ The maximum volume of air that can be inspired at the end of a resting expiration. Averages 3,500 mL.

g. _____ The maximum volume of air that can be expired following a maximum inspiration. Averages 4,500 mL.

h. _____ The volume of air in the lungs at the end of a maximum inspiration. Averages 5,700 mL.

Completion

Fill in the blanks to complete the following narrative.

40. Lung volumes and **(a)** can be measured by a technique known as **(b)**. Other lung measurements take into account the **(c)** of airflow. **(d)** is the total amount of air that flows into or out of the respiratory system in a minute. **(e)** is a measure of the volume of fresh air reaching the alveoli each minute, which is **(d)** corrected for **(f)** volume.

a. _____   d. _____

b. _____   e. _____

c. _____   f. _____

Short Answer

Answer the following questions in 1–4 sentences.

41. Distinguish between lung volume and lung capacity.

42. Describe the difference between obstructive pulmonary disease and restrictive pulmonary disorders.

Multiple Choice

Select the best answer from the choices given.

43. Which of the following changes will accompany the loss of elasticity associated with aging?
   a. increased vital capacity   d. increased total lung capacity
   b. increased tidal volume   e. increased inspiratory reserve volume
   c. increased residual volume

44. Tony inhales as much as he can and then exhales as forcefully as he can. Which of the following has Tony performed?
   a. forced vital capacity   d. residual volume
   b. total lung capacity   e. expiratory reserve volume
   c. functional residual capacity

45. A clinician measures how much air Caroline breathes in and out with each breath. Which of the following is the clinician measuring?

    a. inspiratory capacity

    b. forced vital capacity

    c. functional residual capacity

    d. tidal volume

    e. inspiratory reserve volume

46. Which of the following volumes can be measured with the helium dilution method?

    a. inspiratory capacity

    b. residual volume

    c. inspiratory reserve volume

    d. tidal volume

    e. functional residual capacity

True/False

Label the following statements as true (T) *or false* (F). *If false, change the statement to make it true.*

47. _____ A normal FEV_1 value is approximately 60%.

48. _____ The area of the conducting respiratory passageway that never contributes to gas exchange is known as the anatomical dead space.

49. _____ Total lung capacity is the total amount of air that is normally exchanged with each breath.

Clinical Question

50. An 82-year-old man has trouble breathing and has been referred to a pulmonary specialist. The specialist determines that the man has reduced vital capacity and total lung capacity. What is the likely diagnosis?

Challenge Questions

51. Christine has a minute ventilation of 5,200 mL and a tidal volume of 400 mL. What is her ventilation rate?

52. Given the volumes in Table 15.1, calculate the following volumes and capacities, showing your work: Inspiratory Reserve Capacity (IRV), Expiratory Reserve Volume (ERV), Functional Residual Capacity (FRC), Total Lung Capacity, (TLC). After calculating each volume or capacity, define it.

TABLE 15.1	
Tidal Volume (V$_T$)	450 mL
Residual Volume (RV)	1,100 mL
Inspiratory Capacity (IC)	3,350 mL
Vital Capacity (VC)	4,600 mL

Labeling

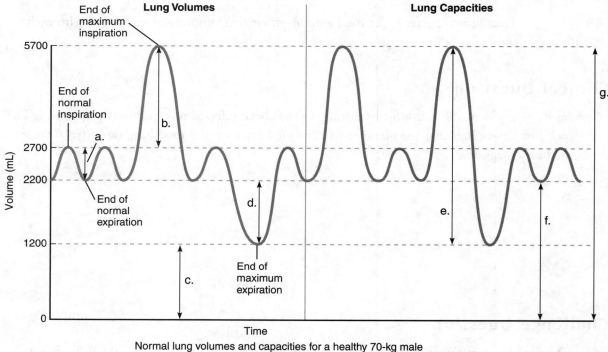

FIGURE 15.2

53. In the space below, identify a–g in Figure 15.2.

16 The Respiratory System: Gas Exchange and Regulation of Breathing

Objectives

We recommend that you review the **Objectives** for this chapter, found on p. 495 of *Principles of Human Physiology*. The **Objectives** outline what you should know from each chapter.

Key Terms

acidosis

alkalosis

carbaminohemoglobin

carbonic anhydrase

central chemoreceptor

chemoreceptor

chloride shift

dorsal respiratory group (DRG)

hemoglobin

hyperpnea

hyperventilation

hypoventilation

peripheral chemoreceptor

phrenic nerve

respiratory quotient

ventilation-perfusion ratio

OVERVIEW OF THE PULMONARY CIRCULATION AND DIFFUSION OF GASES

Matching

1. Match the location in the circulatory system below with its average flow listed here: 200 mL/min; 250 mL/min; 750 mL/min; 882 mL/min; 1,000 mL/min; 2,500 mL/min; 2,700 mL/min.

   a. _____ flow of oxygen from the systemic capillaries into the cells of the body

   b. _____ flow of carbon dioxide in the pulmonary arteries

   c. _____ flow of oxygen in the systemic arteries

   d. _____ the flow of oxygen entering the pulmonary capillaries

   e. _____ the flow of carbon dioxide in the pulmonary veins

   f. _____ the flow of oxygen entering the alveoli

   g. _____ the flow of carbon dioxide leaving the alveoli

Completion

Fill in the blanks to complete the following narratives.

2. The right heart pumps deoxygenated blood to the **(a)** capillaries, where **(b)** diffuses from the alveoli to **(c)**, and **(d)** diffuses from blood to the capillaries. The oxygenated blood returns to the **(e)** side of the heart, where it is pumped to the **(f)** capillaries in the tissues of the body. Here, **(g)** diffuses from the blood to the tissues, and **(h)** diffuses from the tissues to the blood. The now deoxygenated blood returns to the **(i)** side of the heart.

   a. _____   f. _____

   b. _____   g. _____

   c. _____   h. _____

   d. _____   i. _____

   e. _____

3. The pressures of individual gases in a mixture are called **(a)**, and are equal to the fractional concentration of the gas multiplied by the **(b)**. Gases can dissolve in liquids to varying degrees based on their partial pressure and **(c)**. The greater the **(c)** and the greater the partial pressure, the more of the gas dissolves in the liquid. Carbon dioxide is approximately **(d)** times more soluble in liquid than is oxygen.

   a. _____   c. _____

   b. _____   d. _____

Short Answer

Answer the following questions in 1–4 sentences.

4. Define partial pressure. Assuming you are at sea level, what would be the partial pressure of oxygen, nitrogen, and carbon dioxide? Show your work.

5. Calculate the P_{O_2}, P_{N_2}, and P_{CO_2} at an altitude of 5,000 feet, which has a total atmospheric pressure of 619 mm Hg (assume the concentration of the three gases at 5,000 feet is the same at sea level). Show your work.

6. Calculate the P_{O_2}, P_{N_2}, and P_{CO_2} at a depth of 60 feet below sea level (assume the concentration of the three gases under water is the same at sea level). Show your work.

7. If the cells of the body produce 225 mL/min of carbon dioxide, how much carbon dioxide is being exhaled from the lungs? Explain your answer.

Multiple Choice

Select the best answer from the choices given.

8. Lois has a respiratory quotient of 0.85 (which is greater than normal). Which of the following statements is true about her respiration?

   a. She is exhaling too much carbon dioxide.
   b. She is producing too much oxygen.
   c. She is unable to breathe out carbon dioxide sufficiently.
   d. Her carbon dioxide production is less than normal.
   e. She is breathing in an abnormally high amount of oxygen.

9. Assume that an open container is half filled with water. When oxygen in the air above the container is at equilibrium and has a partial pressure of 100 mm Hg, there are 0.15 mmoles/L of oxygen dissolved in the water. What would happen to the concentration of oxygen dissolved in the water if the partial pressure of oxygen in the air above the container were to change to 200 mm Hg?

   a. The concentration of oxygen dissolved in the water would remain unchanged.
   b. The concentration of oxygen dissolved in the water would be 0.30 mmoles/L.
   c. The concentration of oxygen dissolved in the water would be 0.60 mmoles/L.
   d. The concentration of oxygen dissolved in the water would be 0.075 mmoles/L.
   e. The concentration of oxygen dissolved in the water would essentially be zero.

10. Which of the following contains the greatest partial pressure of carbon dioxide?

   a. cells in tissues of body   c. pulmonary veins   e. systemic veins
   b. systemic arteries   d. alveoli in lungs

True/False

Label the following statements as true (T) or false (F). If false, change the statement to make it true.

11. _____ Under most conditions, the concentrations of oxygen and carbon dioxide in the systemic blood are maintained at relatively constant levels.

12. _____ Oxygen is about ten times more soluble in water than is carbon dioxide.

13. _____ At equilibrium, the concentration of gas in the air above a liquid is one-half of the concentration of gas dissolved in the liquid.

Labeling

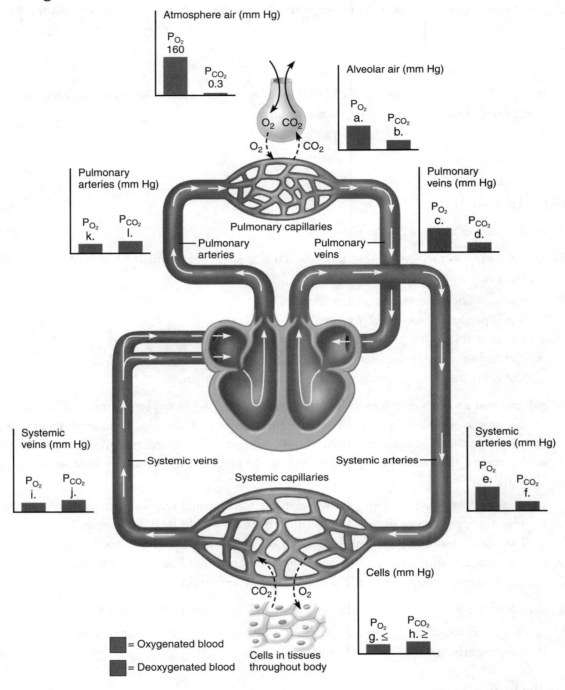

FIGURE 16.1

14. Insert the correct P_{O_2} and P_{CO_2} values for a–l in Figure 16.1.

Sequencing

15. Oxygen passes through or into each of the following structures in the pulmonary circulation. Starting at the alveolar air space, place them in the correct order.

   a. alveolar basement membrane
   b. capillary basement membrane
   c. plasma of bloodstream
   d. endothelial cell in capillary wall
   e. alveolar cells
   f. alveolar air space

   Sequence: _____

Clinical Question

16. Why is a hyperbaric chamber necessary on ships that carry divers who perform long, deep underwater dives?

Challenge Questions

17. The partial pressure of oxygen in a gas mixture is 140 mm Hg. Oxygen is at equilibrium with water. What is the partial pressure of oxygen dissolved in water?

18. Assume that carbon dioxide and oxygen are both dissolved in a liquid. Explain why there is more carbon dioxide (3.0 mmoles/L) dissolved in the water than oxygen (0.15 mmoles/L), even though both gases have the same partial pressure in the air above them (100 mm Hg).

EXCHANGE OF OXYGEN AND CARBON DIOXIDE

Matching

19. Match whether the conditions below will increase (I) or decrease (D) arterial P_{O_2} levels.

    a. _____ a tidal volume of 1,200 mL

    b. _____ increased oxygen consumption by tissues

    c. _____ a drop in breathing rate

    d. _____ breathing 90% oxygen

    e. _____ a drop in minute ventilation

Completion

Fill in the blanks to complete the following narrative.

20. Gas exchange occurs by **(a)** down partial pressure gradients. The amount of carbon dioxide and oxygen moving across a particular systemic capillary depends on the activity of the tissue; more active tissues have **(b)** partial pressure gradients, leading to **(c)** diffusion rates. Normally, alveolar ventilation is matched to **(d)** and carbon dioxide production. If metabolic activity increases, ventilation **(e)** to match the demands of the tissue, a condition called **(f)**.

    a. _____   d. _____

    b. _____   e. _____

    c. _____   f. _____

Short Answer

Answer the following questions in 1–4 sentences.

21. Why do alveolar gas pressures differ from atmospheric pressure?

22. What is mixed venous blood and where does it occur?

Multiple Choice

Select the best answer from the choices given.

23. How does the body alter breathing when arterial P_{O_2} values are lower than normal?

    a. by breathing more slowly

    b. by taking very deep breaths

    c. by tachypnea

    d. by hypoventilating

    e. there is no appreciable change in breathing under these conditions

24. What is the P_{O_2} of mixed venous blood?

    a. 0.3 mm Hg   c. 100 mm Hg   e. ≥ 46 mm Hg

    b. 160 mm Hg   d. 40 mm Hg

25. Which of the following is true during strenuous exercise?

    a. Oxygen and carbon dioxide diffuse faster at the metabolically active tissues.

    b. Carbon dioxide is produced at a much slower rate at the metabolically active tissues.

    c. Oxygen P_{O_2} is near 100 mm Hg in the systemic veins.

    d. Carbon dioxide P_{CO_2} of mixed venous blood is near 100 mm Hg.

    e. Diffusion gradients for both carbon dioxide and oxygen are reduced.

True/False

Label the following statements as true (T) or false (F). If false, change the statement to make it true.

26. _____ When you ascend a mountain to 10,000 feet, atmospheric P_{O_2} does not change appreciably.

27. _____ Most gas exchange takes place in the last two-thirds of the alveolar capillary.

28. _____ The partial pressure gradient determines the direction of gas movement.

29. _____ When alveolar ventilation decreases relative to oxygen consumption and carbon dioxide production, alveolar P_{O_2} decreases and P_{CO_2} increases.

Sequencing

30. Below are locations involved in the exchange of oxygen in the body. Each location has a P_{O_2} value associated with it. Place the locations in order of P_{O_2} value, beginning with the lowest value.

    a. atmosphere air

    b. systemic veins

    c. systemic arteries

    d. cells in tissues throughout body

    Sequence: _____

31. Below are various locations involved in the exchange of carbon dioxide in the body. Each location has a P_{CO_2} value associated with it. Place the locations in order of P_{CO_2} value, beginning with the lowest.

   a. atmosphere air
   b. systemic veins
   c. systemic arteries
   d. cells in tissues throughout body

   Sequence: _____

Clinical Question

32. A patient with respiratory problems comes into the emergency room. Blood gas analysis reveals that the patient's P_{CO_2} is 35 mm Hg, P_{O_2} is 110 mm Hg, and the blood pH is 7.56. Is the patient hyperventilating or hypoventilating? Explain.

Challenge Question

33. When alveolar ventilation decreases below tissue demands, what happens to alveolar P_{CO_2} and P_{O_2}?

TRANSPORT OF GASES IN THE BLOOD

Matching

34. Match whether each statement below is referring to oxygen (O_2), carbon dioxide (CO_2), or both oxygen and carbon dioxide (Both).

   a. _____ binds to hemoglobin

   b. _____ has direct, major effects on blood pH

   c. _____ Most of this gas is dissolved in the blood.

   d. _____ when bound to hemoglobin, has four heme groups associated with it

   e. _____ has a partial pressure of 100 mm Hg in systemic arteries

   f. _____ The Bohr effect promotes the loading of this gas.

   g. _____ The carbamino effect promotes the loading of this gas.

   h. _____ The Haldane effect promotes the unloading of this gas.

Completion

Fill in the blanks to complete the following narrative.

35. Oxygen is transported dissolved in blood and bound to **(a)**. Many factors influence the binding of oxygen to **(a)**. The **(b)** effect is the decreased affinity of **(a)** for oxygen that occurs when hydrogen ions bind to **(a)**. The **(c)** effect is the decrease in affinity of **(a)** for oxygen that occurs when **(d)** binds to **(a)**. The **(e)** effect is the decrease in affinity of **(a)** for hydrogen ions and carbon dioxide that occurs when oxygen bonds to **(a)**. Carbon dioxide is transported in three ways: **(f)** in blood; bound to hemoglobin, and as dissolved **(g)** ions in blood.

a. _____   e. _____

b. _____   f. _____

c. _____   g. _____

d. _____

Short Answer

Answer the following questions in 1–4 sentences.

36. Write the equation for the reaction of carbon dioxide with water in the presence of carbonic anhydrase.

37. Would breathing 100% oxygen cause a large increase in oxygen transport by hemoglobin in a person with normal lung function?

Multiple Choice

Select the best answer from the choices given.

38. The pH of normal arterial blood is approximately _____.

    a. 6.5   c. 7.4   e. 10
    b. 7.0   d. 8.5

39. When conditions cause the hemoglobin-oxygen dissociation curve to shift to the right, there is greater _____.

    a. unloading of carbon dioxide to the tissues
    b. unloading of oxygen in the lungs
    c. unloading of oxygen to the tissues and loading of oxygen in the lungs
    d. loading of carbon dioxide in the lungs
    e. pH produced by the respiring tissues

40. Which of the following statements about the bond between hemoglobin and oxygen is true?

  a. The bond is made stronger by a decreased pH.
  b. The bond is weakened under acidic conditions.
  c. The bond is strengthened by an increase in temperature.
  d. When the bond is stronger, more oxygen is unloaded to the tissues.
  e. An increase in 2,3 DPG increases the bond.

41. Most of the carbon dioxide in the blood is carried _____.

  a. dissolved in the plasma
  b. attached to hemoglobin
  c. as bicarbonate ions
  d. as carbaminohemoglobin
  e. inside the red blood cells

42. When hemoglobin and oxygen combine to form oxyhemoglobin, it is called _____.

  a. the loading reaction
  b. the unloading reaction
  c. the coupling reaction
  d. the oxyheme reaction
  e. positive cooperativity

True/False

Label the following statements as true (T) or false (F). If false, change the statement to make it true.

43. _____ In the systemic capillaries and veins, chloride ions move into the erythrocytes while bicarbonate moves out of erythrocytes and into the plasma.

44. _____ The carbon dioxide content of the blood rises as the P_{O_2} increases.

45. _____ In respiring tissues, the Haldane effect promotes the loading of oxygen.

46. _____ An increase in P_{CO_2} levels in the blood promotes the unloading of oxygen from hemoglobin and the loading of carbon dioxide to hemoglobin.

Challenge Question

47. Fetal hemoglobin has a much higher affinity for oxygen than does the hemoglobin present in the mother's circulatory system (called maternal hemoglobin). Explain why this is important.

Clinical Question

48. Anemia is defined as a reduced oxygen-carrying capacity, and can be caused by various factors. For each of the clinical types of anemia listed below, describe *why* the blood has reduced oxygen-carrying capacity.

Clinical case #1: A 32-year-old male comes to the clinic complaining of shortness of breath. He appears pale. He reports that he recently received a blood transfusion. You find that he has hemolytic anemia caused by the transfusion. In this case, why does the blood have reduced oxygen-carrying capacity?

Clinical Case #2: A 19-year-old woman comes to the clinic complaining that she is cold, fatigued, and short of breath. Her blood analysis reveals that she has iron-deficiency anemia. In this case, why does the blood have reduced oxygen-carrying capacity?

Case #3: A young, African-American girl complains that she is often drowsy, and says she is "tired" and her muscles feel weak. She complains of generalized pain in her torso and muscles of her arms and legs. She exhibits shortness of breath. Her skin is slightly bluish in her fingertips and lips. A blood smear reveals crescent-shaped red blood cells. In this case, why does the blood have reduced oxygen-carrying capacity?

Concept Maps

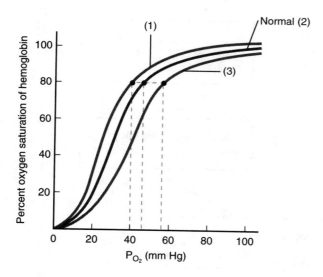

FIGURE 16.2

49. Figure 16.2 shows a normal hemoglobin-oxygen dissociation curve (line 2) and a line on either side of the normal curve. Questions a–c refer to line 2.

    a. Under normal circumstances, what is the approximate percent oxygen saturation when the P_{O_2} is 60 mm Hg? _____

b. What is the P_{O_2} when the blood is 50% saturated with oxygen? _____

c. Approximately what percent oxygen is delivered to the tissues if the P_{O_2} is 50 mm Hg? _____

d. Which line (1–3) represents metabolic alkalosis? _____

e. Which line (1–3) represents high concentrations of 2,3-DPG? _____

f. Which line (1–3) represents a rise in body temperature, like during strenuous exercise? _____

g. Which line (1–3) represents what happens when pH of the blood is 7.4, you are at rest, and your body temperature is 37°C? _____

h. Which line (1–3) represents what happens to the curve when a person falls into cold water and body temperature falls? _____

50. Fill in the boxes in the concept map that shows carbon dioxide exchange and transport in the blood.

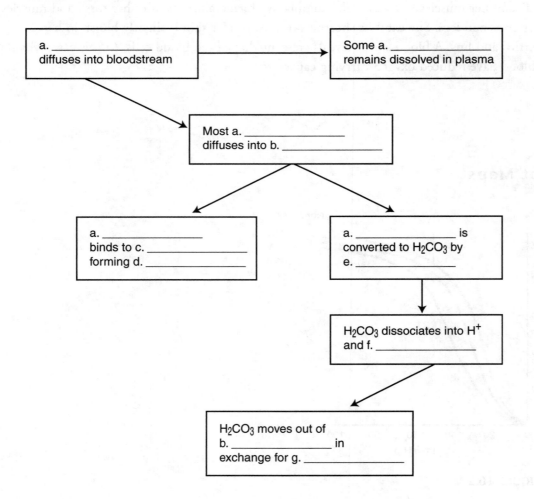

CENTRAL REGULATION OF VENTILATION AND CONTROL OF VENTILATION BY CHEMORECEPTORS

Matching

51. Match whether each statement below is referring to the phase of inspiration (I), expiration (E), or both (B).

   a. _____ This phase is a passive process.

   b. _____ The phrenic nerve is stimulated during this phase.

   c. _____ Neurons on the pontine respiratory group regulate this phase of breathing.

   d. _____ During quiet breathing, this phase is an active process that requires contraction of external intercostals and diaphragm.

Completion

Fill in the blanks to complete the following narratives.

52. The generation of the breathing rhythm requires the action of respiratory centers in the **(a)**. The medullary control center includes the **(b)** and **(c)**. Inspiratory neurons in these regions activate the motor neurons that innervate the inspiratory muscles, causing inspiration. The **(d)** may be involved in the transition between inspiration and expiration. Various stimuli can affect ventilation, including changes in arterial **(e)** and **(f)**, stretch of the lungs, irritants in the airways, baroreceptors, nociceptors, emotions, and voluntary control.

   a. _____   d. _____

   b. _____   e. _____

   c. _____   f. _____

53. **(a)** is the primary stimulus to the peripheral and central chemoreceptors, but its effects are always indirect: **(b)** must first be converted to **(c)**. The peripheral chemoreceptors located in the **(d)** respond directly to changes in **(e)** and to decreases in **(f)** to less than 60 mm Hg. Central chemoreceptors are located in the **(g)** and respond to the pH of the **(h)**.

   a. _____   e. _____

   b. _____   f. _____

   c. _____   g. _____

   d. _____   h. _____

Short Answer

Answer the following questions in 1–4 sentences.

54. Contrast the mechanism of action potentials generated by VRG and DRG neurons during inspiration.

55. Describe the locations of the central and peripheral chemoreceptors in humans.

Multiple Choice

Select the best answer from the choices given.

56. Mary Ann has a severed phrenic nerve. Which muscle(s) will be affected?
    a. internal intercostals only
    b. diaphragm only
    c. external intercostals only
    d. both external intercostals and internal intercostals
    e. diaphragm, external intercostals, and internal intercostals

57. Which network of neurons generates the respiratory rhythm?
    a. ventral respiratory group (VRG)   d. chemoreceptors
    b. pontine respiratory group (PRG)   e. dorsal respiratory group (DRG)
    c. central pattern generator (CPG)

58. Claire begins to breathe more rapidly when she recounts to her friends her near fatal accident while sailing. Besides the cerebrum, which other part of her brain probably was influencing her breathing rate?
    a. hypothalamus   c. pons   e. pineal body
    b. medulla   d. cerebellum

59. Where are inspiratory neurons primarily located?
    a. dorsal respiratory group   d. pineal body
    b. ventral respiratory group   e. hypothalamus
    c. cerebellum

60. An increase in the pH of the CSF will cause _____.
    a. breathing to stop   c. hyperpnea   e. dyspnea
    b. hypoventilation   d. hypercapnea

61. Central chemoreceptors respond directly to _____.

    a. P_{CO_2} c. blood pressure   e. H^+ concentration

    b. P_{O_2} d. nociceptors

True/False

Label the following statements as true (T) *or false* (F). *If false, change the statement to make it true.*

62. _____ Chemoreceptors are sensitive to very slight changes in temperature and/or pressure in the bloodstream and adjust the breathing rate accordingly.

63. _____ Movement of muscles and joints can cause an increase in breathing rate.

64. _____ The pontine respiratory group contains both inspiratory and expiratory neurons.

65. _____ Peripheral chemoreceptors respond only to changes in P_{O_2}.

Clinical Questions

66. You are the trainer on the college swim team. After practice one day you hear two teammates challenge each other to a contest to see who can hold their breath the longest. One of the competitors says that the best way to increase his ability to hold his breath is to hyperventilate so that "My lungs can hold more oxygen." Explain the fallacy of such a statement and why this is a dangerous practice.

67. Marie is playing tennis and loses a very tough match for the state title. She is so emotionally upset at the loss that she begins to hyperventilate. The team trainer calmly advises her to close her mouth and take deep breaths through her nose. Marie finds this difficult to do at first, but eventually the procedure works and she is breathing normally. Explain why this procedure helps someone who is hyperventilating.

Challenge Questions

68. What is the response of respiration to a decreased blood pressure and what is the advantage of this reflex?

69. Explain the relationship between P_{CO_2} and H^+ concentration of the blood when someone is hypoventilating. Also, describe the role of the respiratory system under such circumstances.

Concept Map

70. Fill in the boxes of the concept map of the model of repiratory control during quiet breathing.

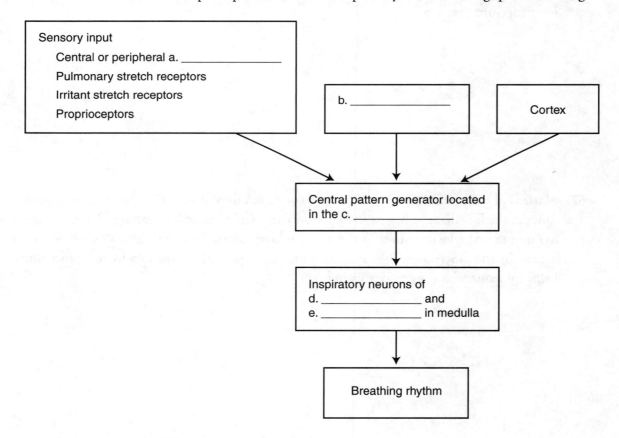

Sensory input
    Central or peripheral a. _____
    Pulmonary stretch receptors
    Irritant stretch receptors
    Proprioceptors

b. _____

Cortex

Central pattern generator located in the c. _____

Inspiratory neurons of
d. _____ and
e. _____ in medulla

Breathing rhythm

LOCAL REGULATION OF VENTILATION AND PERFUSION and THE RESPIRATORY SYSTEM IN ACID-BASE HOMEOSTASIS

Matching

71. Mark whether each of the following conditions in the blood describes acidosis (AD) or alkalosis (AK).

   a. _____ a pH of 7.55

   b. _____ an excess of HCO_3^-

   c. _____ an excess of H^+

   d. _____ a drop in P_{CO_2}

   e. _____ a pH of 7.30

Completion

Fill in the blanks to complete the following narratives.

72. The ratio between airflow to the **(a)** and blood flow to the **(b)** supplying the **(a)** is called the ventilation-perfusion ratio. In normal lungs, airflow and ventilation are matched, and the ventilation-perfusion ratio is equal to **(c)**. If ventilation to a particular alveolus is decreased, perfusion will be decreased by **(d)** to sustain the normal ventilation-perfusion ratio. Likewise, if perfusion to a particular alveolus is decreased, then airflow will be decreased by **(e)**.

   a. _____   d. _____

   b. _____   e. _____

   c. _____

73. The pH of blood is highly regulated between **(a)** and **(b)**. **(c)** is a decrease in pH below **(d)**, whereas **(e)** is an increase in pH to 7.45 or greater. The respiratory and **(f)** systems work together to maintain normal blood pH. The primary contribution of the respiratory system to acid-base balance is the regulation of arterial **(g)**. Because carbon dioxide can be converted to **(h)**, a change in P_{CO_2} can cause either respiratory acidosis or respiratory **(i)**. The respiratory system works in concert with the **(j)** to maintain a ratio of bicarbonate to carbon dioxide of **(k)**.

   a. _____   g. _____

   b. _____   h. _____

   c. _____   i. _____

   d. _____   j. _____

   e. _____   k. _____

   f. _____

Short Answer

Answer the following questions in 1–4 sentences.

74. Lisa has an arterial P_{O_2} of 105 mm Hg and arterial P_{CO_2} of 35 mm Hg. Is her ventilation-perfusion normal? Explain.

75. What will happen to the arterial blood pH:

    a. if the arterial blood $[HCO_3^-]$ increases?

    b. if the arterial blood $[CO_2]$ increases?

Multiple Choice

Select the best answer from the choices given.

76. Valerie has cystic fibrosis and the buildup of fluid in her lungs. Which of the following statements is true about her condition?

    a. Her ventilation-perfusion ratio is greater than 1.

    b. She has bronchodilation to compensate.

    c. She has pulmonary capillaries with lower than normal P_{CO_2} values.

    d. She has pulmonary capillaries with higher than normal P_{O_2} values.

    e. Her pulmonary capillaries P_{O_2} and P_{CO_2} values are normal.

77. When P_{CO_2} of pulmonary capillaries is increased above normal values, which of the following is most likely true?

    a. P_{O_2} levels rise also.

    b. The bronchioles respond by constricting.

    c. There is most likely an airway obstruction.

    d. The pulmonary arteries respond by dilating.

    e. The ventilation-perfusion ratio is greater than 1.

78. After starting a campfire you begin to blow on the flames to keep the fire going. By blowing on the flames you have hyperventilated. Which of the following statements is true?

    a. Your arterial blood pH is increased.

    b. Carbon dioxide has built up in the arterial blood.

    c. Arterial P_{CO_2} levels have not changed.

    d. Your arterial P_{O_2} levels are lower.

    e. Arterial blood pH has not changed.

True/False

Label the following statements as true (T) *or false* (F). *If false, change the statement to make it true.*

79. _____ The lungs regulate the concentration of bicarbonate ions, whereas the kidneys regulate the concentration of carbon dioxide.

80. _____ Hemoglobin is an important buffer present inside of erythrocytes.

81. _____ Hypoventilation can produce respiratory alkalosis.

82. _____ During respiratory alkalosis the pH of the blood increases above 7.45.

Clinical Question

83. Mrs. Tyndall has a blood clot lodged in the pulmonary artery of her left lung. Explain what would happen to her ventilation-perfusion ratio in that lung and how her body would attempt to compensate for it.

Challenge Question

83. Jerome has a ventilation-perfusion ratio of 0.9. What is the general problem with Jerome's ventilation and, physiologically, how do the respiratory and/or circulatory system(s) respond to this mismatch?

17 The Urinary System: Renal Function

Objectives

We recommend that you review the **Objectives** for this chapter, found on p. 532 of *Principles of Human Physiology*. The **Objectives** outline what you should know from each chapter.

Key Terms

Bowman's capsule
clearance
collecting duct
detrusor muscle
external urethral sphincter
filtered load
glomerular filtration
glomerulus
granular cell

juxtaglomerular apparatus
juxtaglomerular cell
loop of Henle
macula densa
micturition
nephron
peritubular capillary
proximal tubule
reabsorption

renal artery
renal pelvis
renal threshold
renal tubule
secretion
urinary system
urine
vasa recta

FUNCTIONS OF THE URINARY SYSTEM AND ANATOMY OF THE URINARY SYSTEM

Matching

1. Match each of the following circulatory system components associated with the urinary system with its appropriate description below: afferent arteriole (AE), efferent arteriole (EA), glomerulus (GL), interlobular vein (IV), peritubular capillary (PC), renal artery (RA), renal vein (RV), vasa recta (VC).

   a. _____ This large vessel branches directly from the abdominal aorta.

   b. _____ This network of capillaries runs adjacent to the loop of Henle and collecting ducts.

   c. _____ This mass of capillaries is contained within Bowman's capsule.

   d. _____ This vessel supplies blood directly into the renal corpuscle.

   e. _____ This large vessel drains directly into the inferior vena cava.

   f. _____ This small vessel branches from the efferent arteriole and surrounds much of the length of the renal tubule.

g. _____ Blood leaves the glomerulus via this vessel.

h. _____ The vessels described by letters **f** and **g** above drain directly into this vessel.

Completion

Fill in the blanks to complete the following narrative.

2. The urinary system consists of the kidneys, ureters, urethra, and **(a)**. The functional units of the kidneys are **(b)**. Filtration occurs at the **(c)**, which includes **(d)** and the glomerulus. The glomerular filtrate resembles **(e)** in composition except that it lacks **(f)**. As filtrate moves through the nephron, its volume and composition change as a result of the reabsorption and **(g)** of **(h)** and solutes. Reabsorbed materials move from the tubular fluid in the lumen of the tubule to the **(i)** fluid that surrounds the tubule, and then into the **(j)** of the peritubular capillaries that surround the tubule. Secretion is the movement of material from the plasma to the **(k)**.

a. _____

b. _____

c. _____

d. _____

e. _____

f. _____

g. _____

h. _____

i. _____

j. _____

k. _____

Short Answer

Answer the following questions in 1–4 sentences.

3. Why are the kidneys considered endocrine glands?

4. Describe the locations of the two types of nephrons present in the kidneys. How do the two nephron types differ?

5. *Principles of Human Physiology* lists five *primary* functions of the kidneys. Briefly describe the *secondary* endocrine and endocrine-like functions of the kidneys.

Multiple Choice

Select the best answer from the choices given.

6. Which of the following is considered the first part of the ureter?

   a. collecting duct   c. major calyx   e. nephron
   b. renal pelvis   d. minor calyx

7. Which of the following is the last structure through which regulated fluid reabsortion occurs?

   a. proximal tubule   c. glomerulus   e. ascending loop of Henle
   b. collecting duct   d. distal tubule

8. Which of the following hormones stimulates red blood cell production?

   a. ADH   d. erythropoietin
   b. renin   e. aldosterone
   c. atrial natriuretic peptide

9. The renal corpuscle is composed of which of the following two structures?

   a. nephron and collecting duct   d. renal tubule and arcade vein
   b. renal artery and renal vein   e. juxtaglomerular apparatus and macula densa
   c. Bowman's capsule and glomerulus

10. Where does filtration occur in the kidneys?

   a. distal convoluted tubule   d. glomerulus
   b. proximal convoluted tubule   e. collecting duct
   c. loop of Henle

11. Which of the following is **not** a function of the urinary system?

   a. regulation of white blood cell production
   b. regulation of blood volume
   c. regulation of plasma osmolarity
   d. regulation of plasma pH
   e. regulation of metabolic waste products in the blood

True/False

Label the following statements as true (T) or false (F). If false, change the statement to make it true.

12. _____ The kidneys can play a role in gluconeogenesis.

13. _____ The kidneys can play a role in regulating blood pressure.

14. _____ The loss of one kidney has major long-term effects on the ability of the body to maintain homeostasis.

15. _____ The arcuate arteries branch from efferent arterioles and run along the loop of Henle and collecting ducts.

Sequencing

16. Place the following structures associated with the anatomy of the urinary tract in order from formation to elimination of urine:

a. bladder
b. glomerulus
c. renal pelvis
d. urethra
e. thick ascending loop of Henle
f. collecting duct

g. descending loop of Henle
h. thin ascending loop of Henle
i. Bowman's capsule
j. ureter
k. proximal convoluted tubule
l. distal convoluted tubule

Sequence: _____

Labeling

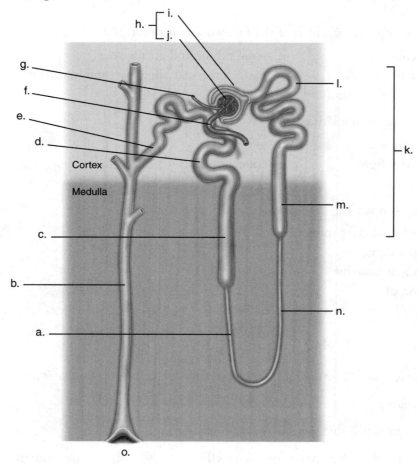

FIGURE 17.1

17. In the space below, identify the structures (a–o) in Figure 17.1.

Clinical Questions

18. A 12-year-old girl notices that the color of her urine is dark. Her father takes her to the pediatrician. Two weeks earlier she was treated for a streptococcal throat infection. Urinalysis reveals red blood cells and protein in her urine. Her pediatrician diagnoses her with acute glomerulonephritis caused by the initial strep infection. What does the word "glomerulonephritis" mean, and why would this girl show the symptoms of blood and protein in her urine?

19. A 7-year-old girl is admitted to the emergency room with cystitis. Describe what part of her body is affected. Why are females more susceptible to cystitis than males?

Challenge Questions

20. Describe the structure and function of the juxtaglomerular apparatus.

21. What effects on glomerular filtration rate might you expect in an individual with a) hypotension? b) hypertension (systolic blood pressure > 180 mm Hg)?

BASIC RENAL EXCHANGE PROCESSES

Matching

22. Match each of the following Starling forces in the renal corpuscle with its description below: Glomerular capillary hydrostatic pressure (GCHP), Bowman's capsule oncotic pressure (BCOP), Bowman's capsule hydrostatic pressure (BCHP), Glomerular oncotic pressure (GOP).

a. _____ This pressure is typically about 15 mm Hg and opposes filtration.

b. _____ This pressure is usually very low but what pressure there is favors filtration.

c. _____ This pressure opposes filtration and is typically about 29 mm Hg.

d. _____ This pressure is about 60 mm Hg and favors filtration.

Completion

Fill in the blanks to complete the following narrative.

23. Glomerular filtration is driven by the four Starling forces that contribute to the glomerular pressure: (1) the glomerular capillary **(a)** pressure, (2) the **(a)** pressure inside **(b)**, (3) the **(c)** pressure of plasma in glomerular capillaries, and (4) the **(c)** pressure of fluid in **(d)**. The normal average glomerular filtration rate is approximately **(e)**.

a. _____   d. _____

b. _____   e. _____

c. _____

Short Answer

Answer the following questions in 1–4 sentences.

24. On average, the kidneys produce 180 liters of filtrate per day. Using the average glomerular filtration rate, show how to calculate this daily average.

25. If a child has 575 mL of plasma flowing through the kidneys each minute and a GFR of 115mL/min., what is the filtration fraction?

26. Describe the glomerular membrane from the lumen to the Bowman's space.

Multiple Choice

Select the best answer from the choices given.

27. Which of the following solutes has the highest filtration rate?
    a. HCO_3^- c. glucose   e. Na^+
    b. urea   d. Ca^{2+}

28. Which of the following is the force that tends to drive water into Bowman's space?
    a. hydrostatic pressure in the collecting ducts
    b. glomerular capillary hydrostatic pressure
    c. Bowman's capsule hydrostatic pressure
    d. glomerular oncotic pressure
    e. systemic venous pressure

29. Which of the following is **least** involved with secretion of H^+?
    a. beginning of proximal tubule   d. distal tubule
    b. end portion of proximal tubule   e. collecting duct
    c. loop of Henle

30. Which of the following is **not** secreted?
    a. glucose   c. K^+ e. creatinine
    b. H^+ d. choline

31. Which of the following is cotransported with Na^+ in the apical membrane of proximal tubule cells of the kidney?
    a. H^+ c. urea   e. glucose
    b. K^+ d. choline

32. To calculate the transport maximum for substance X you need to know the GFR and the
    _____.
    a. rate of secretion of substance X   d. renal threshold of substance X
    b. filtered load of substance X   e. filtration fraction of substance X
    c. plasma concentration of substance X

True/False

Label the following statements as true (T) *or false* (F). *If false, change the statement to make it true.*

33. _____ Within normal blood pressure values when blood pressure rises, GFR rises as well.

34. _____ Myogenic regulation of GFR involves sympathetic stimulation of afferent and efferent arterioles in the kidneys.

35. _____ Mesangial cells secrete renin.

36. _____ Myogenic regulation, tubuloglomerular feedback, and mesangial cells are three examples of GFR autoregulation.

37. _____ When mean arterial pressure falls, glomerular filtration rate also falls.

Sequencing

38. Place the following spaces and membranes in the correct sequence of solute reabsorption in the nephron.
    a. basolateral membrane of tubule epithelial cell
    b. peritubular space
    c. plasma
    d. lumen of tubule
    e. basement membrane
    f. peritubular capillary endothelial cell
    g. apical membrane of tubule epithelial cell

    Sequence: _____

Labeling

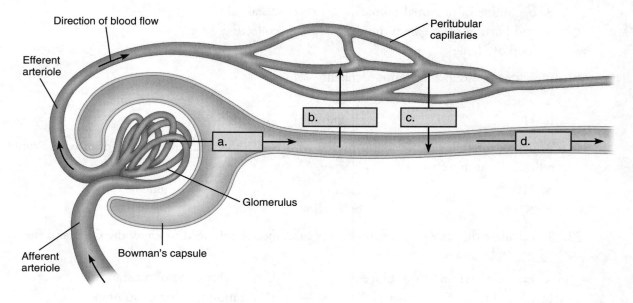

FIGURE 17.2

39. In the space below, identify the boxes lettered a–d in Figure 17.2.

Clinical Questions

40. Raul, an 80-year-old man, has decreased plasma protein production due to cirrhosis of the liver. What will be the likely initial result on his GFR?

41. Frank is taking a drug that blocks the reabsorption of sodium. What will happen to his fluid output?

Challenge Questions

42. A small child has a GFR of 144 liters/day. What is the child's GFR/min.?

43. Describe the movement of glucose through a normally operating kidney.

Concept Map

44. Fill in the blanks of GFR regulation by tubuloglomerular feedback.

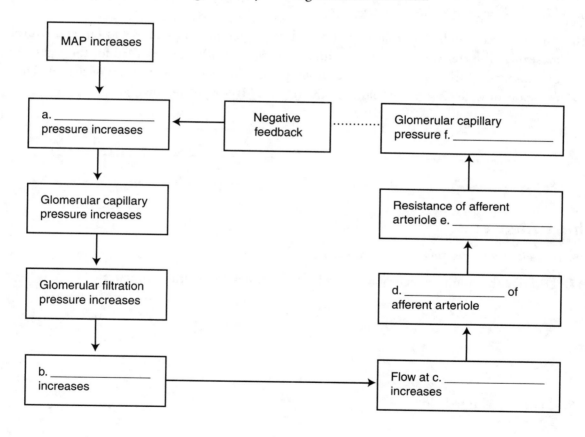

REGIONAL SPECIALIZATION OF THE RENAL TUBULES AND EXCRETION

Matching

45. Match whether each of the following substances is secreted (S), reabsorbed (R), or both (B) by the kidneys.

   a. _____ creatinine

   b. _____ glucose

   c. _____ K$^+$

   d. _____ Na$^+$

   e. _____ PAH

Completion

Fill in the blanks to complete the following narrative.

46. The proximal tubule is specialized to reabsorb large quantities of solutes and **(a)**, and returns most filtered material to the **(b)**. In contrast, the **(c)** and **(d)** are specialized for the regulation of transport, which is important in controlling the volume and composition of the **(e)**. The transport of water and many solutes in the **(c)** and **(d)** is regulated by **(f)**.

   a. _____   d. _____

   b. _____   e. _____

   c. _____   f. _____

Short Answer

Answer the following questions in 1–4 sentences.

47. Describe the voluntary neuronal control that overrides the micturition reflex.

48. Define renal threshold.

Multiple Choice

Select the best answer from the choices given.

49. Which of the following structures is **not** freely permeable to water?

    a. proximal tubule
    b. thick ascending limb of loop of Henle
    c. descending limb of loop of Henle
    d. collecting duct
    e. distal convoluted tubule

50. Which of the following has cells with the largest number of mitochondria?

    a. thick segment of the loop of Henle   d. glomerulus
    b. collecting duct   e. vasa recta
    c. proximal convoluted tubule

51. Which of the following is the function of the collecting ducts?

    a. concentrating the urine   c. secreting aldosterone   e. filtration
    b. secretion of ADH   d. secreting renin

52. The clearance of K^+ is greater than the GFR. Which of the following statements is true?

    a. K^+ was not filtered.
    b. K^+ was reabsorbed in the renal tubule.
    c. K^+ was not present in the urine.
    d. K^+ was not present in the plasma.
    e. K^+ was secreted into the renal tubules.

53. If the flow rate of urine is 8.0 mL/min., the concentration of substance Z is 10 mM/liter in the urine, and the plasma concentration of substance Z is 160 mM/liter, what is the clearance for substance Y?

    a. 0.5 mL/min   c. 5.0 mL/min   e. 10.0 mL/min
    b. 1.0 mL/min   d. 8.0 mL/min

54. Which of the following is innervated by sympathetic neurons?

    a. glomerulus   d. external urethral sphincter
    b. detrusor muscle   e. vasa recta
    c. internal urethral sphincter

True/False

Label the following statements as true (T) or false (F). If false, change the statement to make it true.

55. _____ To estimate GFR one must know the renal clearance and the plasma concentration of a substance.

56. _____ Parasympathetic neurons innervate the detrusor muscle.

57. _____ Most of water reabsorption occurs in the ascending limb of the loop of Henle.

58. _____ The micturition reflex is a spinal reflex that can be overridden in trained individuals.

Labeling

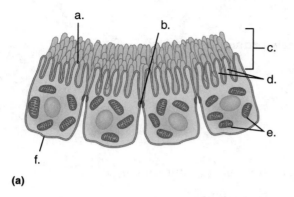

(a)

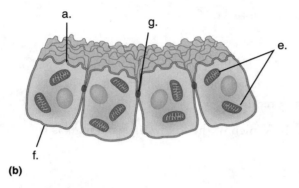

(b)

FIGURE 17.3

59. In the space below, identify the structures (a–g) in Figure 17.3 and indicate which figure illustrates the distal tubule and which illustrates the proximal tubule.

Clinical Questions

60. Explain why a patient with sodium deficiency may also have glycosuria.

61. Helen has diabetes mellitus in which large amounts of glucose appear in the reabsorbed filtrate. What effect will this have on the volume of urine that she produces? Explain.

Challenge Questions

62. Why is reabsorption in the proximal tubule considered nonregulated while reabsorption in the distal tubule is considered regulated?

63. Kenny feels the need to urinate. Describe his micturition reflex.

Concept Map

64. Fill in the blanks of the mechanism of sodium reabsorption in the proximal and distal tubules.

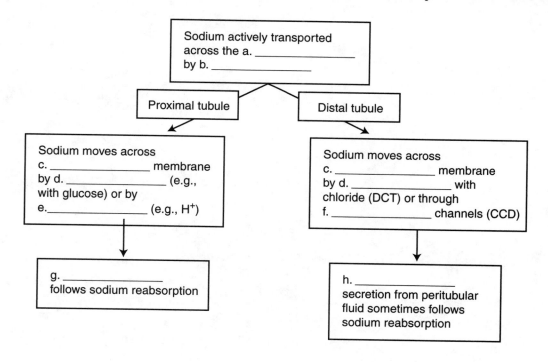

18 The Urinary System: Fluid and Electrolyte Balance

Objectives

We recommend that you review the **Objectives** for this chapter, found on p. 564 of *Principles of Human Physiology*. The **Objectives** outline what you should know from each chapter.

Key Terms

acidosis
aldosterone
alkalosis
calcitonin
calcitrol

hypercalcemia
hyperkalemia
hypernatremia
hypocalcemia
hypokalemia

hyponatremia
osmoreceptor
parathyroid hormone
  (PTH)

THE CONCEPT OF BALANCE AND WATER BALANCE

Matching

1. Fluid flows through each of the following urinary system structures. Mark whether the fluid in each of the structures is hypo-osmotic (OO), iso-osmotic (IO), or hyperosmotic (EO) relative to the plasma.

   a. _____ peritubular fluid

   b. _____ filtrate at the tip of the loop of Henle

   c. _____ fluid entering the descending limb of loop of Henle

   d. _____ fluid entering the distal tubule

Completion

Fill in the blanks to complete the following narrative.

2. To be in balance, the sum of the input and production of a substance must be equal to the sum of the **(a)** and **(b)** of that substance. The **(c)** can gain or lose materials by exchange with **(d)** or extracellular **(e)**. When solutes and **(f)** enter and exit the **(c)** at the same rate, the **(c)** is in balance. For water to be in balance, the input from consumed fluids and **(g)** and from extracellular **(h)** must equal the output in urine, feces, and **(i)**. The control of water excretion by the kidneys regulates plasma volume and **(j)**.

a. _____   f. _____

b. _____   g. _____

c. _____   h. _____

d. _____   i. _____

e. _____   j. _____

Short Answer

Answer the following questions in 1–4 sentences.

3. Describe the role of ADH in regulating blood volume.

4. Describe two functions that the countercurrent multiplier performs for the kidneys.

Multiple Choice

Select the best answer from the choices given.

5. You have just exercised heavily and eaten a salty anchovy pizza without drinking any water. How will your kidneys respond?
   a. stop the release of ADH
   b. produce a highly concentrated, low volume of urine
   c. decrease reabsorption at the loop of Henle
   d. close the pores in the collecting ducts
   e. produce a very dilute, high volume of urine

6. After a marathon race, Bill drinks an excessive amount of water and has a pounding headache. Which condition does he probably have?

    a. hypernatremia   c. acidosis   e. hypovolemia

    b. hyponatremia   d. alkalosis

7. Which of the following is the major solute that produces the osmotic gradient that drives reabsorption of water?

    a. HCO_3^- c. H^+ e. choline

    b. K^+ d. Na^+

8. If the body is in balance, then Input + Production = _____ + Output.

    a. use   c. net loss   e. drinking

    b. net gain   d. reabsorption

9. An increase in plasma volume is called _____.

    a. hypovolemia   c. hypocalcemia   e. hypervolemia

    b. normovolemia   d. hypercalcemia

10. Which of the following might occur if an increase in blood osmolarity goes uncorrected?

    a. a decreased production of ADH

    b. shrinking of red blood cells

    c. production by the kidneys of much dilute urine

    d. ceasing of reabsorption in the tubules

    e. swelling of red blood cells

11. In the kidneys, sodium reabsorption always involves which of the following?

    a. exocytosis   d. ADH

    b. active transport of sodium   e. active transport of water

    c. endocytosis

True/False

Label the following statements as true (T) *or false* (F). *If false, change the statement to make it true.*

12. _____ The thick ascending limb of the loop of Henle is permeable to salt but not to water.

13. _____ The collecting duct actively transports urea into the peritubular fluid.

14. _____ Fluid entering the loop of Henle is hyperosmotic relative to extracellular fluid.

15. _____ Deep in the medulla, solutes enter the vasa recta.

16. _____ The collecting duct is controlled by aldosterone.

17. _____ ADH secretion is dictated by both the blood volume and by the osmolarity of the blood.

Sequencing

18. The following events are associated with the effects of ADH on principal cells lining the late distal tubules and collecting ducts. Place the events in the proper sequence.

   a. Protein kinase A is activated.
   b. ADH binds to receptors on membrane of principal cells.
   c. G protein is activated.
   d. Adenylate cyclase is activated, which catalyzes the formation of cAMP.
   e. Water is reabsorbed into the peritubular capillaries.
   f. New aquaporin-2 is inserted into the apical membrane.
   g. The permeability of the collecting duct to water increases.

   Sequence: _____

Clinical Questions

19. Abby has diabetes insipidus. What is diabetes insipidus, and what are her likely symptoms?

20. Mike is a healthy young man who is intent on winning a regional bodybuilding contest. He decides to take a diuretic to increase his chances of winning. Why would Mike take a diuretic and what are some potentially dangerous consequences of such an action?

Challenge Questions

21. Lasix is a loop diuretic that operates on the loop of Henle. This drug is often used to lower blood pressure. Can you propose a mechanism of action of this drug on the loop of Henle that would cause water loss?

22. Explain how drinking alcohol affects ADH release and urine output.

Concept Map

23. Fill in the boxes is this concept map showing the factors leading to water balance in the body.

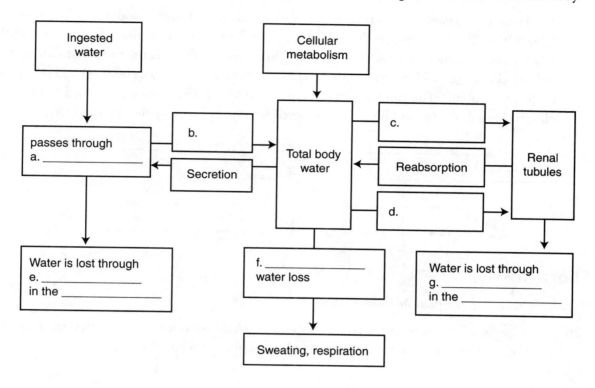

SODIUM, POTASSIUM, CALCIUM BALANCE, AND INTERACTIONS BETWEEN FLUID AND ELECTROLYTE REGULATION

Matching

24. Match each ion with its appropriate description below: Ca^{2+}, K^+, Na^+. Answers may be used more than once.

a. _____ An excess of this ion causes hypernatremia.

b. _____ ANP decreases the reabsorption of this ion.

c. _____ Aldosterone increases secretion of this ion.

d. _____ Intestinal absorption of this ion is enhanced by calcitriol.

e. _____ A decrease in this ion causes hypokalemia.

f. _____ Aldosterone enhances reabsorption of this ion.

Completion

Fill in the blanks to complete the following narrative.

25. The hormones **(a)** and **(b)** regulate sodium reabsorption. **(a)** increases sodium reabsorption and **(c)** secretion. **(b)** is secreted by the cells in the atria of the heart in response to distention of the atrial wall caused by an increased plasma **(d)**. **(b)** increases the glomerular filtration rate and reabsorption of **(e)**, which increases **(e)** excretion. Potassium undergoes both **(f)** and secretion in the renal tubules. Potassium secretion is increased by **(a)**. Calcium can be added to the plasma through the **(g)** and bone, and removed from the plasma by the **(h)** and kidneys.

a. _____   e. _____

b. _____   f. _____

c. _____   g. _____

d. _____   h. _____

Short Answer

Answer the following questions in 1–4 sentences.

26. Describe the effects of too little plasma sodium on blood volume and blood pressure. Describe the effects of too much plasma sodium on blood volume and blood pressure.

27. Compare the movement of potassium in the proximal versus distal tubules.

Multiple Choice

Select the best answer from the choices given.

28. Which of the following is the primary regulator of plasma calcium levels?
    a. parathyroid hormone   c. aldosterone   e. calcitriol
    b. ADH   d. calcitonin

29. _____ increases blood volume by increasing sodium reabsorption.
    a. Aldosterone   c. Glucagon   e. ANP
    b. Insulin   d. Vasopressin

30. Which of the following directly stimulates the release of ANP?

a. a drop in blood volume

b. an increase in blood volume

c. a decrease in plasma sodium levels

d. renin

e. a decrease in plasma osmolarity

31. When mean arterial pressure increases, which of the following compensation mechanisms occurs to lower blood pressure?

a. Renin secretion increases.

b. ADH secretion increases.

c. Angiotensin II causes vasoconstriction.

d. Sodium reabsorption decreases.

e. ANP secretion increases.

32. Tonya has a tumor on the cells of her adrenal gland that causes a decrease in the amount of aldosterone secreted. Which of the following is directly caused by a decrease in aldosterone secretion?

a. Renin secretion increases.

b. ADH secretion increases.

c. Angiotensin II causes vasoconstriction.

d. ANP production decreases.

e. Sodium reabsorption decreases.

33. Calcium ions are transported free in the plasma or _____.

a. bound to Cl^-

b. bound to hemoglobin

c. associated with other positively charged electrolytes

d. bound to carrier proteins

e. dissolved in the plasma membrane of red blood cells

34. Which of the following is an effect produced by calcitrol?

a. increased plasma calcium levels

b. increased heart rate

c. vasoconstriction

d. vasodilation

e. increased bone formation

35. Tulio has eaten some salty breadsticks without drinking any fluids. Secretion of which of the following hormones will increase as a result of increased plasma osmolarity?

a. calcitriol

b. calcitonin

c. PTH

d. calcitrol

e. ADH

True/False

Label the following statements as true (T) *or false* (F). *If false, change the statement to make it true.*

36. _____ Aldosterone decreases the synthesis of Na^+/K^+ pumps in the basolateral membrane of the renal tubules.

37. _____ ANP increases GFR.

38. _____ Regulation of potassium secretion occurs in the proximal tubules and the loop of Henle.

39. _____ Low plasma levels of potassium stimulate aldosterone secretion.

Labeling

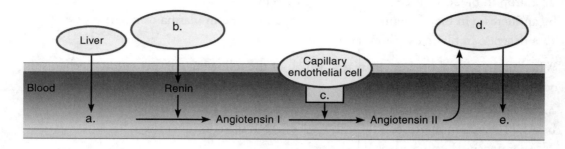

FIGURE 18.1

40. In the space below, identify a–e in Figure 18.1

Clinical Questions

41. ACE inhibitors are often prescribed for people with congestive heart failure. Explain the mechanism of action of these drugs and why they might be used with patients who have a failing heart.

42. Jill has a tumor on one of her parathyroid glands, which increases secretion of parathyroid hormone. What effect will this have on her plasma calcium levels and what are some likely symptoms?

Challenge Questions

43. A man's arm is severed in an automobile accident. Describe the response of the posterior pituitary, the renin-angiotensin-aldosterone system, and ANP to the massive blood loss.

44. Compare and contrast the hormonal regulation of calcium by parathyroid hormone and calcitonin.

Concept Map

45. Fill in the boxes of the concept map of the routes of calcium exchange.

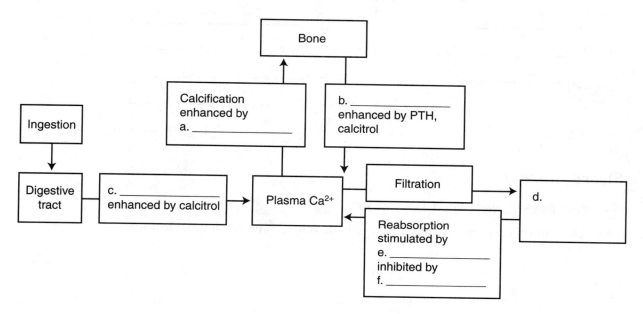

ACID-BASE BALANCE

Matching

46. Each of the following conditions describes or might lead to acidosis (AD) or alkalosis (AK). Mark each accordingly.

a. _____ heavy exercise

b. _____ severe diarrhea

c. _____ prolonged vomiting

d. _____ hypoventilation

e. _____ an excess of H$^+$ in the blood

f. _____ a high-protein diet

g. _____ hyperventilation

h. _____ an excess of bicarbonate addition to the blood due to alteration in renal function

Completion

Fill in the blanks to complete the following narrative.

47. Arterial pH is highly regulated to maintain the normal range between **(a)** and **(b)**. A decrease in pH to below **(a)** is called **(c)**, whereas an increase in pH to above **(b)** is called **(d)**. The respiratory system contributes to acid-base balance by regulating **(e)** levels in the blood. Carbon dioxide can be converted to **(f)** by the enzyme **(g)**. Respiratory acidosis is caused by too much **(h)** and respiratory alkalosis is caused by a decrease in **(h)**. **(i)** and **(j)** are disturbances in blood pH caused by something other than an abnormally low or high P_{CO_2}, respectively.

a. _____   f. _____

b. _____   g. _____

c. _____   h. _____

d. _____   i. _____

e. _____   j. _____

Short Answer

Answer the following questions in 1–4 sentences.

48. Distinguish between the causes of metabolic acidosis and respiratory acidosis.

49. Describe the role of glutamine in renal compensation during severe acidosis.

50. Briefly describe how the kidneys compensate for changes in blood pH.

Multiple Choice

Select the best answer from the choices given.

51. Which of the following is the first response of your body to changes in plasma pH?

   a. respiratory compensation
   b. buffering of sodium ions
   c. excretion of hydrogen ions at the kidneys
   d. reabsorption of hydrogen ions at the kidneys
   e. glutamine formation

52. A blow to his head during football practice caused Jim to begin hyperventilating. Which of the following conditions is true?

   a. He has respiratory acidosis.
   b. He has metabolic acidosis.
   c. His P_{CO_2} is < 40 mm Hg.
   d. His kidneys will begin excreting a larger volume of hydrogen ions than normal.
   e. His plasma pH will be < 7.35.

53. Cory runs a marathon in 4 hours and 17 minutes. After such prolonged heavy exercise, which of the following will be true?

   a. He will have metabolic acidosis.
   b. He will have respiratory alkalosis.
   c. His plasma pH will be > 7.45.
   d. His kidneys will be reabsorbing hydrogen ions and excreting bicarbonate.
   e. His hydrogen ion buffering system will no longer be operating.

54. Patricia has a blood pH of 7.30, and her P_{CO2} is 27 mm Hg. Which condition does she have?

   a. metabolic acidosis   c. metabolic alkalosis   e. These are normal values.
   b. respiratory acidosis   d. respiratory alkalosis

55. Margaret has a blood pH of 7.56, and bicarbonate concentration of 19 mM. Which condition does she have?

   a. metabolic acidosis   c. metabolic alkalosis   e. These are normal values.
   b. respiratory acidosis   d. respiratory alkalosis

56. Which of the following is an important enzyme located within the cytosol of the intercalated cell?

   a. lipase   c. carbonic anhydrase   e. phosphates
   b. hydrogen ions   d. glutamine

57. Which of the following is the most important extracellular buffer?

   a. protein   c. hemoglobin   e. glutamine
   b. bicarbonate   d. phosphate

58. Which of the following is **not** a cause of additional hydrogen ions in the body?

   a. carbon dioxide production by cells   d. severe diarrhea
   b. lactic acid production   e. excessive vomiting
   c. high-protein diet

True/False

Label the following statements as true (T) *or false* (F). *If false, change the statement to make it true.*

59. _____ The nervous system is relatively unaffected by wide changes in plasma pH levels.

60. _____ The two organs of the body that regulate plasma pH levels are the lungs and the kidneys.

61. _____ Proteins, such as hemoglobin, are not very effective in acting as buffers of hydrogen ions.

62. _____ The proximal tubule is responsible for, among other things, secretion of 80–90% of the bicarbonate ions found in the urine.

63. _____ A decrease in plasma pH (< 7.35) and an increase in plasma bicarbonate levels (> 24 mM) indicate compensated respiratory acidosis.

Labeling

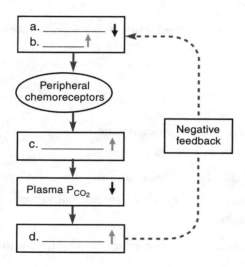

FIGURE 18.2

64. In the space below, identify a–d in Figure 18.2.

Clinical Questions

65. A 6-year-old boy is brought into the emergency room with a virus that causes repeated vomiting. What are the likely effects of this condition on the child's acid-base balance of the blood?

66. A blood chemistry analysis determines that Susie's bicarbonate to carbon dioxide ratio is 19:1. Does she have acidosis or alkalosis? What information would you need in order to know whether the cause is respiratory or metabolic?

Challenge Question

67. *Principles of Human Physiology* states, "Unlike simple hydrogen ion buffering,…respiratory compensation is a true homeostatic regulatory mechanism." What is meant by this statement?

68. Explain how late-stage emphysema can lead to an acid-base imbalance of the blood.

Concept Map

69. Fill in the boxes in the concept map of the summary of acid-base disturbances and the body's compensation.

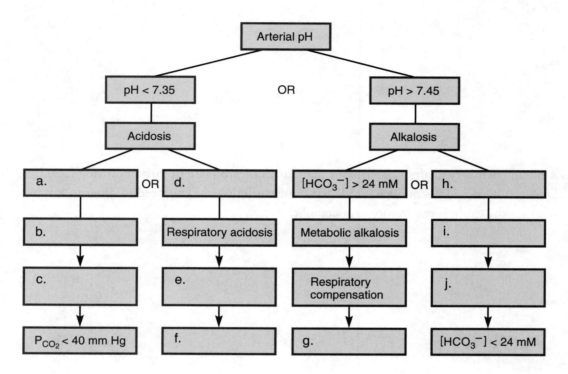

The Digestive System

Objectives

We recommend that you review the **Objectives** for this chapter, found on p. 601 of *Principles of Human Physiology*. The **Objectives** outline what you should know from each chapter.

Key Terms

basic electrical rhythm
bile
bile salt
brush border
chemoreceptor
chief cell
cholecystokinin (CCK)
chylomicron
chyme
crypts of Lieberkuhn
digestion
duodenum
emulsification
enteric nervous system
enterocyte
enterogastrone
enterokinase
esophagus
fundus
gallbladder
gastric mucosal barrier

gastrin
glucose-dependent
    insulinotropic peptide (GIP)
hepatocyte
ileum
intrinsic factor
jejunum
lacteal
large intestine
leptin
lipoprotein
liver
lower esophageal sphincter
mechanoreceptor
mucosa
mucous membrane
muscularis externa
myenteric plexus
osmoreceptor
pancreas
pancreatic juice

parietal cell
pepsinogen
peristalsis
peritoneum
pharynx
potentiation
pylorus
rectum
salivary glands
secretin
secretion
serosa
small intestine
sphincter of Oddi
stomach
submucosa
submucosal plexus
trypsin
villi
zymogen

OVERVIEW OF DIGESTIVE SYSTEM FUNCTION

Matching

1. Match each item in the following list to its definition: chemical digestion (CD), mechanical digestion (MD), absorption (A), secretion (S), and motility (M).

   a. _____ the release of fluids containing enzymes and other substances into the lumen of the digestive tract

   b. _____ the physical breakdown of food into smaller particles

c. _____ the ability of organs within the digestive tract to generate movement

d. _____ the chemical breakdown of nutrient molecules into smaller molecules

e. _____ the transport of molecules from the lumen of the digestive tract into the bloodstream

Short Answer

Answer the following question in 1–4 sentences.

2. Why is it essential that both the mechanical and chemical digestion of food occur within the digestive system?

FUNCTIONAL ANATOMY OF THE DIGESTIVE SYSTEM

Completion

Fill in the blanks to complete the following narrative.

3. The digestive system can be subdivided into two major divisions: the **(a)** , which forms a **(b)** through which food and the products of digestion are transported, and the **(c)** , which are located outside of the **(a)** and which secrete fluids and **(d)** into the lumen of the **(a)**. The **(a)** can also be referred to as the **(e)**.

a. _____   d. _____

b. _____   e. _____

c. _____

Matching

4. Match the following components of the digestive system with their function: pharynx (P), esophagus (E), lower esophageal sphincter (LES), pyloric sphincter (PS), rugae (R), duodenum (D), fundus (F), crypts of Lieberkuhn (CL), brush border (BB), and ileocecal sphincter (IS).

a. _____ ring of smooth muscle that controls the opening between the esophagus and the stomach

b. _____ ring of smooth muscle that controls the movement of chyme from the stomach to the duodenum

c. _____ ring of smooth muscle that controls the movement of chyme from the small intestine to the large intestine

d. _____ folds of the gastric mucosa that flatten as the stomach expands

e. _____ passageway between the mouth and the esophagus

f. _____ pits located in the lining of the small intestine that contain cells that secrete bicarbonate-rich fluid

g. _____ the upper portion of the stomach

h. _____ the tube through which food travels to the stomach

i. _____ the section of the small intestine connected to the stomach

j. _____ microvilli located on the apical surface of the epithelial cells lining the small intestine

Multiple Choice

Select the best answer from the choices given.

5. Which of the following is **not** a component of the digestive tract?

   a. pharynx   c. rectum   e. stomach

   b. liver   d. mouth

6. The innermost layer of the mucosa is called the _____.

   a. muscularis externa   c. mucous membrane   e. lamina propria

   b. muscularis interna   d. submucosa

7. Which of the following is **not** a type of enterocyte?

   a. absorptive cells   c. exocrine cells   e. endocrine cells

   b. hepatocytes   d. goblet cells

8. Which of the following is **not** true of the serosa?

   a. it provides structural support to the gastrointestinal tract (GI tract)

   b. it contains an outer layer of mesothelium that secretes a lubricating fluid

   c. it is continuous with mesenteries that house nerves and blood vessels and interconnect most abdominal organs

   d. it is the outermost layer of the wall of the digestive tract

   e. it consists of a strong inner layer of adipose tissue

9. The exocrine cells of the mucous membrane _____.

   a. absorb nutrients into the blood

   b. secrete enzymes and other fluids into the lumen of the GI tract

   c. secrete enzymes and other fluids into the blood

   d. secrete hormones into the blood

   e. secrete hormones into the lumen of the GI tract

10. Which of the following is **not** true of the submucosa?

   a. It is adjacent to the serosa.

   b. It provides the GI tract the ability to stretch without being damaged.

   c. It contains a network of nerve fibers known as the submucosal plexus.

   d. It contains blood vessels.

   e. It contains lymphatic vessels.

11. Salivary amylase initiates the digestion of _____ in the _____.

    a. carbohydrates : stomach

    b. proteins : stomach

    c. fats : small intestine

    d. carbohydrates : mouth

    e. proteins : mouth

12. Which of the following is **not** true of the human stomach?

    a. Its contractile activity breaks down food into smaller particles and mixes it with gastric juice, producing a substance called chyme.

    b. Its lining contains gastric glands that secrete gastric juice.

    c. It is composed of four major anatomical regions.

    d. It releases food slowly to the small intestine.

    e. It stores food.

13. Which of the following substances is not correctly paired with the cell type from which it is released?

    a. pepsinogen : chief cells

    b. hydrogen ions : parietal cells

    c. intrinsic factor : parietal cells

    d. gastrin : G cells

    e. bicarbonate : chief cells

14. Which of the following is **not** true of the small intestine?

    a. It is a coiled tube about 2.5–3 meters long.

    b. It is composed of three regions: the duodenum, jejunum, and ileum.

    c. It is the site in which the feces are formed.

    d. It is the primary site for both the digestion and absorption of nutrients within the GI tract.

    e. It is the site at which chyme is mixed with pancreatic juice and bile.

15. Which of the following is **not** an accessory gland of the digestive system?

    a. parotid salivary glands

    b. submandibular salivary glands

    c. liver

    d. jejunum

    e. pancreas

16. Which of the following is **not** a component of saliva?

    a. bicarbonate

    b. citrate

    c. mucus

    d. salivary amylase

    e. lysozyme

17. Which of the following substances would **not** be chemically digested by an enzyme in pancreatic juice?

    a. starch and glycogen

    b. fats

    c. proteins

    d. nucleic acids

    e. none of the above

18. Which of the following is **not** a function of the liver?

    a. It eliminates waste products such as bilirubin from the body.

    b. It synthesizes plasma proteins.

    c. It stores bile.

    d. It removes old red blood cells from the blood.

    e. It metabolizes certain nutrients.

True/False

Label the following statements as true (T) or false (F). If false, change the statement to make it true.

19. _____ The digestive tract is a hollow tube that begins at the mouth and ends at the anus.

20. _____ The various epithelial cells of the mucous membrane lining the GI tract are referred to as enterocytes.

21. _____ The submucosa is the layer of the GI tract primarily responsible for motility of the tract.

22. _____ Contraction of the circular muscle layer of the muscularis externa narrows the GI tract's diameter, while contraction of the longitudinal muscle layer decreases its length.

23. _____ The peritoneum is the membrane lining the inside of the abdominal cavity.

24. _____ The mechanical and chemical digestion of food begins in the stomach.

25. _____ Another word for chewing is mastication.

26. _____ Intrinsic factor is an inactive precursor of the enzyme pepsin.

27. _____ The lumen of the stomach is the only location in the GI tract that has an acidic pH.

28. _____ Most of the nutrient absorption in the small intestine occurs within the first 20% of its length.

29. _____ The regions of the colon that specialize in the absorption of water and ions are the ascending colon, transverse colon, and descending colon.

30. _____ Another name for the colon is the small intestine.

31. _____ The internal anal sphincter is composed of skeletal muscle, while the external anal sphincter is composed of smooth muscle.

32. _____ The epithelial cells of the salivary glands and pancreas are arranged in functional clusters called acini.

33. _____ The three pairs of major salivary glands are the parotid glands, sublingual glands, and submandibular glands.

34. _____ Pancreatic juice is a hormone secreted into the blood and small intestine.

35. _____ The gallbladder secretes bile.

36. _____ The sphincter of Oddi controls the release of pancreatic juice and bile into the duodenum.

37. _____ The products of the exocrine pancreas are created by pancreatic islet cells.

Sequencing

38. List the following components of the GI tract in the order in which food/chyme moves through them.

a. stomach
b. jejunum
c. transverse colon
d. pharynx
e. duodenum
f. descending colon

g. esophagus
h. rectum
i. mouth
j. sigmoid colon
k. ascending colon
l. ileum

Sequence: _____

Labeling

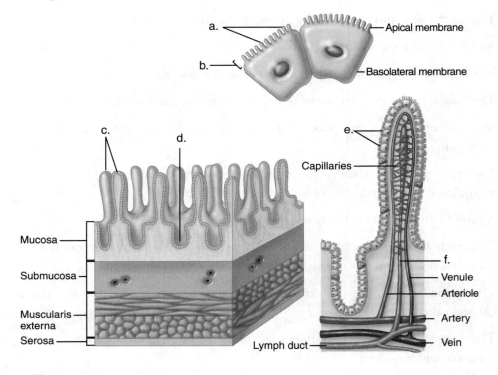

FIGURE 19.1

39. In the space below, identify the structures (a–f) on Figure 19.1.

Short Answer

Answer the following questions in 1–4 sentences.

40. What is the role of mucus within the GI tract, and what cell type secretes it?

41. What is the enteric nervous system?

42. Do the nutrients absorbed in the small intestine directly enter the general circulation when they leave the small intestine in the blood? Explain your answer.

43. Distinguish between the exocrine pancreas and the endocrine pancreas. Include the products secreted by each.

Challenge Questions

44. Why is the environment within the stomach acidic, and why doesn't the low pH damage the stomach lining?

45. In what ways is the mucosa of the small intestine adapted to increase the efficiency of absorption?

46. What are zymogens, and why are they present in the pancreas?

Clinical Questions

47. Define the terms appendicitis and peritonitis. Why are the two conditions sometimes associated with each other? Where might you expect pain resulting from appendicitis to be located?

48. What causes heartburn, and with what typical symptoms is it associated?

DIGESTION AND ABSORPTION OF NUTRIENTS AND WATER

Completion

Fill in the blanks to complete the following narrative.

49. Dietary carbohydrates come in many forms. The majority of dietary carbohydrates are in the form of the polysaccharide **(a)**, which is found in plant products. The main polysaccharide in animal products is **(b)**. Other dietary carbohydrates include the disaccharides **(c)** (table sugar), **(d)** (milk sugar) and **(e)** (found in wheat), and the monosaccharides **(f)**, **(g)**, and **(h)**. Only **(i)** can be absorbed by the small intestine.

a. _____   f. _____

b. _____   g. _____

c. _____   h. _____

d. _____   i. _____

e. _____

Matching

50. Match the digestive enzyme to its action and its site of activity.

Action

a. breaks down starch and glycogen to disaccharides or limit dextrins
b. breaks down limit dextrins to glucose
c. breaks down a disaccharide into monosaccharides
d. breaks down proteins into smaller peptide fragments
e. releases amino acids from peptides
f. breaks down triglycerides into two fatty acids plus a monoglyceride

Site of Activity

a. mouth
b. stomach
c. small intestine

Enzyme	Action	Site of Activity
a. pepsin	_____	_____
b. trypsin	_____	_____
c. salivary amylase	_____	_____
d. pancreatic lipase	_____	_____
e. aminopeptidase	_____	_____
f. pancreatic amylase	_____	_____
g. glucoamylase	_____	_____
h. carboxypeptidase	_____	_____
i. lactase	_____	_____

Multiple Choice

Select the best answer from the choices given.

51. Where are brush border enzymes located?

a. bound to the apical membranes of the absorptive cells of the mucosa in the small intestine
b. bound to the basolateral membranes of the absorptive cells of the mucosa in the small intestine
c. in pancreatic juice
d. in saliva
e. bound to the surface of goblet cells in the mucosa of the small intestine

52. Which of the following is **not** a brush border enzyme?

a. aminopeptidase
b. enterokinase
c. dextrinase
d. maltase
e. trypsin

53. Consider the following statements regarding the mechanisms by which substances are absorbed in the small intestine. Which is incorrect?

a. Glucose and galactose are absorbed via active transport.
b. Some amino acids are absorbed by active transport, others by facilitated diffusion.
c. Water is absorbed by active transport.
d. Fatty acids and monoglycerides are absorbed by simple diffusion.
e. Fructose is absorbed by facilitated diffusion.

54. The digestion of proteins begins in the _____ and ends in the _____.

    a. mouth : stomach
            d. stomach : small intestine

    b. mouth : small intestine
        e. stomach : rectum

    c. mouth : large intestine

55. Which of the following are **active** pancreatic proteases?

    1. chymotrypsinogen
            5. chymotrypsin

    2. aminopeptidase
             6. carboxypeptidase

    3. trypsin
                7. enterokinase

    4. procarboxypeptidase

    a. 1, 2, 3, 4, 5, 6, 7
      c. 2, 3, 6, 7
      e. 5, 6, 7

    b. 3, 5, 6
            d. 1, 3, 5, 7

56. Fats are emulsified by _____.

    a. chylomicrons
      c. cholesterol
      e. triglycerides

    b. micelles
        d. bile salts

57. The large lipid particles that are formed in the absorptive cells of the small intestine after fatty acids and monoglycerides have been absorbed are called _____.

    a. bile salts
        c. cholesterol
      e. chylomicrons

    b. carboxyl groups
    d. adipocytes

58. Which of the following minerals is always absorbed in the small intestine, but is absorbed or excreted to the greatest extent (relative to the others) in the colon depending on its concentration?

    a. potassium
       c. magnesium
      e. calcium

    b. sodium
         d. iron

True/False

Label the following statements as true (T) *or false* (F). *If false, change the statement to make it true.*

59. _____ Bile salts digest lipids.

60. _____ Chylomicrons enter blood capillaries within the villi.

61. _____ The products of protein digestion can be absorbed as amino acids, dipeptides, or tripeptides.

62. _____ Amino acids and monosaccharides enter the bloodstream by diffusing into blood capillaries within villi.

63. _____ The digestion of most lipids begins in the stomach.

64. _____ The chemical digestion of starch or glycogen begins in the mouth and ends in the small intestine.

65. _____ The term dietary fiber refers to carbohydrates that cannot be digested or absorbed, particularly cellulose.

Short Answer

Answer the following questions in 1–4 sentences.

66. Explain how trypsinogen, chymotrypsinogen, and procarboxypeptidase are activated.

67. Define the term emulsification, and explain why it is important to the process of fat digestion.

Challenge Questions

68. What effect, if any, will a very low-fat diet have on the absorption of fat-soluble and water-soluble vitamins?

69. Why are so many different enzymes used in the digestion of carbohydrates?

Clinical Questions

70. Gastroesophageal reflux disease is treated with Prilosec, a medication that greatly decreases the secretion of stomach acid. Would the effects of this drug alter a person's ability to digest proteins? Why or why not?

71. A gastric bypass procedure is a surgery sometimes performed on very obese individuals to assist them with weight loss. In a gastric bypass the stomach is stapled to decrease its size to a capacity of about two tablespoons, and the duodenum is connected to this small section of stomach. Would a person undergoing this procedure be at risk for developing pernicious anemia? Why or why not?

GENERAL PRINCIPLES OF GASTROINTESTINAL REGULATION

Completion

Fill in the blanks to complete the following narrative.

72. Three types of receptors monitor the conditions within the lumen of the gastrointestinal tract. These include **(a)**, which monitor the osmolarity of the contents of the lumen; **(b)**, which detect the degree of distention of the lumenal wall; and **(c)**, which monitor the concentrations of specific substances such as fats and hydrogen ions in the lumenal contents. All of these receptor types are located within the **(d)**. These receptors can send nerve impulses to both the **(e)** nervous system and the **(f)** nervous system.

a. _____   d. _____

b. _____   e. _____

c. _____   f. _____

Multiple Choice

Select the best answer from the choices given.

73. Which of the following is **not** correct?

   a. Many GI functions are controlled by reflexes coordinated by the enteric nervous system.
   b. The central nervous system (CNS) can influence functions coordinated by the enteric nervous system.
   c. Many GI functions are controlled by hormones secreted by endocrine cells located in the stomach or duodenum.
   d. Many of the regulatory mechanisms that control GI function control not only conditions in the lumen of the GI tract, but also conditions in the general internal environment of the body.
   e. Regulatory mechanisms that control GI functions are usually influenced by stimuli from within the GI tract.

74. Which of the following is **not** one of the confirmed hormones of gastrointestinal origin?

   a. cholecystokinin (CCK)
   b. gastrin
   c. secretin
   d. glucose-dependent insulinotropic peptide (GIP)
   e. aldosterone

75. Which of the following phases of gastrointestinal control involves stimuli such as the smell, taste, or thought of food?

   a. cephalic-phase control
   b. gastric-phase control
   c. intestinal-phase control
   d. cerebral-phase control
   e. sensory-phase control

76. Which of the following phases is/are triggered by stimuli that exert their effects via long or short reflex pathways, or by altering the secretion of GI hormones, but don't necessarily trigger involvement of the CNS?

   a. cephalic-phase control
   b. gastric-phase control
   c. intestinal-phase control
   d. a and b
   e. b and c

True/False

Label the following statements as true (T) *or false* (F). *If false, change the statement to make it true.*

77. _____ Increased parasympathetic activity usually increases gastrointestinal activity, while increased sympathetic activity usually decreases gastrointestinal activity.

78. _____ A given region of the GI tract can respond to stimuli within that region of the GI tract, in another region of the GI tract, or outside the GI tract.

79. _____ In general, the GI tract will absorb all the nutrients it can from ingested food, regardless of the needs of the body or the quantities of nutrients present.

80. _____ Effector cells in GI organs include smooth muscle cells, skeletal muscle cells, exocrine cells, and endocrine cells.

81. _____ Short reflex pathways always involve the CNS, while long reflex pathways never do.

Matching

82. Match the hormone to its site of release: ileum (I), jejunum (J), duodenum (D), stomach (S), and colon (C). Answers may be used more than once or not at all, and some hormones may be released from more than one site.

   a. _____ gastrin

   b. _____ CCK

   c. _____ secretin

   d. _____ GIP

Challenge Question

83. Distinguish between the short-term regulation of food intake and long-term regulation. Describe the role of satiety signals in short-term regulation, and the role of leptin in long-term regulation.

Concept Map

84. The following concept map demonstrates the effects of long reflex and short reflex pathways in the digestive system. Fill in the blanks.

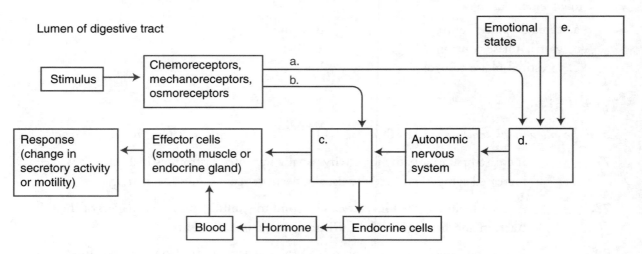

GASTROINTESTINAL SECRETION AND ITS REGULATION

Matching

85. Match the substance to its function(s): gastrin (G), cholecystokinin (CCK), secretin (S), and histamine (H). Do not include potentiating actions.

a. _____ stimulates the secretion of bicarbonate-rich pancreatic juice into the duodenum

b. _____ stimulates the secretion of enzyme-rich pancreatic juice into the duodenum

c. _____ stimulates the secretion of acid and pepsinogen into the stomach

d. _____ stimulates the gallbladder to contract and release bile, relaxes the sphincter of Oddi

e. _____ stimulates the liver to secrete bile

f. _____ inhibits gastric secretion

Multiple Choice

Select the best answer from the choices given.

86. The salivary center controls _____ the salivary glands, and is located in the _____.
    a. autonomic input from : medulla oblongata
    b. autonomic output to : medulla oblongata
    c. somatic output to : medulla oblongata
    d. autonomic output to : pons
    e. somatic output to : pons

87. Which of the following is **not** a typical stimulus for salivation?
    a. the taste of food in the mouth
    b. the texture of food in the mouth
    c. the sight of food
    d. the smell of food
    e. the stimulation of salivary glands by secretin

88. The acid secreted by the stomach is generated in _____ cells by the action of _____.
    a. chief : cholecystokinin
    b. chief : pepsin
    c. chief : bicarbonate
    d. parietal : carbonic anhydrase
    e. parietal : pepsinogen

89. Which of the following is **not** a stimulus for the secretion of acid in the stomach?
    a. parasympathetic nervous activity
    b. sympathetic nervous activity
    c. gastrin
    d. histamine
    e. a and d

90. Which of the following conditions does **not** reduce gastric secretion?
    a. decreased distention of the stomach
    b. increased distention of the duodenum
    c. decreased gastric acidity
    d. increased duodenal acidity
    e. increased fat content in the duodenum

91. Which of the following statements is **not** true?
    a. CCK primarily stimulates the secretion of bicarbonate-rich pancreatic juice; secretin primarily stimulates the secretion of enzyme-rich pancreatic juice.
    b. CCK acts primarily on the acinar cells of the pancreas; secretin acts primarily on the duct cells of the pancreas.
    c. Secretin is secreted primarily in response to the presence of acidic chyme in the duodenum; CCK is secreted primarily in response to the presence of fat-rich and/or protein-rich chyme in the duodenum.
    d. CCK and secretin are secreted into the blood.
    e. CCK and secretin are secreted when chemoreceptors, responding to the appropriate stimulus, send nerve impulses along short and long reflex pathways to endocrine cells in the small intestine.

True/False

Label the following statements as true (T) *or false* (F). *If false, change the statement to make it true.*

92. _____ Hydrogen ions are actively transported from parietal cells into the lumen of the stomach in exchange for potassium ions.

93. _____ The secretion of stomach acid is controlled by cephalic-phase, gastric-phase, and intestinal-phase stimuli.

94. _____ The composition of pancreatic juice can vary according to the type of food a person ingests.

95. _____ The secretion of pancreatic juice is controlled only by intestinal-phase stimuli.

96. _____ When CCK and secretin are both present, they act antagonistically toward one other, a phenomenon known as inhibition.

97. _____ The majority of fluid that enters the GI tract each day is absorbed by the small intestine.

Challenge Questions

98. Why does gastric acidity rise as gastric emptying occurs, and how does this affect gastric secretion?

99. Why is it important that bicarbonate-rich pancreatic juice be secreted into the duodenum when chyme enters from the stomach?

Clinical Question

100. Would the removal of a person's gallbladder impact his or her ability to digest fats? Explain.

Concept Map

101. The flow charts below depict the mechanisms by which gastric secretion is stimulated/regulated. Fill in the blanks.

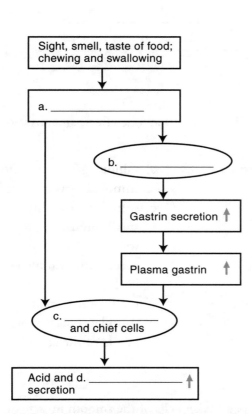

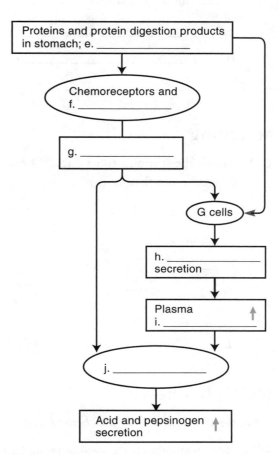

(a) Cephalic-phase control of gastric secretion

(b) Gastric-phase control of gastric secretion

GASTROINTESTINAL MOTILITY AND ITS REGULATION

Completion

Fill in the blanks to complete the following narrative.

102. Under certain circumstances, specialized reflexes occur in the small intestine and colon. Those that occur in the small intestine are coordinated by the **(a)** nervous system, and include: the **(b)** reflex, which inhibits gastric motility and is triggered by distention of the ileum; the **(c)** reflex, which occurs when chyme is present in the stomach and causes increased motility in the ileum; and the **(d)** reflex, resulting from severe distention or injury to any part of the small intestine, and inhibiting contractile activity throughout the rest of the small intestine.

Two specialized reflexes occur in the colon. The **(e)** reflex is triggered by distention of one part of the colon, and results in relaxation of the remaining parts of the colon. When a meal is ingested, the presence of food in the stomach triggers the **(f)** reflex, which causes an increase in colonic motility and an increase in the frequency of mass movements.

a. _____ d. _____

b. _____ e. _____

c. _____ f. _____

Matching

103. Match the stimulus to its effect. Some stimuli may have more than one effect, and answers may be used more than once.

a. _____ moderate distention of the small intestine

b. _____ CCK

c. _____ GIP

d. _____ gastrin

e. _____ secretin

f. _____ parasympathetic stimulation of the GI tract

a. inhibits gastric motility

b. stimulates gastric motility

c. stimulates motility of the small intestine in a general way

d. specifically stimulates ileal motility and relaxes the ileocecal sphincter

e. stimulates mass movements of the colon

Multiple Choice

Select the best answer from the choices given.

104. Slow, spontaneous, graded depolarizations within pacemaker cells of the smooth muscle of the GI tract are called _____.

a. slow waves c. peristaltic waves e. rhythmical waves
b. fast waves d. segmentation

105. When food is chewed and mixed with saliva, it becomes a semisolid mass known as a _____.

a. haustra c. bolus e. micelle
b. chyme ball d. ruga

106. Which of the following is **not** true of the process by which food is swallowed?

a. It begins voluntarily as the tongue pushes the food toward the pharynx.
b. When food reaches the pharynx, the swallowing reflex is triggered.
c. The swallowing reflex is triggered by stimulation of mechanoreceptors.
d. The swallowing reflex is involuntary.
e. The swallowing reflex is mediated by a swallowing center located in the cerebellum.

107. Which of the following is **not** true about the rate of gastric emptying?
    a. The composition of chyme influences the rate of gastric emptying.
    b. The smaller the volume of chyme, the faster the rate of gastric emptying.
    c. The larger the volume of chyme, the stronger the force of gastric contractions.
    d. The greater the force of gastric contractions, the faster the rate of gastric emptying.
    e. More than one of the above is incorrect.

108. Which of the following is **not** true of segmentation?
    a. It involves alternate contraction and relaxation of neighboring segments of the small intestine.
    b. It moves chyme back and forth.
    c. It involves segments of the small intestine called haustra.
    d. It thoroughly mixes the chyme with digestive enzymes, bicarbonate ions, and bile.
    e. It increases the amount of contact between chyme and the brush border enzymes.

109. Which of the following is **not** true of the process of defecation?
    a. The term defecation refers to the elimination of feces from the body.
    b. The process is controlled both voluntarily and by the defecation reflex.
    c. The defecation reflex is triggered by distention of the rectum.
    d. The type of receptors involved in triggering the defecation reflex are stretch receptors.
    e. Defecation may be postponed by voluntary contraction of the internal anal sphincter.

110. Which of the following stimuli would normally inhibit gastric motility?
    a. depression   c. anger   e. b and c
    b. pain   d. a and b

True/False

Label the following statements as true (T) *or false* (F). *If false, change the statement to make it true.*

111. _____ Mass movements are waves of contraction in the colon that move the lumenal contents rapidly forward and occur about 3–4 times per day.

112. _____ During fasting, migrating motility complexes occur in the stomach and small intestine, removing any remaining chyme from these organs.

113. _____ Vomiting is a voluntary process initiated by the vomiting center in the medulla oblongata.

114. _____ Haustration occurs in the large intestine, and it serves to mix the chyme and increase the amount of contact between chyme and the intestinal mucosa, facilitating the absorption of water and electrolytes.

115. _____ Substances that induce vomiting are known as emotives.

116. _____ When food is present, motility in the small intestine includes peristalsis and segmentation.

117. _____ The purpose of peristalsis in the small intestine is to propel chyme forward, but in the stomach it mixes the chyme and propels it forward.

118. _____ Receptive relaxation involves relaxation of the smooth muscle in the upper portion of the stomach, and is triggered by CCK.

119. _____ The chewing reflex produces unconscious chewing, and is triggered when pressure receptors in the mouth are stimulated by the presence of food.

120. _____ Nervous and hormonal stimulation of gastrointestinal smooth muscle usually affects the height of slow waves rather than their frequency.

121. _____ Electrical activity moves within the GI tract from one smooth muscle cell to another through structures called intercalated discs.

122. _____ Gastric motility is influenced by cephalic-phase, gastric-phase, and intestinal-phase stimuli.

Short Answer

Answer the following questions in 1–4 sentences.

123. What is the purpose of the epiglottis?

124. What is a migrating motor complex?

Sequencing

125. Put the following events in the order in which they occur during the swallowing reflex.

   a. The lower esophageal sphincter relaxes.
   b. The upper esophageal sphincter relaxes.
   c. The bolus enters the pharynx.
   d. The bolus enters the stomach.
   e. Peristalsis occurs in the esophagus.
   f. The epiglottis covers the glottis.
   g. The bolus enters the esophagus.

   Sequence: _____

Challenge Question

126. Explain why it is necessary for the rate of gastric emptying to be regulated, and how this is accomplished.

Clinical Question

127. a. What are three physiologic mechanisms by which diarrhea may be produced?

  b. What adverse effects might result from chronic diarrhea?

20 The Endocrine System: Regulation of Energy Metabolism and Growth

Objectives

We recommend that you review the **Objectives** for this chapter, found on p. 640 of *Principles of Human Physiology*. The **Objectives** outline what you should know from each chapter.

Key Terms

adrenocorticotropic hormone	growth hormone	lipoprotein lipase
basal metabolic rate	growth hormone inhibiting	osteoblast
cartilage	hormone	osteoclast
chondrocyte	growth hormone releasing	osteoid
diabetes mellitus	hormone	resorption
epiphyseal plate	hyperplasia	somatomedin
glucagon	hypertrophy	somatostatin
glucocorticoid	insulin	thyrotropin releasing hormone
glucose sparing	insulin-like growth factor	very-low-density lipoprotein

AN OVERVIEW OF WHOLE BODY METABOLISM

Completion

Fill in the blanks to complete the following narrative.

1. Most cellular processes are powered by energy derived from the **(a)** of ATP. ATP is synthesized by two mechanisms within cells—**(b)** phosphorylation and **(c)** phosphorylation. In **(b)** phosphorylation, ATP is synthesized when a phosphate group from a metabolic intermediate is transferred to **(d)** to form ATP. In **(c)** phosphorylation, the energy released from electrons moving down the **(e)** in **(f)** is used to generate ATP. **(c)** phosphorylation is the mechanism by which the majority of cellular ATP is generated.

   a. _____   d._____

   b. _____   e._____

   c. _____   f._____

Short Answer

Answer the following questions in 1–4 sentences.

2. Within cells, what is the most important determinant of the particular metabolic pathways that are active at a given point in time, and the direction in which those metabolic pathways are proceeding?

3. Metabolic pathways can be controlled by compartmentation, which can occur at the cellular or tissue level. Describe the two ways in which compartmentation occurs at the tissue level, and provide one example of cellular compartmentation.

4. Why does the body store nutrients during periods of food intake instead of using all of them immediately to produce energy?

Challenge Question

5. Explain how carbohydrates and proteins can be used to produce energy or to synthesize lipids.

ENERGY INTAKE, UTILIZATION, AND STORAGE

Multiple Choice

Select the best answer from the choices given.

6. Which of the following is **not** a process that ingested nutrients may undergo once they are absorbed by cells?

a. They may be catabolized, releasing energy.

b. They may be used to synthesize other molecules.

c. If present in amounts in excess of those required for immediate cellular use, they may be excreted in the feces.

d. They may be used for the growth, repair, or metabolic functioning of cells.

e. If present in amounts in excess of those required for immediate cellular use, they may be converted to energy storage molecules.

7. What is the class of carbohydrates absorbed within the gastrointestinal tract?

    a. monosaccharides   c. polysaccharides   e. glycogen molecules

    b. disaccharides   d. starch molecules

8. The majority of lipids ingested in the diet are in the form of _____.

    a. cholesterol   c. prostaglandins   e. phospholipids

    b. steroid hormones   d. triglycerides

9. Which of the following is incorrect regarding the form in which the nutrient might be found circulating in the blood?

    a. carbohydrates – glucose

    b. carbohydrates – glycogen

    c. proteins – amino acids and small peptides

    d. lipids – free fatty acids

    e. lipids – lipoproteins

True/False

Label the following statements as true (T) *or false* (F). *If false, change the statement to make it true.*

10. _____ The two primary energy storage molecules in the human body are triglycerides and glucose.

11. _____ The catabolism of cellular proteins to generate energy generally occurs only during periods of starvation.

12. _____ Most cells in the body can release energy by oxidizing glucose, but only a few cell types are capable of efficiently synthesizing glycogen from glucose and storing it.

13. _____ Carbohydrate storage occurs primarily in adipose tissue.

Completion

14. Fill in the following table with the terms that correspond to the definitions given.

Definition	Term
Storage form of carbohydrates in human and other animal cells.	a.
Cell type specialized for fat storage.	b.
Class of carbohydrates into which sucrose and lactose fall.	c.
Break down products of triglycerides.	d.
Name for the process by which triglycerides are broken down.	e.
Primary form in which proteins are absorbed in the gastrointestinal tract.	f.

Concept Map

15. The concept map below depicts what happens to dietary polysaccharides after ingestion. Fill in the steps. Use the squares to specify processes, and circles to indicate products.

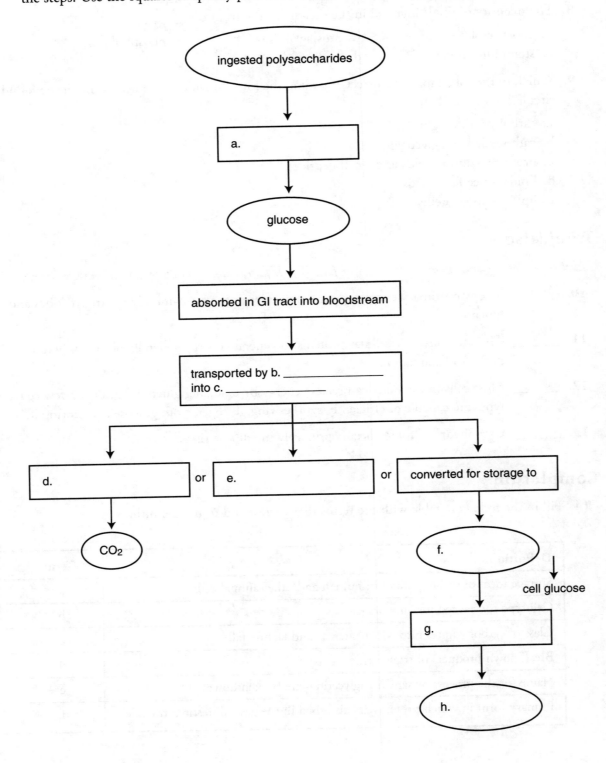

Sequencing

16. List the statements below in the order in which they occur during triglyceride metabolism.

    a. Stored triglycerides can be broken down into glycerol and fatty acids.

    b. Triglycerides located in chylomicrons are absorbed into lymphatic capillaries in the gastrointestinal tract.

    c. Fatty acids within cells are oxidized for energy or are combined with glycerol to form triglycerides, which are stored in the cells.

    d. Triglycerides enter the bloodstream.

    e. Triglycerides arriving at cells are broken down into fatty acids and glycerol by lipoprotein lipase.

    f. Fatty acids enter nearby cells; most glycerol molecules are eventually metabolized by the liver.

    Sequence: _____

ENERGY BALANCE

Matching

17. Match the following definitions to the terms listed: energy content (EC), energy intake (EI), mechanical work (MW), chemical work (CW), transport work (TW), and metabolic rate (MR). Not all terms will be used.

    a. _____ cellular energy-requiring processes that are used to form chemical bonds

    b. _____ total energy content of all the nutrients absorbed by a person

    c. _____ cellular energy-requiring processes that use intracellular protein filaments to generate movement

    d. _____ the quantity of energy released from a molecule when it is oxidized

    e. _____ the amount of energy expended by the body per unit time

Completion

Fill in the blanks to complete the following narrative.

18. The body uses the energy released during catabolic reactions to produce **(a)** or perform cellular **(b)**. About **(c)** percent of the energy in consumed nutrients is used for **(a)** production, while **(d)** percent is used to synthesize **(e)**, which is used to perform cellular **(b)**.

    a. _____   d. _____

    b. _____   e. _____

    c. _____

Multiple Choice

Select the best answer from the choices given.

19. Which of the following statements is **not** true regarding the basal metabolic rate?

    a. It is a measure of the rate of energy expenditure of a person under certain controlled conditions.
    b. It represents the energy required by the body to perform the basic physiologic processes that maintain life such as pumping blood and transporting ions.
    c. It is measured immediately following exercise.
    d. It is measured following a fast of at least 12 hours.
    e. It is measured when a person is awake.

20. Which of the following is **not** a factor that can influence a person's metabolic rate?

    a. age
    b. gender
    c. muscular activity
    d. environmental temperature
    e. eye color

21. Energy output of the body is equivalent to _____.

    a. work performed + heat released
    b. work performed − heat released
    c. energy input − (work performed + heat released)
    d. energy input + (work performed + heat released)
    e. energy input + (work performed − heat released)

22. Which of the following is **not** true of a negative energy balance?

    a. It is created when the rate of energy intake is less than the rate of energy output.
    b. It results in a net synthesis of stored macromolecules.
    c. It is correlated with a decrease in the quantity of energy stored in the body.
    d. It results in weight loss.
    e. It results in the breakdown of glycogen and triglycerides.

23. The system of the body primarily responsible for regulating energy balance, ensuring that a steady supply of nutrients is always available to body cells to meet their energy needs, is the

    _____.

    a. digestive system
    b. nervous system
    c. cardiovascular system
    d. endocrine system
    e. urinary system

True/False

Label the following statements as true (T) or false (F). If false, change the statement to make it true.

24. _____ Most of the expenditure of energy accounted for by the basal metabolic rate is the result of metabolic activity within the digestive system.

25. _____ The amount of energy stored in the body is equivalent to the difference between energy input and energy output.

26. _____ A positive energy balance in the body will usually result in weight gain.

Short Answer

Answer the following questions in 1–4 sentences.

27. The pool of nutrients within cells and the bloodstream, which cells use to generate the energy they need to function, can be replenished in two ways. What are these two mechanisms?

28. When basal metabolic rate is estimated in humans, what is measured, and under what conditions?

29. When can it be said that the body is in energy balance?

Challenge Question

30. Why is the basal metabolic rate expressed as the rate of energy expenditure per unit body weight?

Clinical Question

31. You've been telling your parents recently what you've learned about energy balance in your physiology course, and your mom asks you to tell her how she can achieve a negative energy balance in her body so she can lose weight. What would you tell her?

ENERGY METABOLISM DURING THE ABSORPTIVE AND POSTABSORPTIVE STATES

Multiple Choice

Select the best answer from the choices given.

32. Which of the following statements is **not** true of the postabsorptive state?

    a. It is the time between meals during which nutrients are not being absorbed.
    b. During this state, glucose is used as the primary energy source by cells of the central nervous system, but cells elsewhere in the body use other energy sources, primarily fatty acids, to conserve glucose for the central nervous system (glucose sparing).
    c. During this state, the rate of energy expenditure in the body exceeds energy intake.
    d. During this state, the body is in positive energy balance.
    e. During this state, energy stores are mobilized to provide an energy source for cells.

33. The absorptive state typically lasts _____.

    a. as long as a meal lasts
    b. about 3–4 hours following a meal
    c. about 6–8 hours following a meal
    d. as long as a person is asleep
    e. indefinitely; it is a continual process that does not correspond to eating or sleep

34. Which of the following molecules is/are the **primary** source(s) of energy used by the cells of the body during the absorptive state?

    a. fatty acids   c. glucose   e. triglycerides
    b. glycerol   d. amino acids

35. Which of the following is **not** true about the energy reserves of the body?

    a. The term *energy reserves* refers to the energy stored in the body as macromolecules.
    b. Energy can be stored in the body as carbohydrate, fat, or protein.
    c. Triglyceride stores in the body account for 75–80% of the total energy reserves.
    d. Glycogen stores account for less than 1% of the body's total energy reserves.
    e. The energy stored in protein can maintain cellular functioning for about two months.

36. The synthesis of glucose from non-carbohydrate sources such as amino acids or glycerol is referred to as _____.

    a. glycogenolysis   c. gluconeogenesis   e. lipolysis
    b. glycogenesis   d. glucogenolysis

37. Which of the following is **not** true of the liver?

    a. Liver cells form and store glycogen during the absorptive state.
    b. The liver serves as the primary site of gluconeogenesis during the postabsorptive state.
    c. The liver serves as the primary source of plasma glucose during the postabsorptive state.
    d. The liver converts fatty acids to ketone bodies during the absorptive state.
    e. The liver converts fatty acids to triglycerides during the absorptive state.

Matching

38. Match each of the events listed below to whether it occurs during the absorptive (A) or postabsorptive (PA) state.

a. _____ Amino acids are used for protein synthesis in all cell types, and can be converted to keto acids in the liver.

b. _____ Skeletal muscle cells convert glucose to glycogen for storage.

c. _____ Triglycerides are broken down to fatty acids and glycerol within adipocytes.

d. _____ Glucose is oxidized for energy by all body cells.

e. _____ Proteins within skeletal muscle cells are broken down to amino acids, which are transported to the liver to undergo gluconeogenesis.

True/False

Label the following statements as true (T) *or false* (F). *If false, change the statement to make it true.*

39. _____ The absorptive state is the time following a meal during which the ingested nutrients are absorbed from the gastrointestinal tract.

40. _____ Most body cells catabolize proteins for energy only under extreme conditions (such as starvation).

41. _____ The absorptive state is primarily catabolic, while the postabsorptive state is primarily anabolic.

42. _____ The majority of the body's total stored glycogen is located in skeletal muscle cells.

43. _____ The amount of glycogen stored by skeletal muscle and liver cells is enough to supply the body with energy for a few days.

44. _____ Any nutrient absorbed in excess of the body's needs could be converted to and stored as triglyceride.

45. _____ During prolonged fasting, cells of the central nervous system can use fatty acids for energy.

Completion

Fill in the blanks to complete the following narrative.

46. Triglycerides synthesized in the liver are transported to adipocytes within particles called **(a)**. Once these particles reach the cells, a plasma-membrane-associated enzyme called **(b)** catabolizes triglycerides at the surface of the particles into **(c)** and glycerol. The **(c)** then enter the cells by **(d)** where they are used for **(e)** or are converted into **(f)** for storage.

a. _____   d. _____

b. _____   e. _____

c. _____   f. _____

Short Answer

Answer the following questions in 1–4 sentences.

47. What happens to fats, amino acids, and excess glucose absorbed during the absorptive state?

48. A primary function of the postabsorptive state is to maintain plasma glucose levels. Why is this an extremely important function?

Challenge Questions

49. Why is the glucose formed from glycogen within skeletal muscle cells used for energy only by those cells?

50. Why would storing energy as carbohydrate or protein increase the body's weight more than storing that same amount of energy as fat?

REGULATION OF ABSORPTIVE AND POSTABSORPTIVE METABOLISM

Completion

Fill in the blanks to complete the following narrative describing the roles of insulin and glucagon in regulating absorptive and postabsorptive metabolism.

51. During the absorptive state, the secretion of **(a)** from the **(b)** cells of the **(c)** increases, while **(d)** secretion from the **(e)** cells of the **(c)** increases during the postabsorptive state. These two hormones work antagonistically to help the body regulate its metabolic responses to the absorptive and postabsorptive states, with insulin promoting **(f)** metabolic reactions and

glucagon promoting **(g)** metabolic reactions. One of the most important molecules, whose plasma level is regulated by the antagonistic actions of these two hormones, is **(h)**.

a. _____   e. _____

b. _____   f. _____

c. _____   g. _____

d. _____   h. _____

Multiple Choice

Select the best answer from the choices given.

52. Which of the following stimuli normally inhibits insulin secretion?

    a. the presence of food in the gastrointestinal tract

    b. a decrease in the number of glucose receptors on the surface of cells

    c. a decrease in plasma amino acid levels

    d. decreased gluconeogenesis in the liver

    e. increased parasympathetic nervous activity

53. Which of the following is **not** a stimulus for glucagon secretion?

    a. increased sympathetic nervous activity

    b. increased levels of circulating triglycerides

    c. increased plasma amino acid levels

    d. decreased blood glucose levels

    e. increased levels of circulating epinephrine

54. Which of the following is **not** true of the effect of insulin on cells?

    a. It can trigger the insertion of stored GLUT 4 glucose receptors into the plasma membrane.

    b. It can stimulate the synthesis of new GLUT 4 glucose receptors.

    c. It stimulates the uptake of glucose by most cells of the body by increasing the number of glucose transport proteins in the plasma membranes of the cells.

    d. It has little effect on glucose uptake by exercising skeletal muscle cells.

    e. It increases the permeability of liver and central nervous system neurons to glucose.

55. Hyperglycemia refers to a _____ than normal fasting blood glucose level, and is characterized by a blood level _____.

    a. higher : greater than 140 mg/dL   d. lower : less than 100 mg/dL

    b. higher : greater than 100 mg/dL   e. lower : less than 60 mg/dL

    c. higher : greater than 200 mg/dL

56. Which of the following is **not** true of the actions of insulin on the body?

    a. Insulin decreases plasma glucose concentration.

    b. Insulin promotes the uptake of glucose by cells.

    c. Insulin promotes the breakdown of lipids.

    d. Insulin suppresses gluconeogenesis.

    e. Insulin controls plasma glucose concentration by negative feedback.

True/False

Label the following statements as true (T) or false (F). If false, change the statement to make it true.

57. _____ The role of the sympathetic division of the nervous system in controlling metabolism helps the body adapt to the postabsorptive state, but is **most** important in helping the body respond to stress.

58. _____ The decreased plasma glucose levels that occur during the absorptive state act directly on the beta cells of the pancreas to increase glucagon secretion.

59. _____ Increased plasma amino acid levels can stimulate the secretion of both insulin and glucagon.

60. _____ If plasma glucose concentration decreases, glucagon secretion decreases.

61. _____ Both insulin and glucagon control plasma glucose concentration via negative feedback.

62. _____ Insulin promotes the catabolism of energy stores and inhibits energy storage.

63. _____ Insulin must be present in the blood in order for growth hormone to work normally.

64. _____ In general, the stimuli that trigger the secretion of insulin will inhibit glucagon secretion.

Matching

65. Match each of the following metabolic effects to whether they are produced primarily by insulin (I) or glucagon (G).

    a. _____ stimulates triglyceride synthesis and storage

    b. _____ promotes glycogen synthesis and storage

    c. _____ increases gluconeogenesis

    d. _____ promotes glucose uptake by most cells

    e. _____ increases glycogenolysis

    f. _____ increases amino acid uptake by cells

    g. _____ increases proteolysis

Short Answer

Answer the following questions in 1–4 sentences.

66. Insulin affects exercising skeletal muscle differently from resting skeletal muscle. Explain this differential effect.

67. Explain the role of the sympathetic division of the nervous system during stress in terms of its effect on plasma glucose, fatty acid, and glycerol levels.

Challenge Questions

68. Explain why little change in plasma glucose concentration occurs following a meal rich in proteins but low in carbohydrates, but following a meal rich in both proteins and carbohydrates blood glucose concentration will initially rise and then fall back to normal.

69. Why is it advantageous to the body that glucose uptake by cells of the central nervous system is not affected by insulin?

Clinical Questions

70. What types of symptoms would you expect to be associated with hypoglycemia, and why?

71. The three classic symptoms of diabetes mellitus (although they do not occur in all cases) are polydipsia (excessive thirst), polyphagia (excessive hunger), and polyuria (increased frequency and amount of urination). Explain why these symptoms would occur in untreated diabetes mellitus.

HORMONAL REGULATION OF GROWTH

Multiple Choice

Select the best answer from the choices given.

72. During periods of growth, increases in height are usually the result of _____.

    a. increases in the length of the hip and neck bones
    b. increases in the length of the leg bones
    c. increases in the length of the leg bones and vertebral column
    d. increases in the length of the leg bones and arm bones
    e. increases in the width of the hip bones and leg bones

73. Which of the following is **not** an effect of growth hormone on the body?

    a. It stimulates protein synthesis.
    b. It stimulates cell division.
    c. It increases the size of individual organs.
    d. It causes the elongation of bones.
    e. It increases the deposition of adipose tissue.

74. Which of the following is **not** an indirect mechanism by which growth hormone affects growth?

    a. It increases the plasma concentration of glucose.
    b. It decreases the plasma concentration of fatty acids.
    c. It stimulates gluconeogenesis in the liver.
    d. It inhibits glucose uptake by adipocytes and skeletal muscle cells.
    e. It promotes the uptake of amino acids by cells.

75. _____ refers to an increase in cell size, while _____ refers to an increase in cell number.

    a. Hyperplasia : hypertrophy
    b. Hyperglycemia : hyperkalemia
    c. Hypoplasia : atrophy
    d. Hypertrophy : hyperplasia
    e. Atrophy : hypoplasia

76. Bones lose their ability to increase in length when _____.

    a. the epiphyseal plate closes
    b. cartilage in the epiphyseal plate is completely replaced by bone tissue
    c. bone in the epiphyseal plate is completely replaced by cartilage
    d. a and b are correct
    e. a and c are correct

Matching

77. Match the following terms and definitions: osteoid, osteocytes, osteoblasts, osteoclasts, calcification, resorption, and deposition.

a. _____ bone-forming cells

b. _____ bone-destroying cells

c. _____ organic component of bone tissue

d. _____ process by which new, organic bone tissue is added to bones

e. _____ process by which old/damaged bone tissue is removed from bones

f. _____ mature bone cells

g. _____ process by which calcium phosphate is deposited into bones

True/False

Label the following statements as true (T) *or false* (F). *If false, change the statement to make it true.*

78. _____ Androgens cause the atrophy of skeletal muscle during puberty.

79. _____ Normal body growth requires the actions of growth hormone, thyroid hormones, sex hormones, and insulin.

80. _____ Growth hormone levels usually increase after puberty.

81. _____ In children, growth hormone causes bones and soft tissues to grow, while in adults it maintains bone mass and lean body mass.

Completion

Fill in the blanks to complete the following narrative.

82. Growth hormone is secreted from the **(a)** gland in response to the secretion of **(b)** from the hypothalamus, and its secretion is inhibited by the release of **(c)** from the hypothalamus. Growth hormone can also inhibit its own secretion via the effects of **(d)** on the hypothalamus.

a. _____   c. _____

b. _____   d. _____

Short Answer

Answer the following question in 1–4 sentences.

83. What affect do glucocorticoids have on growth?

Challenge Questions

84. Why is the growth spurt that occurs during puberty followed by the cessation of bone growth in length?

85. What impact, if any, does the nutritional status of the body have on growth?

86. Could a prolonged shortage of sleep during adolescence affect a person's ultimate height? Explain.

Clinical Question

87. Differentiate between the clinical disorders *gigantism* and *acromegaly*, including the cause of the disorders and the age at which the disorders develop, as well as the typical clinical manifestations that would occur with each.

THYROID HORMONES

Multiple Choice

Select the best answer from the choices given.

88. Which of the following dietary substances is a component of thyroid hormones?

a. calcium   c. iodine   e. manganese
b. sodium   d. potassium

89. Which of the following hormones are considered the "thyroid hormones" (those that affect basal metabolic rate)?

    a. parathyroid hormone, tetraiodothyronine (T_4), triiodothyronine (T_3)
    b. calcitonin, T_4, T_3
    c. calcitonin and parathyroid hormone
    d. T_4 and T_3
    e. insulin, growth hormone, calcitonin

90. The precursor molecule for thyroid hormones is _____.

    a. tyrosine
    b. thyroglobulin
    c. parathyroid hormone
    d. thyroxine-binding globulin
    e. calcitonin

91. The hormone that binds to receptors on thyroid gland cells, putting events into motion that ultimately result in the secretion of thyroid hormones from the thyroid gland, is _____.

    a. TSH (thyroid-stimulating hormone)
    b. TRH (thyrotropin-releasing hormone)
    c. T_4
    d. T_3
    e. calcitonin

92. Of the substances listed below, which are protein carriers that can transport thyroid hormones through the blood?

    1. thyroglobulin
    2. thyroxine-binding globulin
    3. transthyrethin
    4. gamma globulin
    5. albumin

    a. 1, 2, 3
    b. 1, 2, 3, 4, 5
    c. 2, 3, 4, 5
    d. 3, 4, 5
    e. 2, 3, 5

93. Other than a low thyroid hormone level in the blood, the only other stimulus for TRH secretion is _____.

    a. exposure to hot temperatures
    b. exposure to cold temperatures
    c. exposure to iodine
    d. exposure to calcitonin
    e. exposure to stress

94. Target cell receptors for thyroid hormone are located _____.

    a. on the plasma membrane
    b. in the mitochondria
    c. in the endoplasmic reticulum
    d. in the nucleus
    e. in lysosomes

95. Which of the following is **not** a **direct** action of thyroid hormones?

    a. They increase the body's basal metabolic rate.
    b. They increase the rate of oxygen consumption at rest.
    c. They enhance the ability of cells to respond to sympathetic stimulation.
    d. They increase the generation of heat in the body.
    e. They increase the rate of activity of sodium/potassium pumps in the cells.

96. Which of the following events would occur in response to a lower than normal concentration of thyroid hormones in the blood?

a. increased glycogenesis and protein synthesis
b. increased glycogenolysis and protein catabolism
c. increased gluconeogenesis
d. increased ketone synthesis
e. increased lipolysis

Matching

97. Match the hormone in the following list to the gland that secretes it: thyroid gland (T), hypothalamus (H), anterior pituitary gland (APG), posterior pituitary gland (PPG), and parathyroid glands (PG). Answers may be used more than once or not at all.

a. _____ thyrotropin releasing hormone (TRH)

b. _____ calcitonin

c. _____ T_4

d. _____ T_3

e. _____ thyroid-stimulating hormone (TSH)

True/False

Label the following statements as true (T) *or false* (F). *If false, change the statement to make it true.*

98. _____ Under normal conditions, thyroid hormone levels in the blood are fairly constant because the primary control of their secretion occurs via negative feedback.

99. _____ T_3 and T_4 must be released from thyroglobulin molecules by lysosomal enzymes before they can enter the blood.

100. _____ TRH secretion is stimulated by stress.

101. _____ The binding of thyroid hormones to cellular receptors alters the rate of transcription of DNA → mRNA within the cell, which ultimately alters protein synthesis within the target cell.

102. _____ Thyroid hormones increase the metabolic rate in all tissues of the body.

103. _____ Untreated hypothyroidism during infancy can lead to mental retardation.

Sequencing

104. List the following events in the order in which they occur.

a. most of the T_4 in the plasma is converted to T_3
b. TSH is secreted
c. TRH is secreted
d. a phagosome containing thyroglobulin fuses with a lysosome
e. T_3 and T_4 diffuse from the thyroid cells into the bloodstream

Sequence: _____

Short Answer

Answer the following question in 1–4 sentences.

105. What is the term for the conversion of T_4 to T_3, and why is this process advantageous to the body?

GLUCOCORTICOIDS

Completion

Fill in the blanks to complete the following narrative.

106. Glucocorticoids are secreted by the **(a)**. The primary glucocorticoid secreted is **(b),** which is secreted in spurts in a pattern associated with the sleep-wake cycle known as a **(c)**, and is also secreted in response to **(d)**. Along with glucocorticoid secretion, other responses typically occur in response to **(d)**, which are collectively known as the **(e)**.

a. _____   d. _____

b. _____   e. _____

c. _____

Multiple Choice

Select the best answer from the choices given.

107. Which of the following is **not** a physiologic effect of glucocorticoids?

a. They are required for growth hormone secretion.
b. They are required in order for blood vessels to respond normally to vasoconstrictive stimuli.
c. At higher than resting levels, they stimulate lipolysis and gluconeogenesis.
d. At higher than resting levels, they decrease the uptake of glucose by cells.
e. At higher than resting levels, they promote protein synthesis.

108. Which of the following is/are pharmacological effects of glucocorticoids?

1. They inhibit inflammation.
2. They inhibit allergic reactions.
3. They promote energy mobilization.
4. They promote glucose sparing.

a. 1   c. 1, 2, 3, 4   e. 1, 4
b. 1, 2   d. 2, 3

109. Which of the following is **not** a stimulus that could trigger cortisol secretion?

    a. surgery
    b. strenuous exercise
    c. exposure to a moderate temperature for a long period of time
    d. burns
    e. infection

110. Which of the following events are part of the general adaptation syndrome?

    1. increased secretion of cortisol by the adrenal cortex
    2. increased activity of the sympathetic division of the nervous system
    3. increased secretion of epinephrine by the adrenal medulla
    4. increased secretion of antidiuretic hormone by the posterior pituitary
    5. increased release of renin by the kidneys

    a. 1, 2, 3   c. 1, 3, 5   e. 1, 2, 5
    b. 2, 3, 4, 5   d. 1, 2, 3, 4, 5

True/False

Label the following statements as true (T) or false (F). If false, change the statement to make it true.

111. _____ Increased secretion of cortisol will decrease the plasma glucose level.

112. _____ Increased secretion of cortisol will strengthen the responses of the immune system.

113. _____ Both physical and emotional stress can trigger cortisol secretion.

Short Answer

Answer the following question in 1–4 sentences.

114. Why are glucocorticoids administered following an organ transplant?

Challenge Question

115. Why are glucocorticoids necessary for survival during prolonged fasting?

Clinical Question

116. What is the cause of Cushing's syndrome? List five clinical manifestations of this disorder.

Concept Map

117. Fill in the blanks in the following concept map depicting the sequence of events that results in or inhibits glucocorticoid secretion. Hormone names should be placed in the circles, and the glands from which the hormones are secreted designated in the squares. The dashed line indicates the mechanism that inhibits glucocorticoid secretion.

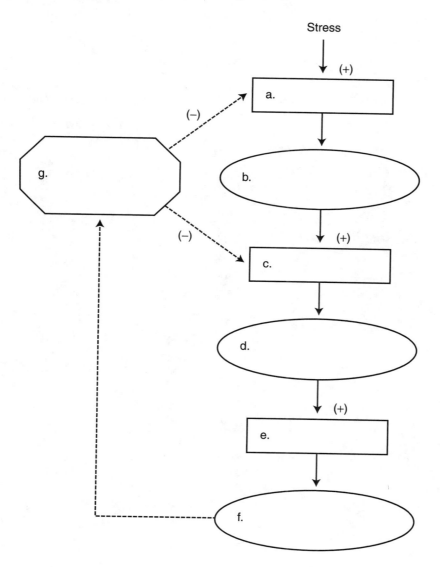

21 The Reproductive System

Objectives

We recommend that you review the **Objectives** for this chapter, found on p. 670 of *Principles of Human Physiology*. The **Objectives** outline what you should know from each chapter.

Key Terms

acrosome
amnion
androgen
blood-testis barrier
bulbourethral gland
cervix
chorion
corpus luteum
diploid
dominant follicle
embryo
endometrium
epididymis
erection
estrogen
fertilization
fetus
follicle
follicle-stimulating hormone (FSH)
follicular phase
gamete
gametogenesis
gonadotropin releasing hormone (GnRH)

gonadotropin
gonad
Graafian follicle
granulosa cell
haploid
implantation
inhibin
lactation
Leydig cell
luteal phase
luteinizing hormone (LH)
mammary gland
meiosis
menopause
menstrual cycle
Müllerian-inhibiting substance (MIS)
oogenesis
ovary
ovulation
ovum
oxytocin
parturition
penis
placenta

placental lactogen
progesterone
prolactin
prostate gland
scrotum
seminal vesicle
seminiferous tubule
Sertoli cell
sex hormone
spermatogenesis
spermatozoa
testes
umbilical cord
uterine cycle
uterine tube
uterus
vagina
vas deferens
vulva
zygote

AN OVERVIEW OF REPRODUCTIVE PHYSIOLOGY

Matching

1. Match each of the following structures or chemicals associated with the male reproductive system with its appropriate description below: androgen (AG), Müllerian ducts (MD), Müllerian-inhibiting substance (MIS), secondary sex characteristics (SSC), spermatozoa (SZ), srY gene (srY), testes (TS), Wolffian ducts (WD).

   a. _____ a male gamete

   b. _____ rudimentary female reproductive systems

   c. _____ sex hormone secreted by the testes after puberty

   d. _____ genetic molecule that determines whether the fetus will be male or female

   e. _____ chemical that operates in conjunction with testosterone to develop the fetus into a male

   f. _____ rudimentary male reproductive systems

   g. _____ primary reproductive organs in males

   h. _____ develop during puberty

Completion

Fill in the blanks to complete the following narrative.

2. Human reproduction involves the fundamental processes of gametogenesis, **(a)**, pregnancy, and **(b)**. Reproductive ability develops during **(c)**, during which the reproductive organs mature, gametogenesis begins, and **(d)** sex characteristics develop. **(e)** are able to reproduce continually through adulthood, but in **(f)** reproductive capacity is lost at **(g)**.

   a. _____ e. _____

   b. _____ f. _____

   c. _____ g. _____

   d. _____

Short Answer

Answer the following questions in 1–4 sentences.

3. Distinguish between autosomes and sex chromosomes.

4. Why are the testes considered to have endocrine tissue?

5. Describe the number and arrangement of chromosomes in a gamete compared to the chromosome number and arrangement in a zygote.

Multiple Choice

Select the best answer from the choices given.

6. Which of the following is true about a zygote?

    a. It is haploid.

    b. It has 22 autosomes and 1 sex chromosome.

    c. It has 44 autosomes and 2 sex chromosomes.

    d. It has no sex chromosomes.

    e. It is also known as a germ cell.

7. Which of the following is true about gametic crossing over?

    a. It occurs in the zygote.

    b. Maternal and paternal chromosomes exchange genetic information.

    c. It can occur among any two chromosomes during meiosis.

    d. It always occurs between the X and Y chromosomes.

    e. It happens during meiosis II.

8. Which of the following hormones is primarily produced in the ovaries?

    a. testosterone   d. estradiol

    b. androgens   e. aldosterone

    c. Müllerian-inhibiting substance

9. Which of the following is a result of gametic independent assortment?

    a. All spermatozoa are identical.

    b. Meiosis II is halted.

    c. It increases genetic variation in the offspring.

    d. The resulting spermatozoa each contain 46 chromosomes.

    e. Sister chromatids exchange genetic information.

10. What is the alternative name for gestation?

    a. fertilization   c. sex differentiation   e. sex determination

    b. parturition   d. pregnancy

11. What role does the srY gene play in the reproductive cycle?
    a. It determines whether the fetus will be a male or female.
    b. It transforms Müllerian ducts into ovaries.
    c. It regulates hormones of the ovaries.
    d. It influences the release of testosterone from the adrenal medulla.
    e. It acts directly on the hypothalamus to influence the "sex drive."

True/False

Label the following statements as true (T) *or false* (F). *If false, change the statement to make it true.*

12. _____   Parturition is also known as birth.

13. _____   After normal meiosis, each egg and sperm contain only one sex chromosome.

14. _____   Most egg and sperm cells are fully mature just before puberty.

15. _____   The reproductive tract is present only in the female.

Sequencing

16. Place the following stages of meiosis in the correct sequence:
    a. Homologous chromosomes separate into two different cells.
    b. The original DNA is replicated, forming sister chromatids.
    c. Homologous chromosomes group together.
    d. Sister chromatids separate into two different cells.
    e. Crossing over may occur.
    f. A diploid germ cell contains 46 unduplicated chromosomes.
    g. Pairs of homologous chromosomes line up along a plane, bisecting the cell.

    Sequence: _____

Clinical Question

17. Down syndrome (also known as Trisomy 21) occurs in about 0.5% of all conceptions and in 1/900 live births. It is the leading cause of childhood mental retardation and occurs as a result of an extra number 21 chromosome present in the diploid cells of the offspring. Explain how an extra chromosome might occur in the zygote.

Challenge Questions

18. Describe the roles of testosterone and Müllerian-inhibiting substance (MIS) in sex differentiation.

19. Describe the reproductive capacity of males and female after puberty.

THE MALE REPRODUCTIVE SYSTEM

Matching

20. Match each of the following hormones with its description or function below: follicle-stimulating hormone (FSH); gonadotropin releasing hormone (GnRH); inhibin (INH); luteinizing hormone (LH); testosterone (TST).

a. _____ This hormone is produced in the anterior pituitary and targets the Sertoli cells to promote spermatogenesis.

b. _____ This hormone targets the Leydig cells and leads to testosterone secretion.

c. _____ This hormone is produced in the hypothalamus.

d. _____ This hormone promotes secondary sex characteristics.

e. _____ This hormone is produced in the Sertoli cells and suppresses the release of FSH.

Completion

Fill in the blanks to complete the following narrative.

21. The male reproductive system includes the **(a)**, external genitalia, the reproductive tract, and **(b)**. Sperm are formed in the testes in the **(c)**, which are lined by **(d)** cells. Reproductive function in males is controlled by **(e)** and other hormones, including gonadotrophs from the **(f)** and the hypophysiotropic hormone **(g)**.

a. _____   e. _____

b. _____   f. _____

c. _____   g. _____

d. _____

Short Answer

Answer the following questions in 1–4 sentences.

22. Describe the blood-testis barrier and explain its immunological significance.

23. Explain the role of nitric oxide in achieving an erection in males.

24. Sertoli cells are sometimes called "nurse cells." Explain why.

Multiple Choice

Select the best answer from the choices given.

25. What is the function of the fluid secreted from the seminal vesicles?
    a. It contains citrate, which the sperm use as an energy source.
    b. It neutralizes the acidic environment encountered in the vagina.
    c. It assists in producing spermatozoa under the influence of testosterone.
    d. It acts as a lubricant.
    e. It suppresses the motility of the sperm cells.

26. Initially, an enlarged prostate can lead to which of the following conditions?
    a. difficulty in urination
    b. inability to produce sperm cells
    c. inability to produce testosterone
    d. inability to produce androgen-binding protein
    e. a breakdown of the blood-testis barrier

27. Which structure in the sperm cell directly enables the sperm to fuse with the egg?
    a. centriole   c. acrosome   e. midpiece
    b. microtubules   d. tail

28. Sven produces lower-than-normal levels of testosterone at puberty. Which of the following symptoms is he likely to have?

   a. reduced muscle and bone mass
   b. a deeper voice
   c. increased facial hair
   d. increased oil production in the skin
   e. increased spermatogenesis

29. Which of the following molecules act as an energy source for swimming sperm cells?

   a. ketone bodies
   b. lipids
   c. carbohydrates
   d. choline
   e. ATP

30. Which of the following processes is involved in the positive feedback loop of an erection?

   a. increased activity of sympathetic neurons to penis
   b. decreased activity of parasympathetic neurons to penis
   c. compression of veins draining erectile tissue
   d. release of GnRH from the anterior pituitary
   e. activation of inhibin

True/False

Label the following statements as true (T) *or false* (F). *If false, change the statement to make it true.*

31. _____ LH stimulates the secretion of androgens.

32. _____ FSH is produced in the hypothalamus.

33. _____ The bulbourethral glands produce secretions that aid in nutrition of the sperm.

34. _____ Steroid hormones are hydrophobic and, therefore, they can easily diffuse through the Leydig cells.

35. _____ The parts of the body associated with sexual arousal that are sensitive to mechanical stimulation are known as erogenous zones.

Sequencing

36. Place the following structures of the male reproductive tract and accessory glands in the proper order in which sperm cells travel from their site of production to ejaculation.

   a. vas deferens
   b. prostate
   c. urethra of penis
   d. seminiferous tubule
   e. seminal vesicle
   f. bulbourethral gland
   g. epididymis

   Sequence: _____

Labeling

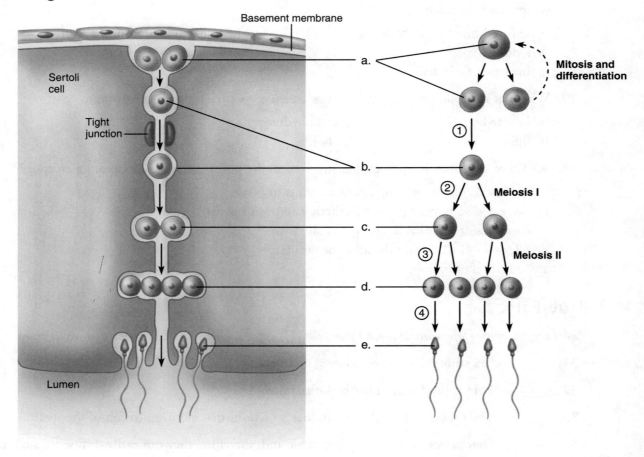

FIGURE 21.1

37. In the space below, label each of the letters (a–e) in Figure 21.1 that correspond to the cells present in the testes. Indicate whether each cell is haploid (n) or diploid (2n).

Clinical Questions

38. A couple, Paul and Prudy, have been trying to conceive a child for six years. After extensive testing it is determined that Prudy is reproductively normal. Paul, however, is an avid bike rider, often wearing tight nylon biking shorts. He works in a factory that has consistently elevated air temperatures, and he wears tight briefs. Explain one possible cause for the couple's infertility. What action would you recommend the couple take?

39. Mike and Beth have three children and have decided that Mike will have a vasectomy to prevent further pregnancies. Mike arrives at the clinic and expresses his concern that his ejaculate volume will be greatly diminished due to this procedure. What do you tell Mike?

Challenge Questions

40. Some body builders use anabolic steroids (chemicals similar to testosterone) to obtain substantial muscle mass. However, use of steroids can have severe side effects. Explain why anabolic steroid use leads to hypogonadism in males, while females may have withdrawal of the frontal hair line, male pattern baldness, lowering of the voice, and increased facial hair growth.

41. During spermatogenesis, why is it important for the spermatogonia to undergo mitosis *before* they begin meiosis?

Concept Map

42. Fill in the blanks in the following concept map of hormonal regulation of reproductive function of males.

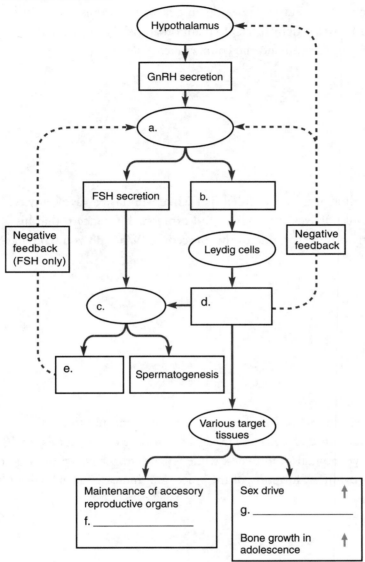

THE FEMALE REPRODUCTIVE SYSTEM

Matching

43. Match each of the following hormones with its description or function below: estrogen (EST); follicle-stimulating hormone (FSH); luteinizing hormone (LH); progesterone (PRG).

a. _____ This hormone causes the follicle to increase in size.

b. _____ This hormone causes granulosa cells and theca cells to begin to differentiate.

c. _____ This hormone promotes the development of female secondary sex characteristics.

d. _____ This hormone promotes growth of glandular tissue in breasts.

Completion

Fill in the blanks to complete the following narrative.

44. The female reproductive system includes the **(a)**, the reproductive tract, and the external genitalia. The menstrual cycle, which lasts about **(b)** days, is marked by cyclic changes in **(c)** and ovarian hormone secretion, and begins with **(d)**, the shedding of tissue and blood from the endometrium. Ova develop from a set of **(e)** cells whose number is fixed at **(f)** and do not fully mature until **(g)** has occurred.

a. _____   e. _____

b. _____   f. _____

c. _____   g. _____

d. _____

Short Answer

Answer the following questions in 1–4 sentences.

45. Describe meiotic arrest in the human female.

46. Describe the benefits of the acidic environment in the vagina. Why aren't all of the sperm killed by these acidic conditions?

Multiple Choice

Select the best answer from the choices given.

47. Which of the following hormone levels peaks prior to ovulation?

    a. progesterone   c. LH   e. inhibin

    b. estrogen   d. FSH

48. Which of the following hormone levels peaks after ovulation?

    a. estrogen   c. progesterone   e. LH

    b. inhibin   d. FSH

49. Which of the following pairs of hormone levels peak on the day of ovulation?

    a. LH and FSH
        d. LH and estrogen
    b. estrogen and progesterone
        e. FSH and inhibin
    c. LH and inhibin

50. What is the term used for the degeneration of germ cells in the ovary?

    a. endometriosis
        c. menstruation
        e. atresia
    b. ovulation
        d. menopause

51. Collectively, the female external genitalia are referred to as which of the following?

    a. vulva
        c. uterus
        e. cervix
    b. vagina
        d. mons pubis

52. Where does fertilization normally occur?

    a. cervix
        c. fallopian tube
        e. ovary
    b. vagina
        d. uterus

True/False

Label the following statements as true (T) *or false* (F). *If false, change the statement to make it true.*

53. _____ The proliferation phase of the menstrual cycle is marked by the onset of menstruation.

54. _____ The cervix is also known as the *neck* of the uterus.

55. _____ The Graafian follicle helps to maintain the endometrium when implantation occurs.

Sequencing

56. Place the following events of the ovarian cycle in the correct sequence.

    a. A dominant follicle develops.
    b. Ovulation occurs.
    c. The oocyte enters the uterine tube.
    d. The follicles begin to develop, the oocyte grows in size, and the granulosa cells proliferate.
    e. Meiosis I occurs and Graafian follicles are present.
    f. The corpus luteum is formed.
    g. The zona pellucida forms between the oocyte and granulosa cells, and the antrum forms.

Sequence: _____

Labeling

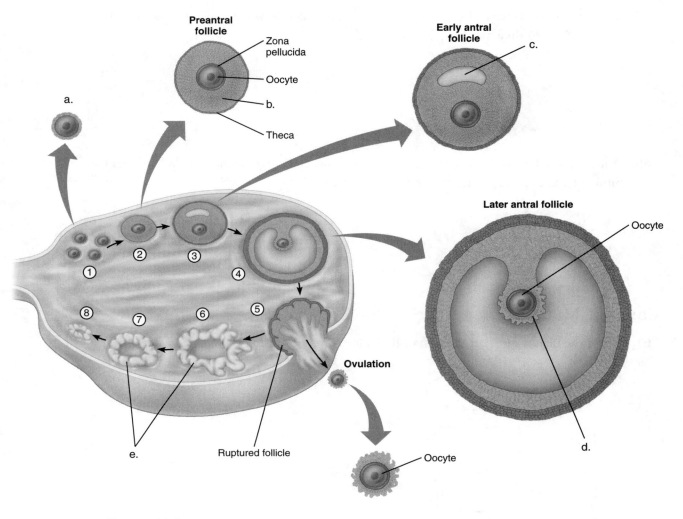

FIGURE 21.2

57. In the space below, identify the structures (a–e) in Figure 21.2.

Clinical Question

58. At menopause women may require estrogen replacement therapy to combat osteoporosis. Explain why.

Challenge Questions

59. What criterion do physiologists and clinicians use to decide when a female's menstrual cycle begins? Why do they use this criterion?

60. When do the human male sperm cells *begin* meiosis and *complete* meiosis? When does the human female egg *begin* meiosis and *complete* meiosis?

Concept Map

61. Fill in the blanks of the regulation of hormone secretion during the *late follicular* phase.

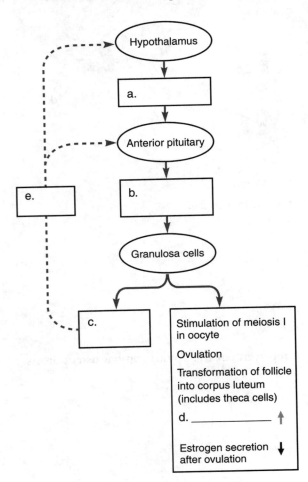

FERTILIZATION, IMPLANTATION, AND PREGNANCY, AND PARTURITION AND LACTATION

Matching

62. Match each of the following hormones with its description or function below: estrogen (EST); human chorionic gonadotropin (hCG); placental lactogen (PLG); progesterone (PRG); prolactin (PRL); oxytocin (OXT). Each statement may have more than one right answer.

a. _____ This hormone maintains the corpus luteum during the first three months of pregnancy.

b. _____ This hormone prepares the breasts for lactation.

c. _____ This hormone works with estrogen to promote breast development and mobilize energy stores.

d. _____ This hormone stimulates uterine contractions and aids in milk ejection.

e. _____ After parturition this hormone stimulates milk production.

f. _____ This hormone inhibits uterine contractions during pregnancy.

g. _____ This hormone promotes contractions of the uterine smooth muscle.

Completion

Fill in the blanks to complete the following narratives.

63. After fertilization, which normally occurs in the **(a)**, the zygote is transformed into a **(b)**, which implants in the **(c)** of the uterus. At the point of implantation, embryonic and endometrial tissue develop into a **(d)**, which permits the exchange of materials between the mother and the developing embryo. During pregnancy, estrogen and **(e)** promote many effects, including growth and development of the **(f)** glands, secretion of prolactin by the **(g)**, and maintenance of **(h)** phase uterine conditions.

a. _____   e. _____

b. _____   f. _____

c. _____   g. _____

d. _____   h. _____

64. **(a)** usually occurs 40 weeks after fertilization and is marked by a wave of strong uterine contractions, dilation of the **(b)**, expulsion of the fetus from the uterus, and separation of the **(c)** from the uterine wall. After delivery, nourishment is provided to the infant by milk secreted from the **(d)**. Suckling of the infant triggers the secretion of the hormone **(e)**, which promotes milk **(f)**, and the hormone **(g)**, which promotes **(h)**.

a. _____   e. _____

b. _____   f. _____

c. _____   g. _____

d. _____   h. _____

Short Answer

Answer the following questions in 1–4 sentences.

65. Describe capacitation of sperm.

66. Describe the roles of elevated plasma estrogen levels during pregnancy.

67. What is a breech birth and why is it a dangerous situation for the fetus and the mother?

Multiple Choice

Select the best answer from the choices given.

68. Besides estrogen, which of the following hormones is released from the corpus luteum early in pregnancy?

    a. oxytocin
    b. progesterone
    c. placental lactogen
    d. prolactin
    e. human chorionic gonadotropin

69. The acrosome reaction in the sperm results in _____.

    a. ovulation
    b. capacitation of the sperm
    c. the contents of the acrosome being released to the outside
    d. the formation of a morula
    e. the decidual response

70. Cells of the morula are considered to be _____.

    a. totipotent
    b. part of the amnion
    c. in contact with the placenta
    d. involved in polyspermy block
    e. part of the acrosome reaction

71. Which of the following is formed early in placental development and contains fetal capillaries?

    a. blastocyst
    b. chorion
    c. amnion
    d. morula
    e. chorionic villus

72. Which of the following contains vascular tissue and is the link between the fetus and the placenta?

    a. umbilical cord
    b. chorion
    c. amnion
    d. myometrium
    e. endometrium

73. Which of the following is **not** a function of progesterone during pregnancy?
  a. growth of glandular breast tissue
  b. suppression of uterine smooth muscle contractions
  c. stimulation of prolactin secretion from the anterior pituitary
  d. maintenance of secretory-phase uterine conditions
  e. negative feedback on the hypothalamus that suppresses LH and FSH

True/False

Label the following statements as true (T) *or false* (F). *If false, change the statement to make it true.*

74. _____ During an entire pregnancy, estrogen and progesterone are secreted from the corpus luteum.

75. _____ The placenta can be considered to have endocrine tissue.

76. _____ The decidual response is produced by the blastocyst.

77. _____ The inner cell mass of a blastocyst eventually gives rise to the embryo.

Clinical Questions

78. A woman discovers that she is going to have twins. Explain to her the difference between fraternal twins and identical twins.

79. The level of hCG present in the urine is often used to test for pregnancy. Why must a woman wait at least seven days (sometimes longer) after ovulation to test her urine for the presence of hCG? Why might the result be negative even after seven days?

80. A new mother is debating whether to breastfeed her newborn infant. Explain to her the physiological benefits of breastfeeding.

Challenge Questions

81. Describe polyspermy. Explain how it is prevented.

82. A physician may sample fetal cells through a process called amniocentesis. In amniocentesis, a syringe needle is inserted through the abdominal and uterine walls to collect a small volume of amniotic fluid. This fluid contains fetal cells that can be used for biochemical or cytogenetic studies. Why is it that sampling the amniotic fluid yields fetal cells?

Labeling

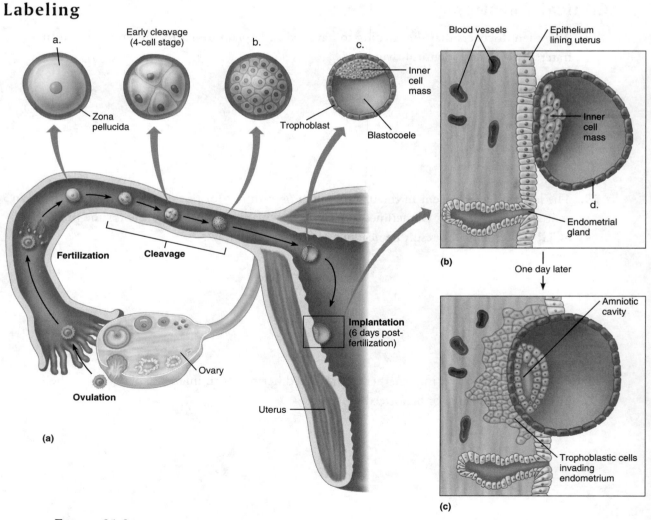

FIGURE 21.3

83. In the space below, identify the structures (a–d) in Figure 21.3.

Concept Map

84. Fill in the blanks of the concept map of hormonal regulation of lactation in response to infant suckling.

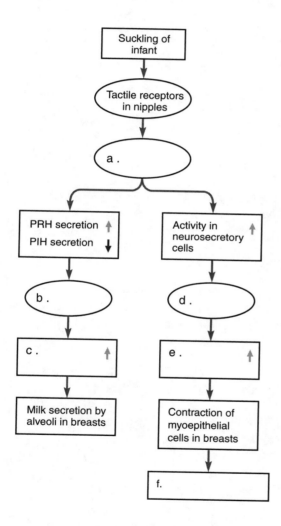

22 The Immune System

Objectives

We recommend that you review the **Objectives** for this chapter, found on p. 708 of *Principles of Human Physiology*. The **Objectives** outline what you should know from each chapter.

Key Terms

active immunity
agglutination
antibody
antigen
B lymphocyte
basophil
cell-mediated immunity
central lymphoid tissue
chemotaxis
Class I MHC
Class II MHC
clonal selection
complement system
cytokine
cytotoxic T cell
effector cell
eosinophil

epitope
fragmentin
helper T cell
histamine
humoral immunity
immunoglobulin (Ig)
inflammation
interferon
macrophage
major histocompatibility
    complex (MHC)
mast cell
memory cell
monocyte
natural killer (NK) cell
neutralization
neutrophil

non-specific immunity
opsonin
passive immunity
perforin
peripheral lymphoid tissue
phagocytosis
plasma cell
primary immune response
prostaglandin
pyrogen
secondary immune response
self-tolerance
specific immunity
T cell receptor (TCR)
T lymphocyte
T-dependent antigen
T-independent antigen

INTRODUCTION & ANATOMY

Matching

1. Match each term in the following list with its description or examples below: immunity (I), pathogenic agents (PA), immune response (IR), autoimmune diseases (AD), leukocytes (L), lymphoid tissues (LT). Each can be used once or more than once.

   a. _____ white blood cells, responsible for producing a wide range of immune responses

   b. _____ bacteria, viruses, parasites, and other disease-generating organisms and substances

   c. _____ bone marrow, spleen, and lymph nodes, areas where leukocytes come in contact with foreign material

   d. _____ the capacity to protect an individual from disease

e. _____ a series of physiological events leading to the destruction and elimination of foreign substances

f. _____ result when a person's immune system attacks his or her own tissues and cells

Completion

Fill in the blanks to complete the following narrative.

2. There are five major types of **(a)**. Some types are **(b)**, engulfing and destroying foreign matter. The most numerous of these are the **(c)**, which circulate in the blood for 8–10 hours before migrating to the **(d)**. A type of agranulocyte, **(e)** are activated only after they grow 5–10 times their original size; they are then known as **(f)**. The **(g)**, known for their bright red granules, defend against parasites along with the **(h)** and are involved in allergic reactions. The **(i)** are divided into three groups, the **(j)**, which damage foreign cells directly, the **(k)**, which fight viruses specifically, and finally the **(l)**, which mature into **(m)**, which secrete antibodies.

a. _____   h. _____

b. _____   i. _____

c. _____   j. _____

d. _____   k. _____

e. _____   l. _____

f. _____   m. _____

g. _____

Short Answer

Answer the following questions in 1–4 sentences.

3. List, compare, and contrast the functions of the granulocytic leukocytes.

4. Define phagocytosis. Which types of cells exhibit this characteristic? Name two sites where one would find "fixed" cells and explain their significance.

5. Describe the peripheral lymphoid tissues and their location. Explain the importance of location in the function of these tissues. Where are the *central* lymphoid tissues located?

Multiple Choice

Select the best answer from the choices given.

6. Of the circulating lymphocytes, which make up the smallest population?

   a. B cells
   b. T cells
   c. natural killer cells
   d. cytotoxic T cells
   e. macrophages

7. Which of the following statements about basophils is false?

   a. They are not phagocytic.
   b. They constitute less than 1% of all leukocytes.
   c. They release histamine.
   d. They are thought to defend against large parasites.
   e. After they are stained, bright red granules fill their cytoplasm.

8. The term *hematopoietic* refers to _____.

   a. the ability to cause disease
   b. the ability to prevent disease
   c. cells that engulf foreign cells
   d. blood forming cells
   e. blood cell destroying cells

9. Neutrophils engulf(s) _____.

   I. microorganisms
   II. abnormal cells
   III. foreign particles

   a. I and II only
   b. II and III only
   c. I only
   d. I, II, III
   e. II only

10. All but which of the following are thought to result from autoimmune responses?

    a. rheumatoid arthritis
    b. Parkinson's disease
    c. diabetes mellitus
    d. multiple sclerosis
    e. systemic lupus erythematosus

True/False

Label the following statements as true (T) *or false* (F). *If false, change the statement to make it true.*

11. _____ The spleen is the largest lymphoid organ.

12. _____ All blood cells develop from precursor cells located in the bone marrow.

13. _____ Peripheral lymphoid tissues are the sites of lymphocyte maturation.

14. _____ When T cells contact antigens they develop into plasma cells that secrete immunoglobulins.

15. _____ Of the cells of the immune system, only neutrophils, monocytes, and some T lymphocytes become phagocytic.

Labeling

Central Lymphoid Tissues

Peripheral Lymphoid Tissues

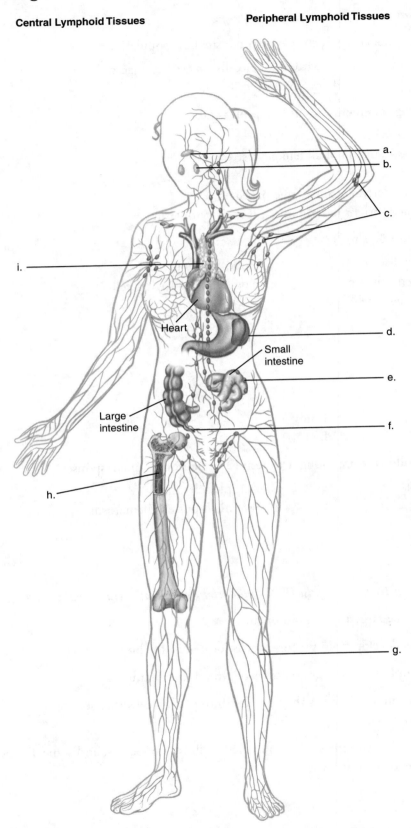

a.

b.

c.

i.

Heart

d.

Small
intestine

e.

Large
intestine

f.

h.

g.

FIGURE 22.1

16. In the space below, identify the central and peripheral lymphoid tissues (a–i) in Figure 22.1.

Clinical Question

17. Your throat hurts and, in general, you don't feel well. Examination by your doctor reveals swollen lymph nodes in your throat. What causes the swelling in your lymph nodes? Blood is drawn, and your results show an elevated leukocyte count. What causes this elevated count? Which cell numbers are most likely to be elevated? Why?

Challenge Questions

18. Your 4-year-old comes home from day care with chicken pox, which is caused by a virus. She gets the disease, but you don't, although you had it when you were her age. Specifically, what cells help you stay well? Briefly explain how these cells work to prevent you from showing symptoms of chicken pox.

19. What effect on the immune system would you expect in an adult who undergoes a splenectomy surgery to remove the spleen? Would you expect different effects in a five-year-old child? Explain your answer.

20. Describe the relationships among blood plasma, tissue fluid, lymph, and peripheral lymphoid tissues. How do these systems work together?

ORGANIZATION OF THE BODY'S DEFENSES

Matching

21. Mark each of the following mechanisms as either *specific* (S) or *nonspecific* (NS).

    a. _____ complement system

    b. _____ immunoglobulins

    c. _____ inflammation

    d. _____ natural killer (NK) cells

    e. _____ memory cells

    f. _____ interferons

    g. _____ helper T cells

Completion

Fill in the blanks to complete the following narrative.

22. Intact, the **(a)** and the **(b)** that line the digestive, urinary, and other systems provide excellent initial barriers to most **(c)** and **(d)**. **(e)** also produce a viscous **(f)** that traps foreign matter and potential pathogens. Chemical defenses also protect the **(g)**, such as **(h)** and **(i)**, that help lower the pH enough to prevent colonization by **(j)**.

    a. _____   f. _____

    b. _____   g. _____

    c. _____   h. _____

    d. _____   i. _____

    e. _____   j. _____

Concept Map

23. Fill in the blanks in this concept map that outlines the organization of the **body's specific and non-specific defense systems**.

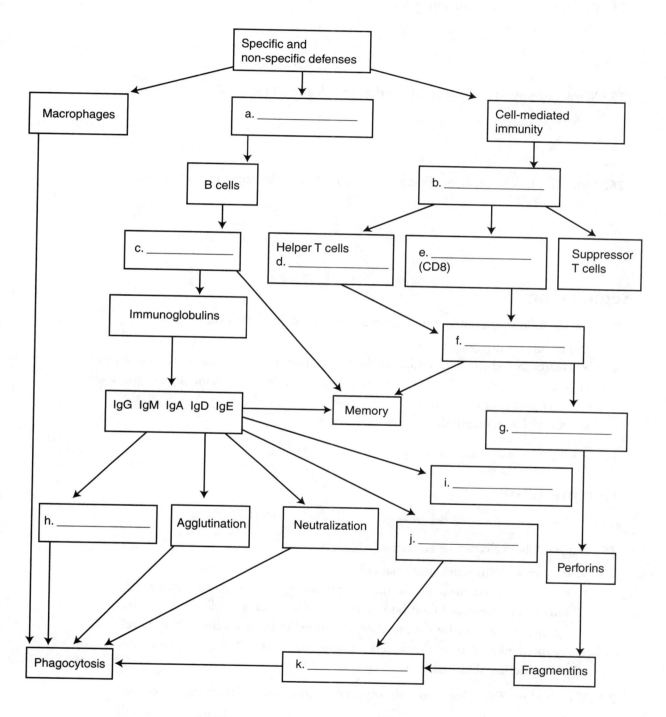

Short Answer

Answer the following questions in 1–4 sentences.

24. Explain the events of inflammation.

25. What category of pathogens do interferons defend you from? Summarize how this occurs.

26. How did the complement system get its name? What are some important outcomes of its activation?

Sequencing

27. Put the following events of inflammation in the order of their occurrence.

    a. Leukocytes migrate to the region.
    b. Nearby blood capillaries dilate and become more permeable to proteins and fluid.
    c. Recruited leukocytes continue to help clear the infection, mainly by phagocytosis.
    d. Foreign matter is contained.
    e. Macrophages engulf debris and foreign matter.

Sequence: _____

Multiple Choice

Select the best answer from the choices given.

28. Natural killer cells can be activated _____.

    a. only by encountering abnormal cells
    b. only by interleukin-2, which may appear during certain immune responses
    c. only in the presence of antibodies from T cells or plasma cells
    d. by interleukin-2 or by the presence of antibodies from T cells or plasma cells
    e. by interleukin-2 or by the presence of antibodies from T cells or plasma cells, or by encountering abnormal cells

29. Which of the following is **not** an important part of the inflammatory process?

    a. Local macrophages are activated in order to engulf bacteria and foreign cells.
    b. Vasodilation and increased capillary permeability allow blood to bring in additional leukocytes and defensive proteins.
    c. Complement is activated to fulfill the actions of uncompleted protein reactions.

d. The area of damage is walled off by clotting factors, which helps prevent the spread of bacteria.

e. Leukocytes are recruited to the site to continue to clean up the debris.

30. Which of the following terms is incorrectly paired with its definition?

a. margination : leukocyte movement toward the walls of blood vessels

b. chemotaxis : a type of movement used by leukocytes to crawl between cells of the capillary wall

c. phagocytosis : engulfment of cellular particles or debris

d. interferons : related proteins that are secreted by B cells and bacteria and induce other cells to resist infection

e. vasodilation : increased blood vessel diameter

31. An endogenous pyrogen _____.

a. raises body temperature

b. triggers the release of blood-clotting factors

c. coats foreign material with protein so it can be more readily ingested

d. causes a four- to five-fold increase in the number of circulating neutrophils

e. binds to the surface of a bacteria so that a phagocyte can find it

True/False

Label the following statements as true (T) *or false* (F). *If false, change the statement to make it true.*

32. _____ Complement is a single molecule of a protein that normally circulates in the plasma.

33. _____ Opsonization is a process required in order for foreign material to be ingested.

34. _____ Interferons are a family of related proteins that help other cells resist infection by a virus.

35. _____ Mast cells, like basophils, are damaged when the skin is damaged, stimulating the early events of inflammation.

36. _____ Once cellular damage has occurred, chemicals are released from the damaged cells that summon other members of the immune system to the site.

Clinical Question

37. How do sprains and strains differ from one another, and how are they alike? Recommendations for recovering from sprains include "RICE" — **R**est – **I**ce – **C**ompression – **E**levation of the affected part. How do those recommendations fit with what you now know about the process of inflammation?

Completion

Fill in the blanks to complete the following narrative.

38. B and T cells provide for the features of *specific immune responses*: **(a)**, **(b)**, **(c)**, and **(d)**. In the **(e)**, antigen-activated B cells develop into plasma cells that secrete antibodies. Antibodies bind to and target specific antigens, but recruit other defenses, like phagocytic cells, to destroy the antigens. In the **(f)**, cytotoxic T cells detect antigens presented by **(g)** molecules (on virus-infected cells or tumor cells) and become active killers. They destroy their targets in two ways: by releasing **(h)** that lead to target cell lysis, and **(i)** that induce apoptosis in the target cell. Both humoral and cell-mediated responses are supported and regulated by cytokines secreted by helper T cells that have been induced by antigens presented by **(j)** molecules on macrophages or activated B cells.

a. _____   f. _____

b. _____   g. _____

c. _____   h. _____

d. _____   i. _____

e. _____   j. _____

Challenge Questions

39. Why is it important that the activities of the immune system have both specific and non-specific mechanisms of activation?

40. Why are vasodilation and capillary permeability important to the immune system? What compounds enhance the mechanisms of the immune system? Design a table to list as many compounds as you can find in the chapter that affect these properties. Include each factor's source.

41. What is the importance of pain in the immune response?

IMMUNE RESPONSES

Matching

42. Mark whether the part listed below is part of the Antigen (Ag) or the Lymphocyte (L) by writing the correct letters in the blank.

    a. _____ epitope

    b. _____ antigen receptor

    c. _____ membrane immunoglobulin

    d. _____ antigenic determinant

    e. _____ virus

    f. _____ T cell receptor

Short Answer

Answer the following questions in 1–4 sentences.

43. What is meant by clonal selection? What cells undergo clonal selection?

44. Compare and contrast the terms *heavy chains, light chains, constant* and *variable regions.*

45. Compare and contrast the terms *humoral immunity* and *cell-mediated immunity.* Explain the origin of these terms.

46. What characteristics distinguish a specific immune response from a non-specific response?

Multiple Choice

Select the best answer from the choices given.

47. The term describing the fact that a given lymphocyte will only respond to a given antigen is _____.

    a. antigenic determinant   c. phagocytosis   e. humoral immunity
    b. specificity   d. cell-mediated immunity

48. The variable region of an antibody molecule _____.

    a. results from a unique sequence of amino acids
    b. binds to a unique antigen
    c. allows the formation of covalent bonds with specific antigens
    d. results from a unique sequence of amino acids and binds to a unique antigen
    e. results from a unique sequence of amino acids, binds to a unique antigen, and allows the formation of covalent bonds with specific antigens

49. Self-tolerance is a term that describes _____.

    a. a lymphocyte's ability to bind to an antigen
    b. a lymphocyte's ability to produce several thousand copies of itself
    c. the immune system's ability to recognize foreign cells and attack them without attacking its own body's tissue
    d. the need for cytotoxic T cells to directly contact their targets
    e. the ability of B lymphocytes to mature into plasma cells

50. Which response is incorrectly matched with its effector cell?

    a. B cells — plasma cells — antibody secretion
    b. lymphocytes — cytotoxic T cells — kill abnormal cells
    c. lymphocytes — clone — effector and memory cells
    d. T cells — natural-killer cells — antibody secretion
    e. monocytes — macrophages — engulf bacteria

51. Programmed cell death is correctly termed _____.

    a. self-tolerance   c. apoptosis   e. humoral immunity
    b. epitopisis   d. cell-mediated immunity

Challenge Question

52. When blood plasma is collected from donors, it contains the elements of humoral immunity that the donor possessed, but not those of cell-mediated immunity of the donor. Why?

Graphing

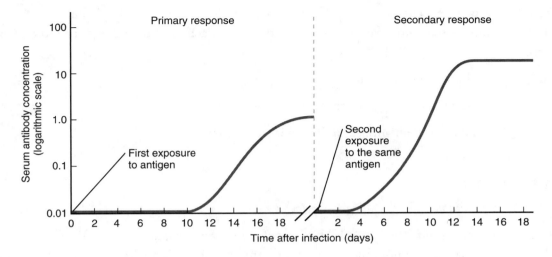

FIGURE 22.2

53. Look at the graph in Figure 22.2. What are three important conclusions that can be drawn from this graph regarding the differences between the primary and secondary responses?

HUMORAL AND CELL-MEDIATED IMMUNITY

Short Answer

Answer the following questions in 1–4 sentences.

54. Compare and contrast T-dependent and T-independent antigens. Which specific type of T cell responds to these different antigens?

55. List and distinguish among the different classes of antibody molecules and their functions.

56. What are the three major types of T lymphocytes and how do they differ? How are they alike?

Matching

57. Match each item in the following list of terms with its description or example below: neutralization (N), agglutination (A), opsonization (O). Each can be used once or more than once.

   a. _____ clumping of antigens

   b. _____ coating an antigen to encourage phagocytosis

   c. _____ binding to an antigen and blocking its activity

Completion

Fill in the blanks to complete the following narrative.

58. Each of our cells is identified as "self" by a set of **(a)** (in humans, known as **(b)**), of which there are two classes. **(c)** molecules are found on the surface of all nucleated cells—that is, on almost every cell of the body. **(d)** molecules are found on only a few specialized cell types, including macrophages, activated B and T cells, and the cells that make up the interior of the **(e)**. In the **(e)**, T cells develop into two different types, depending on the class of **(a)** to which they bind. Those cells that bind to **(c)** molecules develop into cytotoxic T cells, whereas those that bind to **(d)** molecules develop into helper T cells.

   a. _____   d. _____

   b. _____   e. _____

   c. _____

Short Answer

Answer the following questions in 1–4 sentences.

59. Compare and contrast the Class I MHC molecule with the Class II MHC molecule.

60. Explain the interactions among macrophages, helper T cells, B cells, and cytotoxic T cells during an effective immune response.

Sequencing

61. Put the following events in the order of their occurrence.

   a. Released pathogens are opsonized or are eliminated by phagocytosis.
   b. The infected cell's membrane becomes increasingly permeable to ions and water.

c. Perforins are released.

d. The infected cell swells, lyses, and dies.

e. The cytotoxic T cell is activated.

f. An inactive cytotoxic T cell binds with a class I MHC foreign antigen complex on the surface of a virus-infected cell, while simultaneously receiving a signal of IL-2 from a helper T cell.

g. Cytotoxic T cells release proteins called *fragmentins*, which enter the cell.

Sequence: _____

IMMUNE RESPONSES IN HEALTH AND DISEASE

Matching

62. Match each situation below with the appropriate type of immunity: active (A), or passive (P). Each can be used once or more than once.

a. _____ A gamma globulin shot is given to someone exposed to Hepatitis B.

b. _____ Immunizations are required before a child can start school.

c. _____ A child has chicken pox and recovers.

d. _____ A one-month-old infant nurses.

63. In the table below, specify the letters of the **antigen** present in a person of the given blood type. Also, write the letters of **antibodies** in that same person's blood. Use **both** or **neither** if needed.

Antigen		Antibody
_____	Type A blood	_____
_____	Type O blood	_____
_____	Type B blood	_____
_____	Type AB blood	_____

Short Answer

Answer the following questions in 1–4 sentences.

64. Explain the advantages of active immunity over passive immunity.

65. Briefly explain what tissue typing is, and why it is important.

True/False

Label the following statements as true (T) *or false* (F). *If false, change the statement to make it true.*

66. _____ Passive immunity typically lasts a few weeks.

67. _____ A person with Type A blood will have type B antibodies in his blood even if he has never been exposed to type B blood.

68. _____ People with blood type AB are considered to be universal donors.

69. _____ Cyclosporin A helps organ transplants to be successful by inhibiting the production of IL-2.

70. _____ In bone marrow transplants, the greatest risk is that the recipient's immune system will attack the donated marrow.

71. _____ The most common allergies involve antibodies of the IgE class.

Completion

Fill in the blanks to complete the following narrative.

72. The most serious consequence of an acute allergic response is **(a)**, a life-threatening reaction to injected or ingested **(b)**. **(a)** occurs when there is widespread degranulation of **(c)** cells throughout the body, which triggers abrupt and widespread **(d)** of peripheral blood vessels, causing a precipitous drop in total peripheral resistance and mean arterial pressure. As a consequence of the drop in pressure, **(e)** may occur within a few minutes.

a. _____   d. _____

b. _____   e. _____

c. _____

Multiple Choice

Select the best answer from the choices given.

73. Beta cells of the pancreatic islets appear to become the target of a cell-mediated immune response in which disease?

    a. rheumatoid arthritis

    b. multiple sclerosis

    c. insulin-dependent diabetes mellitus

    d. systemic lupus erythematosus

    e. Parkinson's disease

Clinical Question

74. Dwight mows ten acres of pasture. He is allergic to bee stings and has been told he could die unless he quickly administers a particular drug that he takes with him on the tractor in case a bee stings him while he's mowing, since there are no phones nearby and the closest hospital is ten miles away. How could complications, including death, occur? What drug has he been advised to carry? Why?

Challenge Question

75. Explain how it is possible that there is a genetic component to autoimmune diseases like diabetes mellitus or rheumatoid arthritis?

23 The Whole Body: Integrated Physiological Responses to Exercise

Objectives

We recommend that you review the **Objectives** for this chapter, found on p. 741 of *Principles of Human Physiology*. The **Objectives** outline what you should know from each chapter.

PRINCIPLES OF PHYSIOLOGICAL INTEGRATION AND THE START: TRANSITION FROM REST TO EXERCISE

Matching

1. From the following list of metabolic pathways, choose the one that would most probably be in use during levels of exercise listed below: aerobic lipolytic metabolism (ALM), anaerobic glycolysis (ANG), creatine phosphate (CP).

   a. _____ the third minute of a light jog around the block

   b. _____ the first few seconds of a high-intensity, 100-yard sprint

   c. _____ the last few seconds of a high-intensity, 100-yard sprint

Completion

Fill in the blanks to complete the following narratives.

2. Exercise places many demands on the body, which can be met only through the activities of different organ systems working together. One such demand is an increased need for **(a)** to power skeletal muscle contractions, which can be supplied for very brief periods by molecules stored within the muscle cells themselves (ATP, **(b)**, glucose, and **(c)**). More prolonged activity requires increased delivery of **(d)** and fuels (glucose and fatty acids, for example) to the muscle cells from other sources. Within specific systems, adjustments are regulated by **(e)** (intrinsic control or autoregulation), **(f)**, and hormonal signals (extrinsic control). Under most conditions, blood flow to muscles and other organs is controlled by **(g)** mechanisms. When conditions become more stressful, organs begin to compete with each other for blood delivery and **(f)** and hormonal signals assume a greater role.

   a. _____

   b. _____

   c. _____

   d. _____

   e. _____

   f. _____

   g. _____

3. Often, exercise is preceded by an anticipatory increase in **(a)** nervous activity (and epinephrine secretion) and a decrease in **(b)** activity. Cardiac output increases, as does plasma **(c)** concentration. At the start of exercise, **(d)** (a feedforward mechanism arising in the cerebral cortex) helps orchestrate the cardiovascular and respiratory adjustments that occur. The proportion of fuels used depends on exercise **(e)** and duration. Early on (before oxygen delivery can be increased), **(f)** is the predominant ATP-generating mechanism in exercising muscle cells; afterward, aerobic metabolism (fatty acid oxidation and **(g)**) becomes predominant.

a. _____   e. _____

b. _____   f. _____

c. _____   g. _____

d. _____

Short Answer

Answer the following questions in 1–4 sentences.

4. John is about to take his morning 5K run. Explain the importance of central command in increasing his heart rate at the beginning of his run.

5. Barb is in mile 2 of her 3-mile run. Explain the two types of pulmonary reserve capacity in Barb's body that help to deliver more oxygen to her lungs and exercising tissues.

Multiple Choice

Select the best answer from the choices given.

6. Which of the following is not an energy source stored within muscles?

  a. ATP   c. creatine phosphate   e. glucose

  b. fatty acids   d. glycogen

7. Which of the following organs receives unchanging blood flow despite the changing metabolic demands of the rest of the body?

  a. lungs   c. brain   e. large skeletal muscles

  b. heart   d. kidneys

8. During which of the following activities would autoregulation primarily dictate blood flow to and from skeletal muscle?

  a. sprinting a 40-yard dash   d. sleeping

  b. swimming a 50-meter race   e. running a marathon

  c. taking a bicycle ride around the block

9. Which of the following is not the result of increased sympathetic activity during exercise?
   a. dilation of airways
   b. increased sweating
   c. constriction of blood vessels leading to skeletal muscles
   d. increased venous return
   e. increased secretion by alpha cells of the pancreas

10. Which of the following physiological responses occurs during moderate exercise?
    a. Feedback mechanisms are involved in increased ventilation.
    b. Fewer pulmonary capillaries are recruited to carry oxygen.
    c. Tidal volume decreases.
    d. The time each red blood cell remains in the capillaries of the alveoli is increased.
    e. Mechanoreceptors and chemoreceptors originate feedforward signals to initiate increased breathing rate.

True/False

Label the following statements as true (T) or false (F). If false, change the statement to make it true.

11. _____ During exercise, the body experiences widespread increases in sympathetic nervous activity.

12. _____ When arterial blood pH levels fall, the hemoglobin saturation curve shifts to the right.

13. _____ During heavy exercise, blood is shunted away from the brain and toward the exercising muscles.

14. _____ The hypothalamus is the body's thermoregulatory center.

15. _____ During moderate exercise in a hot environment, blood is shunted away from the skin.

Clinical Question

16. You are a trainer for the track and field team at a local college. Explain to the runners why they should eat a meal high in complex carbohydrates the day before a long run.

Challenge Question

17. Describe the role of the sympathetic nervous system (including the receptors and the neurotransmitters involved) in mediating blood flow to and from the skin during exercise.

THE LONG HAUL: ALMOST STEADY STATE

Matching

18. For each situation listed below, mark the place(s) in the body where most blood is distributed: muscle (M), skin (S), or viscera (V). Assume that vital organs receive optimal blood flow in each situation and that each situation can have more than one right answer.

    a. _____ resting, neutral environment

    b. _____ resting, warm environment

    c. _____ moderate exercise, cool environment

    d. _____ moderate exercise, hot environment

Completion

Fill in the blanks to complete the following narrative.

19. After the initial shift from anaerobic to aerobic metabolism that occurs in prolonged exercise, fuel use settles into a relatively steady state. However, **(a)** and body fluids are continually being used. Mobilization of energy stores is regulated by changes in plasma levels of **(b)**, epinephrine, and **(c)** (which all rise), and **(d)** (which falls). Plasma glucose rises initially due to epinephrine-stimulated glycogenolysis and **(e)**, but eventually begins to decline. **(f)** rises due to the initial burst of anaerobic metabolism, but levels off due to the rise in aerobic metabolism coupled with increased **(e)**. **(g)** levels rise steadily due to an increased glucagon to insulin ratio.

    a. _____   e. _____

    b. _____   f. _____

    c. _____   g. _____

    d. _____

Short Answer

Answer the following questions in 1–4 sentences.

20. What is the benefit of a metabolite-regulated rise in blood pressure during exercise?

21. Explain the source of the steroid hormones in males and females and describe how these hormones may drive energy usage in the two sexes during exercise.

Multiple Choice

Select the best answer from the choices given.

22. Which of the following is true during strenuous exercise?

a. Oxygen and carbon dioxide diffuse faster at the metabolically active tissues.

b. Carbon dioxide is produced at a much slower rate at the metabolically active tissues.

c. P_{O_2} is near 100 mm Hg in the systemic veins.

d. P_{CO_2} of mixed venous blood is near 100 mm Hg.

e. Diffusion gradients for both carbon dioxide and oxygen are reduced.

23. After the marathon race described on p. 18 of *Principles of Human Physiology*, Bill lost a significant volume of water with the diarrhea. What other condition will Bill likely have?

a. hypovolemia

b. hypervolemia

c. acidosis

d. alkalosis

e. hypocalcemia

24. Which of the following adrenergic receptors is paired correctly with its physiological response on the respiratory airways?

a. α_2 adrenergic receptors increase airway resistance.

b. α_1 adrenergic receptors decrease the diameter of the airway.

c. β_2 adrenergic receptors increase the diameter of the airway.

d. Nicotinic receptors increase the diameter of the airway.

e. Muscarinic receptors increase airway resistance.

25. After exercising heavily on a hot day, the kidneys will _____.

a. stop the release of ADH

b. produce a highly concentrated, low volume urine

c. decrease reabsorption at the loop of Henle

d. close the pores in the collecting ducts

e. produce a very dilute, high volume urine

26. When mean arterial pressure increases, which of the following compensation mechanisms occurs to lower blood pressure?

a. Renin secretion increases.

b. ADH secretion increases.

c. Angiotensin II causes vasoconstriction.

d. Sodium reabsorption decreases.

e. ANP secretion decreases.

True/False

Label the following statements as true (T) *or false* (F). *If false, change the statement to make it true.*

27. _____ At the onset of low-intensity exercise, ATP production in exercising muscle cells occurs primarily through aerobic metabolism.

28. _____ At the onset of exercise, an increase in pulmonary ventilation is the result of an increase in breathing rate.

29. _____ By gradually increasing exercise intensity a person can help to conserve the body's stores of fatty acids.

30. _____ Women rely more heavily than men on fatty acid oxidation during heavy exercise.

Labeling

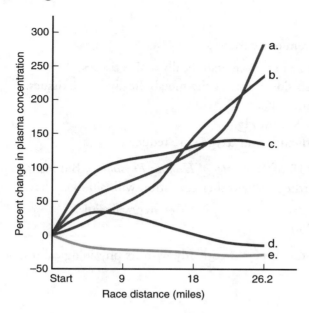

FIGURE 23.1

31. In the space below, label the lines (a–e) in Figure 23.1 with the following terms: Lactate, Insulin, Epinephrine, Glucose, Free fatty acids. Provide a brief explanation for the status of each line at the *end* of the race.

Clinical Questions

32. Explain the hormonal response of the pancreas to moderate exercise (a 2-mile light jog).

33. Jim spends five hours on a hot afternoon playing golf and loses a significant volume of water through sweat. He drinks until he is no longer thirsty. However, when he gets out of bed in the middle of the night to get a drink of water he passes out and comes to on the bedroom floor. Jim goes to see his physician, who diagnoses him with dehydration and administers intravenous fluids. Explain why Jim passed out when he got out of bed.

Challenge Questions

34. Describe the forces involved in active inspiration and expiration during exercise.

35. Describe the role of the sympathetic nervous system (including the receptors and the neurotransmitters involved) in mediating blood flow to and from the gastrointestinal tract during exercise.

Concept Map

36. Fill in the blanks (a–g) in the following concept map of the roles of metaboreceptors and central command in mean arterial pressure during exercise.

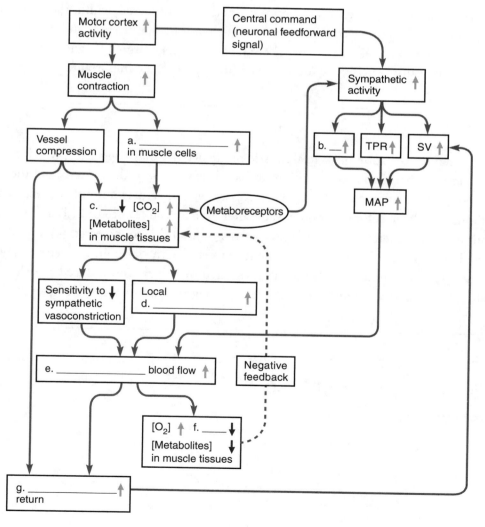

THE DECLINE TO THE END: "THE WALL" OR THE FINISH LINE? AND THE AFTERMATH

Matching

37. Match each of the following conditions with its physiological cause below: delayed-onset muscle soreness (DOMS); muscle fatigue (MF); postexercise fever (PEF); syncope (SYN); water intoxication (WI).

   a. _____ a buildup of hydrogen ions

   b. _____ an increase of water concentration inside of central nervous system cells

   c. _____ cytokines operating on the hypothalamus

   d. _____ breakdown of Z disks and disruption of plasma membranes of muscle cells

   e. _____ lack of blood flow and oxygen delivery to the brain

Completion

Fill in the blanks to complete the following narratives.

38. Prolonged exercise ultimately leads to **(a)**, which arises due to **(b)** factors within the exercising muscles, systemic factors influenced by metabolic and environmental stresses, and psychological factors. **(c)** depletion is most likely the pivotal event that triggers terminal fatigue in endurance exercise; in high-intensity exercise, accumulation of **(d)** appears to be important.

   a. _____   c. _____

   b. _____   d. _____

39. At the end of exercise, cessation of skeletal muscle pump activity may trigger **(a)**, which is actually beneficial in that it ends competition for blood flow between the muscles and the brain, reduces **(b)** production by muscles, and increases **(c)** and cardiac output. Replacement of lost body fluids with large volumes of pure water after exercise can lead to cell **(d)** and water intoxication. Following exercise, a person may experience fever due to increased **(e)** levels, which act on hypothalamic thermoregulatory centers to elevate the set point. A person may also experience **(f)**, a symptom of inflammation triggered by contraction-induced muscle damage. This inflammatory response normally sets the stage for eventual muscle **(g)**.

   a. _____   e. _____

   b. _____   f. _____

   c. _____   g. _____

   d. _____

Short Answer

Answer the following questions in 1–4 sentences.

40. Explain the response of the concentration of circulating neutrophils to moderate exercise.

41. Describe the fuel sources and primary pathway of ATP synthesis used for each of the following activities:

  a. the first few seconds of a marathon run

  b. the first two miles of a marathon at top speed

  c. the first two miles of a marathon at a moderate speed

Multiple Choice

Select the best answer from the choices given.

42. Before the race, which of the following osmotic conditions exist?
  a. The ECF is hypo-osmotic relative to the ICF.
  b. The ECF and ICF are iso-osmotic.
  c. The ECF is hyperosmotic relative to the ICF.
  d. Water is lost from the plasma to the interstitial fluid.
  e. Cells in the brain swell as water enters the intercellular spaces.

43. Which of the following can lead to syncope?
  a. hypernatremia
  b. hypervolemia
  c. increased blood pressure
  d. increased cardiac output
  e. hypovolemia

44. Which of the following is not implicated in fatigue of skeletal muscle?

    a. accumulation of lactic acid

    b. inhibition of hormone-sensitive lipase

    c. phosphate ions displacing calcium from troponin

    d. hydrogen ions displacing calcium from troponin

    e. hydrogen ions inhibiting phosphofructokinase

45. After training for their marathon race, all of the following physiological adaptations should have been observed in Bill and Jane **except** _____.

    a. some fast glycolytic fibers are converted to fast oxidative fibers

    b. some slow-twitch fibers are converted to fast-twitch fibers

    c. the muscle fiber oxidative capacity has increased

    d. the muscle fibers are more resistant to fatigue

    e. the number of mitochondria increase

46. High-intensity exercise would result in which of the following adaptations of skeletal muscle?

    a. Oxidative capacity increases.

    b. Some fast glycolytic fibers are converted to fast oxidative fibers.

    c. Fiber diameter decreases.

    d. New fibers are synthesized.

    e. Muscles are less resistant to fatigue.

47. Assuming all other factors are equal, which is probably true about the composition of urine at the end of a marathon when compared to urine composition at rest?

    a. The urine pH is higher after the marathon compared to at rest.

    b. The urine is more basic after the marathon compared to at rest.

    c. The urine is more acidic after the marathon compared to at rest.

    d. The urine is slightly basic after the marathon compared to at rest.

    e. The urine composition does not change much after the marathon compared to at rest.

True/False

Label the following statements as true (T) *or false* (F). *If false, change the statement to make it true.*

48. _____ Delayed onset muscle soreness is thought to be produced by the buildup of lactic acid.

49. _____ Fast glycolytic fibers contain fast myosin and can produce ATP quickly through glycolysis.

50. _____ Slow oxidative fibers contain slow myosin and produce most of their ATP through oxidative phosphorylation.

Clinical Questions

51. Explain why someone with severe trauma to skeletal muscles may experience plasma hyperkalemia.

52. Following a rigorous 12-month training schedule to prepare for a marathon, Sherri, a 20-year-old athlete, visits her doctor because she is no longer menstruating. Can you propose a cause for her amenorrhea?

Challenge Questions

53. Karen is hiking down into the Grand Canyon on a hot day, and has heard stories about how other hikers have become dehydrated. She vows that this will not happen to her, so she continually drinks water as she descends into the canyon. She refills her water bottles at stations along the way, and does not eat any food during her hike. By the time she reaches the bottom she has drunk an enormous volume of water and is sweating. She is dazed, confused, and nauseated. A park ranger at the bottom of the canyon quickly recognizes her symptoms and gets her to eat some food rich in sodium. What condition does Karen likely have?

54. Compare and contrast the types of muscles recruited during Bill's high-intensity start to the race, and the types of muscles recruited during Jane's more steady, moderate pace.

Concept Maps

55. Fill in the blanks in this concept map showing the effects of epinephrine on the body during moderate exercise.

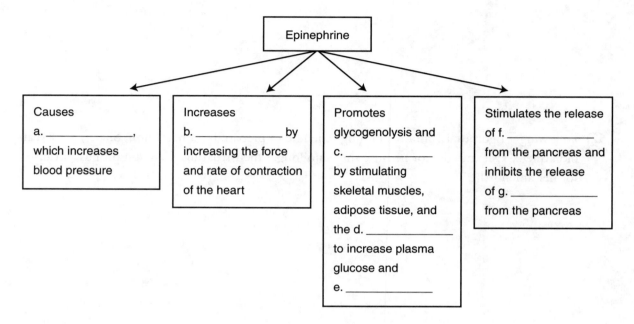

Epinephrine

Causes
a. _____,
which increases
blood pressure

Increases
b. _____ by
increasing the force
and rate of contraction
of the heart

Promotes
glycogenolysis and
c. _____
by stimulating
skeletal muscles,
adipose tissue, and
the d. _____
to increase plasma
glucose and
e. _____

Stimulates the release
of f. _____
from the pancreas and
inhibits the release
of g. _____
from the pancreas

56. Fill in the blanks of the effects of cytokines on the body following sustained moderate exercise.

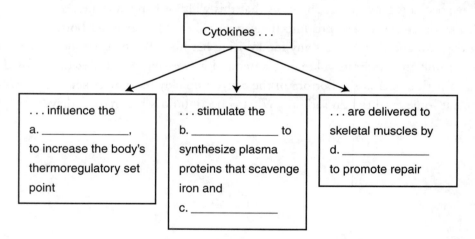

Cytokines . . .

. . . influence the
a. _____,
to increase the body's
thermoregulatory set
point

. . . stimulate the
b. _____ to
synthesize plasma
proteins that scavenge
iron and
c. _____

. . . are delivered to
skeletal muscles by
d. _____
to promote repair

Answer Key

CHAPTER 1

ORGANIZATION OF THE BODY

Matching

1. a. C, **b.** M, **c.** E, **d.** C, **e.** N, **f.** N.

Completion

2. a. four, **b.** Muscle, **c.** involuntary, **d.** Neurons, **e.** Connective tissue, **f.** Epithelial.

3. a. external, **b.** epithelial, **c.** internal, **d.** interstitial fluid, **e.** plasma, **f.** intracellular fluid, **g.** total body water.

Short Answer

4. Physiology is the study of how the body performs its various functions.

5. Epithelial tissues separate the various fluid compartments of the body. Any substance that enters or leaves the body has to cross an epithelium. **Epithelial tissue is considered semipermeable.** That is, it can allow *some* substances to cross the tissue. On the other hand, epithelial tissue also **acts as a barrier** to prevent the movement of substances into and out of the various fluid compartments.

6. a. Endothelial (epithelial) tissues line the insides of hollow organs, including the arteries and veins. **b. Muscle tissue** (smooth muscle in this case) aids in constricting blood vessels. **c. Connective tissue** is responsible for protection and support in arteries and veins.

Multiple Choice

7. d   **8.** b   **9.** e   **10.** d   **11.** a   **12.** c
13. b   **14.** a   **15.** d   **16.** a

True/False

17. F Muscle cells are generally elongated, but they **do not line the inside of hollow organs**; epithelial tissues do.

18. T

19. F Most cells of the body are **in contact with other cells**.

20. T   **21.** T

Labeling

22. a. neurons: conduct electrical signals **b. muscle cells:** generate mechanical forces, contract **c. epithelial cells:** cover a body surface or line a body cavity **d. connective tissue cells:** binding and support, protection, insulation, transportation of substances.

Sequencing

23. b, d, a, c

Challenge Question

24. The skin is considered an organ because it contains three of the four tissue types. Each of these tissues can be seen in Figure 1.2. **Epithelial tissue** present on the outer surface of the skin acts as a barrier to the outside world, thus protecting the inner organs from dehydration, disease, shock, abrasions, and UV light. **Connective tissue** can be seen in the deeper parts of the skin. Here, connective tissue helps to anchor the upper epithelial layers and also acts as a site of energy storage. **Nerve endings and nerve receptors** can also be seen in the skin. They transmit information about the external environment to the brain.

Concept Map

25. a. intracellular fluid, **b.** interstitial fluid, **c.** plasma.

HOMEOSTASIS

Matching

26. a. E, **b.** IC, **c.** ES, **d.** SP, **e.** S.

27. a. NF, **b.** NF, **c.** PF, **d.** PF, **e.** PF.

Completion

28. a. negative feedback, **b.** set point, **c.** error signal, **d.** sensor, **e.** integrating center, **f.** effectors.

Short Answer

29. Homeostasis is the maintenance of near constant internal conditions within the body.

30. The three aspects of the extracellular fluid that do not change much are its **temperature**, **volume**, and **composition**. Under normal homeostatic conditions, the body regulates the ECF and ICF temperatures at or near 37°C and the overall fluid volume, and solute concentrations also change very little.

31. The three types of thermoregulatory effectors are **sweat glands**, **blood vessels of the skin**, and **skeletal muscles**. They respond in the following ways to a drop in body temperature. Sweat glands respond by **decreasing output,** resulting in a reduction of evaporative water loss. **Blood flow to the skin decreases** and thus reduces heat loss. **Shivering** of skeletal muscles is stimulated by the thermoregulatory centers and acts to generate heat.

Multiple Choice

32. a   **33.** a   **34.** c   **35.** e

True/False

36. F **Negative feedback** is the more common form of regulating homeostasis.

37. T

38. F Conduction is thermal energy transfer between objects in direct contact. During radiation, thermal **energy is transferred from the body to the environment** in the form of electromagnetic waves.

39. F The body's thermoregulatory center is the **hypothalamus**.

40. T **41.** T

42. F Insensible water loss is the **loss of water on a continual basis without us being aware of it**. Water is lost through mucus membranes, the skin, and lungs. Sweat is lost through sweat glands in the skin and is regulated according to our body's needs.

43. T

44. F **Homeothermic** animals can regulate their body temperatures within a narrow range. Poikilothermic animals have little internal control over body temperatures and therefore their temperatures fluctuate widely.

Sequencing

45. f, a, e, b, c, d

Clinical Question

46. Fever is an elevated body temperature caused by a shifting in the body's temperature set point. This shift is often caused by either a bacterial or viral infection. This is accomplished by pyrogens that are secreted by white blood cells and act to stimulate the thermoregulatory center to increase the set point. **The fever is the body's way of trying to create an unsuitable environment for the invader.** By giving the child aspirin and reducing the slight fever, the mother is short-cutting the body's natural defense against the infection.

Challenge Questions

47. Both negative and positive feedback are similar in that they **help to maintain homeostasis** in the body. They are different in that **negative feedback** acts in a direction opposite to the initial stimulus, while **positive feedback** acts in the same direction as the initial stimulus. They also differ in that the response from negative feedback generally takes somewhat longer to occur as compared with responses generated by positive feedback. Positive feedback is less common than negative feedback in the human body.

48. When Mary Jane visits the desert, she tends to gain heat and her body responds by trying to cool her down. Her body attempts to transfer heat to the external environment in three ways: 1) **increased sweating** induces evaporative heat loss, 2) **increased blood flow to the skin** transfers heat to the environment through radiation, and 3) the hypothalamus lets Mary Jane know that she is thirsty and she will drink more water, which **hydrates** her body and aids in cooling her down.

49. Convection ovens have fans inside of them to move the air inside of the oven. This **moving air** helps to distribute the heat more evenly. Physiologically, this is important because **convection (moving air) helps to transfer heat away from your body** when it is warm. The body has no control over external moving air. However, we can increase our exposed surface area to take advantage of convection. When it is cold outside, we add more clothing to reduce heat loss due to convection. Conversely, when it is hot outside, we wear less clothing to increase heat loss due to convection.

Concept Map

50. a. set point, **b.** integrating center, **c.** effector organ, **d.** regulated variable, **e.** sensors.

CHAPTER 2

BIOMOLECULES

Matching

1. a. C, **b.** N, **c.** P, **d.** L, **e.** L, **f.** C.

Completion

2. a. biomolecules, **b.** Nucleotides, **c.** DNA, **d.** Carbohydrates, **e.** Proteins, **f.** polypeptides, **g.** lipids.

Short Answer

3. Saturated fatty acids have only single covalent bonds between the carbon atoms, whereas **unsaturated fatty acids** have one or more double bonds between carbon atoms.

4. Polypeptides are chains of amino acids joined together by peptide bonds. These amino acids are joined by dehydration synthesis with the amine end of one amino acid linked to the acid end of the next amino acid.

5. a. The complimentary strand of DNA would be **TTAACGTTACT**. **b.** The base sequence of an RNA molecule made from the DNA base sequence AATTGCAATGA would be **UUAACGUUACU**. **c.** There are a total of **seven pyrimidines** (five uracils and two guanines) and **four purines** (three adenines and one guanine) present in the RNA molecule.

Multiple Choice

6. e **7.** a **8.** e **9.** d **10.** e

True/False

11. F Amphipathic means that a molecule **has both polar and nonpolar components** associated with it.

12. T **13.** T

14. F Eicosanoids are modified fatty acids that **function in intercellular communication between cells.** DNA and RNA are the genetic material of cells.

15. T

Clinical Question

16. The biomolecule he would suggest you eat more of is **cellulose**, which is a polysaccharide (carbohydrate) found in plant cells. Human digestive tracts are not well adapted to digest and absorb cellulose. **This indigestible fiber adds bulk to the feces and aids in stimulating defecation.**

Challenge Questions

17. **Plasma is composed primarily of water, a polar substance. Steroid hormones** such as testosterone and estrogen **are nonpolar.** Because of their nonpolar nature, **testosterone and estrogen are poorly dissolved in the plasma and prefer cellular lipid membranes.** Therefore, they are bound to specific transport proteins that aid in transporting the hormones from their site of production to where they will exert their effects.

18. Both **DNA** and **RNA** are composed of structural units called **nucleotides.** Each nucleotide is composed of a nitrogen-containing base, a phosphate group, and a 5-carbon carbohydrate. **DNA is a double-stranded** molecule composed of the bases adenine (A), guanine (G), thymine (T), and cytosine (C) plus the carbohydrate deoxyribose. **RNA is usually single stranded** and contains the bases adenine, guanine, and cytosine, **but has uracil (U) instead of thymine, and also contains the carbohydrate ribose** instead of deoxyribose. **The function of DNA is storage** of genetic information within the nucleus, while **RNA is necessary for the expression of the DNA** and can be located in either the nucleus or cytoplasm.

19. **Hydrogen bonds** form between hydrogen atoms in the amine group of one amino acid and the oxygen atom in the carboxyl group of another amino acid in the same polypeptide. **These bonds produce the secondary protein structures such as alpha helices** and **beta-pleated sheets**, which contribute to the three-dimensional nature of proteins. When these hydrogen bonds are disrupted by abnormal pH or temperatures, this folding pattern is disrupted and the protein cannot perform its physiological function.

20. **Tendons are composed of fibrous proteins** (e.g., collagen) that are elongated and that attach muscle to bone. **Myoglobin is a globular protein** whose structure is coiled and bulky and functions in carrying oxygen.

CELL STRUCTURE

Matching

21. a. NM, **b.** M, **c.** NM, **d.** M, **e.** NM, **f.** NM, **g.** M, **h.** NM.

Completion

22. a. phospholipid bilayer, **b.** Membrane proteins, **c.** transmembrane proteins, **d.** integral membrane proteins, **e.** Peripheral membrane proteins, **f.** Carbohydrates, **g.** lipids.

23. a. intermediate filaments, **b.** examples include actin and microvilli, **c.** microtubules

Short Answer

24. The **plasma membrane** is considered "**fluid**" because the molecules associated with the membrane (phospholipids, proteins, cholesterol, etc.) are **able to move about because they are not linked by chemical bonds.** The plasma membrane is considered a "**mosaic**" because of the many different parts that make up the membrane.

25. **Proteins are manufactured at ribosomes** that are either associated with the endoplasmic reticulum, or with free ribosomes in the cytosol. The **ribosomes associated with the rough endoplasmic reticulum** synthesize proteins that are secreted from cells. Proteins that are **made in association with free ribosomes** will remain in the cytosol, enter a mitochondrion, the nucleus, or peroxisomes.

26. **Mitochondria have a double membrane.** The **outer membrane** surrounds the entire organelle, while the **inner membrane** contains numerous folds called **cristae.** This folding increases the surface area exposed to the fluid contents, or **matrix,** of the mitochondrion. It is on the inner membrane where the **electron transport chain** is located. The area between the two membranes is called the **intermembrane space.**

Multiple Choice

27. a **28.** e **29.** c **30.** d **31.** b **32.** c
33. e **34.** d

True/False

35. F The cytosol is the **fluid of the cytoplasm.**

36. F Ribosomes can be free in the cytoplasm or **associated with the endoplasmic reticulum.**

37. F The number of mitochondria in various cells is **dependent upon the energy needs of the cells.** Muscle cells that are actively involved in movement have many more mitochondria that do most skin cells.

38. T **39.** T **40.** T

41. F The type of protein that insulin binds to is a **transmembrane protein.** Peripheral proteins are associated with the cytoskeleton and are involved in cellular support.

Labeling

42. a. The functions of **vaults** is still not clear, but it is thought that one function is in assisting in the transfer of molecules around the cell.

b. The **nucleus** serves as a site of DNA storage and provides the instructions for protein synthesis.

c. The **mitochondrion** provides the cell with most of its ATP supply.

d. **Rough endoplasmic reticulum** is where the integral proteins, phospholipids, and cholesterol associated with the plasma membrane are synthesized.

e. **Free-floating ribosomes** are a site of synthesis of proteins that will stay in the cytosol.

f. The **smooth endoplasmic reticulum** has enzymes involved in lipid metabolism and detoxification of drugs in the liver and kidneys.

g. The **centrioles** are important animal organelles involved in cell division.

h. The **Golgi apparatus** functions to modify, concentrate, and package the proteins made at the rough endoplasmic reticulum.

43. a. A **carbohydrate bound to lipid** functions in forming the glycocalyx, which is a protective layer that holds the cell together.

b. Glycolipids are carbohydrates bound to lipids; they can function in cell recognition or in forming the glycocalyx.

c. Integral membrane proteins can serve as carrier proteins that transport molecules from one side of the membrane to the other.

d. Peripheral membrane proteins often function to help form the cytoskeleton.

e. The **cytoskeleton** is a group of proteins that gives the cell structure and support.

f. Carbohydrates bound to proteins function in forming the glycocalyx, which is a protective layer that holds the cell together.

g. Glycoproteins are carbohydrates bound to proteins; they can function in cell recognition.

h. Cholesterol decreases the ability of water to cross the lipid bilayer.

i. The **phospholipid bilayer** provides a barrier to large polar molecules.

j. Phospholipid heads are hydrophilic and face the inside and outside of the cell.

k. Fatty acid tails are hydrophobic and face each other.

Challenge Questions

44. Microtubules are most likely the organelles affected by drugs such as nicotine. **Cilia are the main propellers of substances across the cell surfaces.** A cilium is composed of ten pairs of microtubules; disruption in the microtubules would likely lead to the cell's inability to effectively propel substances across its surface.

45. The **carbohydrate chains** associated with membrane lipids and membrane proteins **function in cell recognition**. This allows the body's immune system to recognize normal membrane glycoproteins and glycolipids as "self" rather than as "foreign." This recognition system **keeps your immune system from attacking your cells, but allows it to recognize and destroy foreign cells**. In order for this recognition to operate, the glycoproteins and glycolipids must be on the outside of the cell membrane where other cells of the body can communicate with them and recognize them as "self."

46. Integral membrane proteins are part of the membrane structure and are firmly inserted in the lipid bilayer. All integral membrane proteins have both hydrophobic and hydrophilic regions. They can **function as receptors for chemical messengers, transport, or act as carriers** that bind a substance and move it through the membrane. **Peripheral membrane proteins** are not embedded in the lipid bilayer at all and are usually associated with exposed parts of integral proteins or the lipid bilayer. Most of them are on the inside of the cell **associated with the cytoskeleton and provide cellular support**. Some peripheral proteins also have **enzymatic functions**.

47. There appears to be an association between the number of **vaults** and the **multidrug resistance** of cancer patients. Individuals who have multidrug resistance have a greater concentration of vaults in their cells. There has yet to be shown, however, any cause and effect correlation between these two variables.

CELL-TO-CELL ADHESIONS

Matching

48. a. D, **b.** GJ, **c.** GJ, **d.** TJ, **e.** D, **f.** TJ

Short Answer

49. These are both ways for substances to travel across epithelia. In **paracellular movement, the substances move around cells**, whereas in **transepithelial transport**, substances (such as polar solutes) **travel through the epithelial cell layer** from one side to the other.

True/False

50. T

51. F **Both membranes**, apical and basolateral, face the extracellular fluid.

52. F Gap junctions are most often located between **smooth muscle cells and cells of the heart**.

53. T

Labeling

54. a. Desmosomes can be found between cells of the skin. They have cadherins that link to the intracellular filaments of adjoining cells.

b. Gap junctions are most notably found in the heart and smooth muscle. The cells are connected by connexons.

c. Tight junctions have integral membrane proteins called occludins that fuse adjacent cells together. Epithelial cells lining the organs often have tight junctions.

Clinical Question

55. In order for all of the cells of the atria or ventricles to beat at the same time they must communicate with each other. **Gap junctions allow for free movement of ions between cells, which coordinates muscular contractions**. These gap junctions join cells together by an interlocking of membrane proteins called *connexons*. Because these connexons are channel proteins, they form small passageways, which let small molecules and ions flow freely from cell to cell.

Challenge Question

56. Epithelial tissue that lines hollow organs **acts as a barrier, separating the contents of the lumen from the environment surrounding the hollow organ**. Often the contents of the hollow organ are different from the contents outside of the organ (think of the inside of the stomach with its very acidic juices compared to the organs within the abdominal cavity). The epithelial tissue that lines the hollow organs must act to contain the contents.

Tight junctions and the associated adhesion molecule, occludin, help to form a tight barrier to the outside world. These interlocking occludins tightly bind the lipid portions of the adjoining cell membranes. This attachment is so tight that these junctions can prevent the passage of water and solutes between cells.

GENERAL CELL FUNCTIONS

Matching

57. a. T, **b.** EX, **c.** RME, **d.** PH, **e.** PI.

Completion

58. a. exocytosis, **b.** receptor-mediated endocytosis, **c.** phagocytic vesicle (phagolysosome), **d.** endocytic vesicle, **e.** receptors, **f.** coated pit.

Short Answer

59. Metabolism is the sum total of all of the chemical reactions that occur inside the cells of the body.

60. The breakdown of larger molecules into smaller ones is an example of **catabolism**, which liberates energy.

Multiple Choice

61. e   **62.** b   **63.** b   **64.** d   **65.** c

True/False

66. T   **67.** T

68. F During transcytosis, **macromolecules are moved across epithelial cells**. Exocytosis functions to add components to the cell membrane.

69. F Transcytosis is **common to epithelial tissue**.

Sequencing

70. e, a, c, b, d

Challenge Question

71. Endocytosis and **exocytosis** are similar in that they **move large substances using the formation of vesicles**. They are also similar because both processes **require energy** to perform their tasks. The two are different in the direction in which large molecules are moved. **Endocytosis moves large molecules into the cell, whereas exocytosis moves particles out of the cell.**

Concept Map

72. a. exocytosis, **b.** transcytosis, **c.** phagocytosis, **d.** pinocytosis, **e.** receptor-mediated endocytosis.

PROTEIN SYNTHESIS

Matching

73. a. TL, **b.** TR, **c.** TR, **d.** TL, **e.** TR, **f.** TL.

Completion

74. a. cytosol, **b.** rough endoplasmic reticulum, **c.** leader sequence, **d.** mitochondrion, **e.** Golgi apparatus.

Short Answer

75. Transcription occurs in the nucleus when a complimentary copy of mRNA is made from DNA. The mRNA molecule then moves out of the nucleus to the ribosomes. **Translation occurs in the cytoplasm** in association with ribosomes where amino acids are assembled in the correct sequence to form proteins.

76. A **gene** is the genetic information carried in the DNA sequence and codes for a particular protein or proteins.

77. Polyribosomes are a number of ribosomes associated with one mRNA molecule present during translation. Polyribosomes are formed because **each mRNA is assembled at more than one ribosome at the same time.**

Multiple Choice

78. b   **79.** a   **80.** d   **81.** e   **82.** c   **83.** e
84. a   **85.** c

True/False

86. T

87. F In the cytosol, proteins are degraded by **proteases**. RNA polymerase is an enzyme that helps to break the two strands of DNA.

88. T

89. F The mRNA codon for the DNA triplet AAT would be **UUA**; U replaces T in RNA.

90. T

91. F If protein synthesis occurs at the rough endoplasmic reticulum, the leader sequence and associated ribosome will bind to **signal recognition proteins**.

Sequencing

92. d, e, a, j, i, b, g, h, c, f

Clinical Question

93. The drug *clotrimazole* likely exerts its effects in the **cytoplasm** since transcription takes place in the cytoplasm and is associated with the ribosomes.

Challenge Questions

94. DNA is the template for making mRNA. **RNA polymerase** attaches to the DNA at the appropriate promoter sequence and initiates the separation of DNA into two strands. **RNA polymerase** also catalyzes the formation of bonds between the nucleotides. **mRNA** is made through transcription of DNA in the nucleus. mRNA then moves out of the nucleus through nuclear pores to the ribosomes where translation takes place. **tRNA** carries the appropriate amino acid to the ribosomes. The **ribosomes** align the mRNA with the appropriate anticodon on the tRNA.

95. The **leader sequence** is a sequence of amino acids that determines whether a protein will be synthesized in the cytosol or associated with the endoplasmic reticulum. By contrast, the **promoter sequence** is a sequence of DNA to which the RNA polymerase binds in order to initiate transcription.

96. a. Each of the three bases on an mRNA molecule that codes for an amino acid is called a codon, so this mRNA molecule has a total of **nine codons**. **b.** The first codon is called an initiator codon and codes for the first amino acid, which starts the process of translation. Each of the next seven codons codes for one amino acid. The last codon is the termination codon and does not code for an amino acid. Therefore, a total of **eight amino acids** is coded for by this mRNA sequence.

Concept Map

97. a. vesicle buds off of smooth endoplasmic reticulum

b. vesicle empties contents into lumen of Golgi apparatus

c. Golgi apparatus sorts and packages proteins into vesicles

CELL DIVISION

Matching

98. a. M, **b.** PM, **c.** I, **d.** T, **e.** P, **f.** A, **g.** C.

Completion

99. a. Meiosis, **b.** mitosis, **c.** cell division, **d.** S, **e.** protein, **f.** grows.

Short Answer

100. During **semiconservative replication,** the DNA molecule is copied with each strand of DNA serving as a template. Each new DNA molecule synthesized consists of an old strand that serves as both a template and a new strand. **This occurs during the S phase of interphase.**

Multiple Choice

101. d   **102.** b   **103.** c

True/False

104. F **Proto-oncogenes are mutations that have serious effects** on unregulated cell growth and cause cancer.

105. T   **106.** T

107. F Chromosomes are coiled around proteins called **histones**. Proteosomes help to break down proteins.

Clinical Question

108. Centrioles and spindle fibers are important for moving the chromosomes around the cell during mitosis. **Interruption of this chromosome movement would prevent the cell from dividing.** These chemotherapy drugs also affect non-cancerous cells, which is why the rapidly dividing cells that produce your hair are also inhibited from reproducing, thus resulting in hair loss.

Challenge Questions

109. During mitosis, each chromosome is divided in half; one chromatid of each chromosome goes into each of the two daughter cells. This means that **each of the daughter cells now has only half of the DNA that each needs**. During the S phase of the next cell cycle, each daughter cell replicates the DNA. **This restores the correct amount of DNA in each cell.**

110. Interphase occurs between cell divisions. DNA is replicated, proteins are made, and the cell increases in size in anticipation of cell division. **Mitosis** is the process of nuclear division of the cell, whereas **cytokinesis** is the process of division of the cell's cytoplasm.

111. The cell would have gone through mitosis, so **two nuclei would exist**. However, the cell fails to proceed with cytokinesis, **so both nuclei would exist within a single cell**.

112. All of the cells of your body that have **23 pairs of chromosomes** are identical in their genetic makeup because **a single fertilized egg went through mitosis to produce all of the cells of your body**. Mitosis simply splits each of the chromosomes in half and, during the S phase of interphase, each of these split chromosomes is replicated. This process produces two genetically identical cells; each of these cells then goes through mitosis, thus producing the 100 trillion genetically identical cells of your body. (But, as you will see later in Chapter 21, your reproductive cells are not all genetically the same).

Concept Map

113. a. G0, **b.** G1, **c.** S, **d.** G2, **e.** prophase, **f.** prometaphase, **g.** metaphase, **h.** telophase, **i.** cytokinesis, **j.** mitosis

CHAPTER 3

TYPES OF METABOLIC REACTIONS

Matching

1. a. OR, **b.** DR, **c.** CR, **d.** OR, **e.** OR, **f.** RR

Completion

2. a. energy, **b.** biomolecules, **c.** work, **d.** future use, **e.** energy metabolism.

Multiple Choice

3. b   **4.** a   **5.** e   **6.** d   **7.** c   **8.** d

True/False

9. F Hydrolysis reactions are **catabolic** reactions.

10. F A phosphorylation reaction involves the addition of a **phosphate group** to a molecule.

11. T   **12.** T   **13.** T   **14.** T

Short Answer

15. Metabolism is all the chemical reactions that occur within cells.

16. Catabolic reactions are energy-releasing reactions that break down larger molecules into smaller molecules. **Anabolic reactions** are energy-requiring reactions that produce larger molecules from smaller reactants.

Challenge Questions

17. The technical definition of an **oxidation reaction** is that it is one in which **electrons are removed from a molecule**. If the molecule affected was originally electrically neutral, it will become positively charged when it is oxidized. An oxidation reaction can also be defined as the **reaction of any molecule with oxygen**, because oxygen atoms tend to pull electrons away from other atoms to which they are bound. Oxidation reactions can also be defined as the **removal of hydrogen atoms from a molecule**; as each hydrogen atom contains an electron, so electrons are removed when hydrogen atoms are removed.

18. The terms **forward and reverse refer to the direction of the <u>net</u> reaction**. A forward reaction is one in which the majority of chemical activity involves reactants being converted to products. In a reverse reaction, most of the activity involves products being converted to reactants.

Clinical Question

19. Since Sara is not ingesting food, the **energy will come from the energy stores** within her body (e.g., glycogen stores and fat stores). **Catabolic reactions** include the breakdown of glycogen to glucose and the breakdown of fats to fatty acids and glycerol.

Labeling

20. A + B → C + D
reactants **products**

METABOLIC REACTIONS AND ENERGY

Matching

21. a. ERL, **b.** ERQ, **c.** ERQ, **d.** ERQ, **e.** ERL, **f.** ERL

Completion

22. a. raw materials, **b.** urine, **c.** pumping, **d.** multiplication/proliferation, **e.** contraction or relaxation

Multiple Choice

23. b **24.** c **25.** a **26.** e **27.** e

True/False

28. T **29.** T

30. F An increase in the concentration of reactants relative to products will cause a reaction to proceed spontaneously in the **forward** direction.

31. F The transition state is the high energy state in which **reactants exist before being converted to products**.

32. T

Short Answer

33. Anabolic and catabolic reactions are coupled within cells such that the energy released from catabolic reactions is used to drive anabolic reactions.

34. Thermal motion is the source of the kinetic energy present in atoms and molecules. It refers to the **random movement/vibration of atoms** that occurs at temperatures above absolute zero.

35. ΔE represents the energy change of a reaction. It is the difference between the energy of the products and the energy of the reactants.

$$\Delta E = E_{products} - E_{reactants}$$

Challenge Questions

36. Even though energy-releasing reactions proceed spontaneously in the forward direction once the reaction is started, **activation energy is required to put the reactants into the transition state that enables the reactants to begin chemically interacting**. Once the reaction begins, it will proceed spontaneously without energy input.

37. The **law of mass action** says that **an increase in reactant concentration relative to product concentration will drive a reaction forward, while an increase in products relative to reactants will drive a reaction in the reverse direction.** This occurs because, as the concentration of molecules increases, the number of collisions between molecules increases, which thereby increases the energy of those molecules.

38. Molecular collisions generate the potential energy needed to overcome the activation energy barrier. Molecules collide with each other because they are in constant thermal motion. When these collisions occur, some of the kinetic energy is converted to potential energy. When the amount of potential energy exceeds the activation energy barrier, the molecules will enter the transition state.

REACTION RATES

Matching

39. a. D, **b.** D, **c.** I, **d.** I, **e.** D, **f.** D

Completion

40. a. enzyme, **b.** cofactor, **c.** substrate, **d.** coenzyme, **e.** active site, **f.** regulatory site, **g.** modulator

True/False

41. F The chemical composition of an enzyme is **NOT** altered by the chemical reactions in which it participates.

42. F Enzymes will interact **only with specific substrates**.

43. F The reaction rate in an enzyme-catalyzed reaction will increase **only until the enzyme is 100% saturated**.

44. T

45. F Dephosphorylation reactions are catalyzed by **phosphatases**; phosphorylation reactions are catalyzed by protein kinases.

46. T

Multiple Choice

47. d **48.** b **49.** a **50.** c **51.** b

Labeling

<pre>
                    enzyme-
                    substrate
                    complex
52. E + S ⇔ E • S → P + E
        binding   catalytic
         step   step
</pre>

53. **a.** enzyme, **b.** substrate, **c.** enzyme-substrate complex, **d.** product, **e.** product, **f.** active site.

Short Answer

54. The **rate of a chemical reaction** measures how fast it consumes reactants and generates products. The **net rate** is the difference between the rate of the forward reaction and the rate of the reverse reaction.

55. **Affinity** refers to how tightly a substrate molecule binds to the active site on an enzyme.

Challenge Questions

56. **Feedback inhibition and feedforward activation are similar** in that both regulate the activity of enzymes involved in metabolic pathways and both do so as the result of the influence of a molecule or molecules within the pathway on an enzyme's activity. Both can be used to keep the reaction rates of a metabolic pathway steady.

The **difference between the two** is that in **feedback inhibition**, a pathway product or intermediate downstream from an enzyme inhibits the activity of that enzyme and, in **feedforward activation**, a pathway intermediate upstream from an enzyme activates the enzyme.

57. The **lock-and-key hypothesis is less accurate than the induced-fit hypothesis** as it implies that a substrate will fit exactly into an active site just as a key fits into a lock. In actuality, **when a substrate enters an active site it induces a slight conformational change in the active site, causing it to fit the shape of the substrate more precisely.**

58. As **temperature increases, the kinetic energy of individual molecules increases** and, therefore, the energy converted to potential energy when these molecules collide will increase as well. Increased temperature also **increases the number of molecular collisions**. Therefore, as temperature increases, the **rate of the reaction will increase** because the proportion of molecular collisions with energy sufficient to overcome the activation energy barrier will increase.

59. Increasing the reactant concentration will **increase the number of molecular collisions that occur**, thus increasing the energy of the reactants, which will increase the rate of the reaction.

Clinical Question

60. The **ingestion of aspirin made Bob's blood acidic.** Since enzyme activity within cells is highly dependent on the pH of the internal environment, **many of the enzymes in Bob's cells will no longer work properly**

under acidic conditions. Therefore, many of the metabolic reactions within Bob's cells will stop working normally, resulting in abnormal cellular functioning.

Concept Map

61. **a.** regulatory site on enzyme, **b.** active site, **c.** catalytic rate, **d.** affinity for substrate

GLUCOSE OXIDATION: THE CENTRAL REACTION OF ENERGY METABOLISM

True/False

62. F The oxidation of one mole of glucose **releases** 686 kcal of energy.

63. T   64. T

Short Answer

65. The primary **purpose of glucose oxidation within human cells** is to **release energy from glucose** that is used to **generate ATP**, which is the energy source for cellular work.

66. 6 carbon dioxide molecules, 6 water molecules, 38 ATP molecules

67. **ATP is the form of energy used by cells to perform their functions.** (This is the primary function—it has other biochemical functions as well. For example, the second messenger cAMP is formed from ATP.)

68. The chemical name of ATP is **adenosine triphosphate**.

69. **ATP → ADP + P_i + energy.** This is a **hydrolysis reaction.**

Challenge Question

70. **Glucose oxidation and ATP synthesis are coupled** because some of the energy released during glucose oxidation is used to **drive ATP synthesis**.

Clinical Question

71. **While some of the energy released during glucose oxidation is used to generate ATP, not all of it is.** This **remaining energy is dissipated as heat** and contributes to the maintenance of body temperature. Since Joe is metabolizing a lot of glucose to meet the high energy needs of his muscle cells, a lot of heat is being generated, thus increasing his body temperature.

STAGES OF GLUCOSE OXIDATION: GLYCOLYSIS, THE KREBS CYCLE, AND OXIDATIVE PHOSPHORYLATION

Matching

72. **a.** IMM, **b.** MM, **c.** ISM, **d.** C, **e.** MM

Sequencing

73. c, b, d, a

74. b, d, a, c, f, e

Completion

75. a. 2, **b.** 0, **c.** 0, **d.** 2, **e.** 2, **f.** 0, **g.** 2, **h.** 0, **i.** 6, **j.** 2, **k.** 4, **l.** 2, **m.** 0, **n.** 0, **o.** 0, **p.** 34

Multiple Choice

76. d **77.** b **78.** c **79.** b **80.** b **81.** c
82. a **83.** b **84.** c **85.** e

Labeling

86. a. 2 NADH + 2 H$^+$, **b.** 2 ATP, **c.** 2 NADH + 2 H$^+$, **d.** 2 CO_2, **e.** 6 NADH + 6 H$^+$, **f.** 2 $FADH_2$, **g.** 4 CO_2, **h.** 2 ATP, **i.** 12 H_2O, **j.** 34 ATP

Challenge Questions

87. Oxygen serves as the final electron acceptor of the electron transport chain. Without it, the electron transport chain won't function and ATP can be synthesized only by glycolysis. Cells cannot function on the 2 ATPs per molecule of glucose produced anaerobically—they require the much greater amount of ATP produced aerobically in order to survive.

88. Sugars, such as fructose and galactose, are first converted by enzymes to intermediates of the glycolytic pathway. They then enter the pathway at the appropriate step and proceed to be oxidized just as glucose is.

Clinical Questions

89. Because the patient was in cardiac and respiratory arrest, there was **very little oxygen available to his cells.** Therefore, **most cells were generating ATP anaerobically**, which results in the **production of lactic acid.** The lactic acid built up in his blood, producing the acidosis reflected in his pH value.

90. It would have the same effect as the absence of oxygens to the cells. Refer to the importance of the electron transport chain in the answer to Question 87.

True/False

91. T **92.** T

93. F The anaerobic production of ATP occurs in the **cytosol.**

94. F The Krebs cycle generates ATP by **substrate-level phosphorylation.**

95. F Glycolysis produces **two molecules of pyruvate** for every molecule of glucose that enters it.

96. F ATP synthase is involved in **aerobic** ATP production.

Concept Map

97. a. lactate dehydrogenase, **b.** acetyl CoA, **c.** lactic acid, **d.** Krebs cycle, **e.** NADH, **f.** $FADH_2$, **g.** chemiosmosis

ENERGY STORAGE AND UTILIZATION: METABOLISM OF CARBOHYDRATES, FATS, AND PROTEINS

Matching

98. a. K, **b.** G, **c.** T, **d.** A

Completion

99. a. lipolysis, **b.** gluconeogenesis, **c.** proteolysis, **d.** glycogenolysis, **e.** glycogenesis, **f.** lipogenesis, **g.** C, **h.** A, **i.** C, **j.** C, **k.** A, **l.** A

Multiple Choice

100. c **101.** e **102.** d **103.** d **104.** b **105.** a
106. c **107.** d **108.** b **109.** e

True/False

110. T **111.** T

112. F Proteins are broken down **only** into amino acids; ammonia is converted to urea.

113. T

114. F Some amino acids can be converted to glucose.

115. T **116.** T

Short Answer

117. A **bypass reaction** is a reverse reaction that bypasses the enzymes of the forward reaction.

Challenge Questions

118. No. One-way reactions, although often referred to as irreversible, are simply reactions that rarely run in the reverse direction because to do so requires the input of large quantities of energy.

119. Nervous tissue does not store glycogen, and it is very difficult for nerve cells to switch to alternate sources of energy. Therefore, **if the supply of glucose is limited, brain cells will not be able to generate adequate amounts of ATP and will not function normally**, which can result in loss of consciousness.

Clinical Questions

120. A molecule of fat generates much more ATP than a molecule of glucose or protein because many molecules of acetyl CoA can be produced from a single fatty acid molecule, and the catabolism of fatty acids produces a number of NADH and $FADH_2$ molecules that participate in oxidative phosphorylation. Therefore, fat is a higher calorie food than carbohydrates or proteins, and eating a high-fat diet will slow or prevent weight loss.

121. 1. Her blood glucose level has steadily dropped.

2. Glycogen stores are being used up.

3. Fat and protein are broken down and are used for energy.

4. The break down of fat generates ketones that cause her breath to have a fruity odor.

5. Continued low blood glucose levels result in less than optimum functioning of her nervous tissue, resulting in tiredness and sluggishness.

Concept Map

122. a. glycolysis, **b.** pyruvate, **c.** acetyl CoA, **d.** Krebs cycle, **e.** oxidative phosphorylation

CHAPTER 4

FACTORS AFFECTING THE DIRECTION OF TRANSPORT

Matching

1. a. AT, **b.** AT, **c.** PT, **d.** PT, **e.** AT.

Completion

2. a. chemical, **b.** electrical, **c.** electrochemical, **d.** net.

Short Answer

3. When the **equilibrium potential** is zero, **the electrical driving force is equal and opposite to the chemical driving force**. This situation makes the electrical driving force equal to zero and **no net diffusion** of the molecule will occur into or out of the cell.

4. Membrane potential is the difference in electrical potential that exists across the cell membrane.

5. Cations are positively charged ions. Examples include K^+, Ca^{++}, and Na^+. **Anions** are negatively charged ions. Examples include Cl^- and HCO_3^-.

6. If this cell is to gain more calcium it will have to move the calcium up the electrochemical gradient. To accomplish this, the cell will need to use **active transport**.

Multiple Choice

7. a   **8.** b   **9.** b   **10.** e   **11.** d

Labeling

12. a. inward, **b.** outward, **c.** inward, **d.** inward, **e.** outward, **f.** inward

True/False

13. F Most cells are **negatively charged**.

14. F Passive transport **does not require energy;** active transport does.

15. T   **16.** T

17. F The electrical and chemical forces must be **equal and in opposite directions** for an equilibrium potential to exist.

Sequencing

18. Cl^- , Na^+ , Ca^{++}

Clinical Question

19. The sodium is positively charged and the chloride negatively charged. When the epithelial cells secrete chloride ions into the lumen, **sodium is attracted to the lumen due to the electrical driving force of the chloride ions. Water follows due to an osmotic driving force.**

Challenge Questions

20. Passive and active transport are similar in that they are important **mechanisms for transporting substances across the cell membrane.** They differ in important ways: **passive transport** moves substances down the electro-chemical gradient and thus does not require energy, whereas **active transport** moves substances up the electrochemical gradient and requires energy input from the cell.

21. Chemical and electrical driving forces are different in the ways that they act on the movement of molecules. **Chemical driving force** is the force generated by the concentration gradient of molecules. Molecules are moved from areas of high concentration to areas of low concentration by the chemical driving force. The **electrical driving force** moves molecules based on the charges associated with the molecules. Similar charges will repel each other, while opposite charges are attracted to each other.

Concept Map

22.

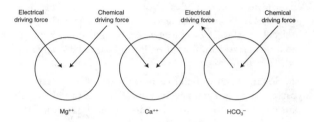

FACTORS AFFECTING THE RATE OF TRANSPORT

Matching

23. Passive transport: a. D, **b.** I, **c.** I

   Active transport: d. I, **e.** D

Completion

24. a. flux, **b.** unidirectional, **c.** net, **d.** magnitude, **e.** surface area, **f.** permeability, **g.** pump, **h.** number

Short Answer

25. Net flux is the difference between two unidirectional fluxes.

26. The **permeability** of a cell membrane is the ease with which molecules are able to move through it.

Multiple Choice

27. b   **28.** a

True/False

29. T

30. F **Diffusion continues to happen** when a cell and its environment come to equilibrium but the net flux is zero.

31. T

32. F The greater the concentration difference between the inside and the outside of the cell, the **faster** diffusion takes place.

33. F The rate of actively transported substances depends on the **rate at which individual protein pumps operate** (also on the **number of pumps** in the membrane).

Labeling

34. Line A indicates higher permeability than line B. We know this because, at any concentration, the net flux for A is always greater than that for B.

Clinical Question

35. The **surface area of the lungs decreases** by the pathological destruction and clogging of the alveoli and the closing off of the air sacs. This means that less oxygen can diffuse into the bloodstream and less carbon dioxide can diffuse out of the bloodstream.

Challenge Question

36. Because Na^+ is moving both into and out of the cell, the **flux is in both directions.** However, the **net flux is into the cell,** with the majority of sodium ions moving into the cell.

Concept Map

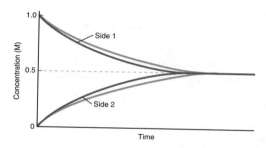

37. By reducing the surface area of the membrane, diffusion takes longer. This is evident by each line taking longer to reach equilibrium. That is, the decrease in surface area of the membrane reduces the time it takes for diffusion to occur.

SIMPLE DIFFUSION: PASSIVE TRANSPORT THROUGH THE LIPID BILAYER

Matching

38. a. HP, **b.** HP, **c.** LP, **d.** LP.

Short Answer

39. Simple diffusion is the random movement of molecules down their concentration gradient. The four factors that affect membrane permeability in simple diffusion include the following: 1) the **lipid solubility** of the diffusing molecule. Since the membrane is composed of lipids, the more lipid soluble a substance is the faster diffusion will occur. 2) The **size and shape of the molecule** diffusion through the membrane. Smaller and more regularly shaped molecules can diffuse through the membrane faster than larger, irregularly shaped molecules. 3) The **thickness of a tissue layer.** The thinner the tissue layer, the faster diffusion takes place. 4) **Temperature.** The trend is for higher temperatures to produce faster rates of diffusion. This, however, is not a common factor when dealing with human physiology.

40. The inner portion of the **lipid bilayer is composed of fatty acids (hydrophobic molecules)** that act as a barrier to most hydrophilic substances. **Fatty acids, steroid hormones, and vitamin E are all hydrophobic** and can therefore move easily across the lipid bilayer.

41. The lipid solubility of a molecule will have the strongest influence on membrane permeability.

Labeling

42. a. Line C represents the permeability of an epithelial tissue that has had its surface area reduced by one-half. The reduction in surface area decreases the rate of diffusion. **b.** Very small molecules can cross the epithelial tissue faster than larger molecules. **Line A** represents the rate of diffusion by a small molecule. **c.** By contrast, larger, irregularly shaped molecules cross epithelial tissue layers at a much slower rate, which is represented by **line C.**

Clinical Question

43. Most likely, these drugs are able to make their way into cells more effectively because they contain **hydrophobic** material that can pass easily through the cell membrane. Further, they may contain **small, regularly shaped molecules.**

Challenge Question

44. No, individual molecules do not always move down their concentration gradient, but rather, move at random. However, the population of molecules diffusing will move down the concentration gradient. **Diffusion is the random movement of molecules as a result of the molecules moving down their concentration gradient** due to the thermal energy of the molecules.

FACILITATED DIFFUSION: PASSIVE TRANSPORT THROUGH MEMBRANE PROTEINS

Matching

45. a. CH, **b.** CR, **c.** CH.

Completion

46. a. carriers, **b.** conformational, **c.** pores, **d.** transport, **e.** number.

Short Answer

47. Carrier proteins operate by **first binding to the substance** that is being transported. The carrier then undergoes a **conformational change** that exposes the binding site to the other side of the cell membrane. **The transported substance is then released** to the other side of the membrane.

48. Facilitated diffusion is necessary because cells require substances, such as glucose and amino acids, that cannot diffuse through the lipid bilayer. These hydrophilic substances are not lipid soluble and therefore cannot pass through the lipid bilayer and into the cell without the help of transport proteins.

Multiple Choice

49. e **50.** d **51.** a **52.** e

True/False

53. T **54.** T

55. F Facilitated diffusion transports substances **down their concentration gradient**.

56. F **Hydrophilic substances** are transported by facilitated diffusion. Some hydrophobic molecules can pass directly through the lipid bilayer.

57. T

Sequencing

58. b, a, c, d

Clinical Question

59. For nerve and muscle cells to perform their functions, ions must move across their cell membranes. Inorganic ions, such as Na^+, cannot cross the membrane through the lipid bilayer. Instead, it is transported by **facilitated diffusion through protein channels**. Saxitoxin blocks the voltage-dependent Na^+ channels present in nerve and muscle cells so that these cells cannot perform their functions. The blocking of Na^+ channels in nerves causes the tingling, while the blocking of Na^+ channels in muscles causes the uncoordinated muscle movements.

Challenge Question

60. This cell is using a **channel protein** to transport the substance through **facilitated diffusion**. The fact that the substance is moving down the concentration gradient tells us that it is using diffusion. Further, the fact that a protein is involved with the transport tells us it is facilitated diffusion. Lastly, because binding sites are open at both ends of the membrane at the same time, we know the cell is using channels for transport.

Concept Maps

61. Figure 4.4a shows saturation while Figure 4.4b shows simple diffusion. Note that in Figure 4.4a, at increasing concentrations, the rate of transport levels off (or plateaus). This indicates a saturation of the substance being transported. **Saturation is a characteristic of facilitated diffusion by carrier proteins** and so Figure 4.4a indicates facilitated diffusion.

62. a. molecule binds to the binding site on a carrier

b. carrier undergoes a conformational change

c. the molecule is free to be released

ACTIVE TRANSPORT

Matching

63. a. SAT, **b.** SAT, **c.** PAT, **d.** PAT.

Completion

64. a. energy, **b.** electrochemical gradient, **c.** primary active transport, **d.** secondary active transport, **e.** energy, **f.** cotransport, **g.** different, **h.** same.

Short Answer

65. Primary active transport uses energy in the form of ATP to drive substance up their electrochemical gradients, whereas **secondary active transport** uses the electrochemical gradient of another solute to move a substance up its electrochemical gradient.

66. Cells leak due to passive transport. Substances, either pass through the lipid bilayer or, more commonly, through protein channels where facilitated diffusion occurs.

Multiple Choice

67. a **68.** e **69.** b **70.** c **71.** e **72.** d

True/False

73. F Since the Na^+/K^+ pump is pumping ions up their electrochemical gradients, it **requires energy**.

74. T **75.** T **76.** T

77. F Primary active transport is used when a substance needs to be transported **up its concentration gradient**.

Sequencing

78. b, a, f, c, e, d

Challenge Questions

79. The cell is able to accumulate calcium through **active transport**. The sarcoplasmic reticulum of the muscle cells has numerous Ca^{++} pumps that it uses to move calcium against its electrochemical gradient.

80. If the primary active transport pumps in a cell were to fail, **the Na+ and K+ concentrations would eventually come to equilibrium**. The cells would still leak Na^+ and K^+, but there would be no mechanism to pump Na^+ back out of the cell and K^+ back into the cell. Therefore, Na^+ would move down its electrochemical gradient into the cell and K^+ would move down its electrochemical gradient and out of the cell until **the net flux of both would be zero**.

81. You can tell whether a substance is being transported actively or passively by **whether or not the cell uses energy** to accomplish the task. **Active transport** moves substances up their electrochemical gradient, whereas in **passive transport,** substances flow down their electrochemical gradients, which requires no energy.

82. Cells transport glucose by **secondary active transport**. Sodium is moved into the cell down its electrochemical gradient and releases energy that drives glucose into the cell against its concentration gradient. This form of secondary active transport is known as **sodium-linked glucose transport**.

Concept Map

83. a. simple diffusion, **b.** facilitated diffusion with a channel, **c.** facilitated diffusion with a carrier, **d.** primary active transport, **e.** secondary active transport

OSMOSIS: PASSIVE TRANSPORT OF WATER ACROSS MEMBRANES

Matching

84. a. T, **b.** O, **c.** HPT, **d.** HPO, **e.** I, **f.** IO, **g.** HPR, **h.** HOT.

Completion

85. a. osmosis, **b.** passive, **c.** tonicity, **d.** isotonic, **e.** hypotonic, **f.** hemolysis, **g.** shrink.

Short Answer

86. Hypertonic solutions cause cells to shrink. **Hypotonic** solutions cause cells to swell. **Isotonic** solutions have no effect on cell size.

87. Osmosis is the passive movement of water down its concentration gradient.

Multiple Choice

88. e   **89.** a   **90.** d   **91.** d

True/False

92. T

93. F Water moves from areas that are **hypotonic to areas that are hypertonic**.

94. T

Clinical Question

95. a. The child's blood is **iso-osmotic** relative to normal blood (since 300 mOsm is within the normal range for plasma). **b.** This tells you that, while the child lost water, she also lost solutes in the vomit. In other words, **the vomit has a solute concentration of 300 mOsm** and so this loss did not affect the osmolarity of the blood.

Challenge Questions

96. The **total particles dissolved in solution is what is important for osmolarity**. Sodium chloride dissociates into two particles (Na^+ and Cl^-). Therefore, a solution containing sodium chloride at a concentration of 150 mOsm has twice the osmolarity.

97. Water will move from hypo-osmotic solutions to hyperosmotic solutions. That is, from areas of high water concentration (low solute concentration) to areas of lower water concentrations (high solute concentration). Therefore, in this example, since water has moved from side A to side B, water moved from an area that was hypo-osmotic (side A) to an area that was hyperosmotic (side B). **Side B initially had a higher solute concentration than side A.**

Concept Map

98.

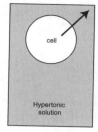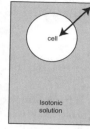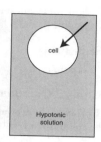

Hypertonic solution   Isotonic solution   Hypotonic solution

MOVEMENT OF MOLECULES ACROSS TWO MEMBRANES: EPITHELIAL TRANSPORT

Matching

99. a. AM, **b.** BM, **c.** AM, **d.** BM, **e.** BM.

Completion

100. a. internal, **b.** external, **c.** apical border, **d.** basal membrane, **e.** Absorption, **f.** epithelial, **g.** polarized.

Short Answer

101. Water transport across epithelia is considered secondary to solute transport because **the differences in solute concentrations drive the movement of the water:** water follows the solutes. The active transport of the solutes into one area of the epithelium makes that area hyperosmotic. Water then follows behind the solute in an attempt to dilute the hyperosmotic area.

Multiple Choice

102. b   **103.** b   **104.** a

True/False

105. T

106. F The movement of glucose into intestinal epithelial cells is **secondary-active transport**.

107. T   **108.** T

109. F **Tight junctions** usually occur between epithelial cells; gap junctions occur between cardiac muscle, smooth muscle cells, and some epithelial cells.

110. T

Labeling

111. a. lumen: central space within a passageway, exchanges material with the apical membrane

b. apical membrane: exchanges materials with the lumen

c. basolateral membrane: exchanges materials with the blood

d. basement membrane: anchors the basolateral membrane and supports the epithelial layer

e. interstitial fluid: highly regulated fluid compartment outside of cells

f. tight junction: joins cells together and permits fluids on either side of the cell layer to differ in composition

Sequencing

112. e, b, d, a, c

Clinical Question

113. No. The seawater is **hyperosmotic** relative to your body fluids and will actually draw water out of your cells (intracellular dehydration), eventually resulting in death.

Challenge Question

114. Tight junctions allow for each cell to have control over the transport of solutes across it. Without tight junctions, all cells of the epithelium would have to transport the same substance at the same rate. These tight junctions allow the cells to be somewhat independent of each other.

Concept Map

115. a. pumps in the basolateral membrane actively transport solute molecules into the interstitial fluid; **b.** solute concentration of the interstitial fluid rises; **c.** water flows from the lumen to the interstitial space

CHAPTER 5

INTERCELLULAR COMMUNICATION

Completion

1. a. secreting **b.** target **c.** receptors **d.** signal transduction mechanisms **e.** chemical messenger

Multiple Choice

2. a   **3.** d

Short Answer

4. Connexins are the plasma membrane proteins that form connexons. **Connexons** form the channels that make up gap junctions.

Challenge Question

5. Cells must be able to **communicate** in order for **homeostasis to be maintained.** Examples of situations in which **cellular communication** occurs include (but are not limited to):

—feeling the warmth of the sun (or other sensation) on your skin

—producing movements of the arms and legs

—producing movements of the digestive tract

—activities of the immune response

—regulating kidney activity in response to dehydration

—process of growth and development

CHEMICAL MESSENGERS

Matching

6. a. C **b.** H **c.** P **d.** NH **e.** A **f.** NT

7. a. CA, P, AU, CY **b.** S, T **c.** P, A

Multiple Choice

8. b   **9.** e   **10.** c   **11.** d   **12.** a   **13.** d
14. d   **15.** c   **16.** a   **17.** e   **18.** d

True/False

19. F The term lipophilic refers to molecules that are lipid soluble, easily cross the plasma membrane, and are **not soluble in water.**

20. T   **21.** T

22. F Histamine is an example of a **paracrine messenger.**

23. T

24. F Neurohormones are secreted by **neurosecretory cells.**

25. F Glutamate, aspartate, glycine, and GABA are **amino acid messengers.**

26. T   **27.** T   **28.** T

29. F **Some** carrier proteins are specific for particular hormones.

30. T

Completion

31. a. tyrosine **b.** amine **c.** 3-phosphoglycerate **d.** amino acid **e.** arachadonic acid **f.** eicosanoid **g.** glucose **h.** amino acid **i.** glutamate **j.** amino acid

Labeling

32. a. paracrines **b.** autocrines **c.** cytokines **d.** neurotransmitters **e.** hormones **f.** neurohormones

Sequencing

33. c, a, b

34. d, b, a, c

Short Answer

35. Presynaptic cells are neurons, while **postsynaptic cells** can be neurons, glands, or muscle cells.

36. The **biological half-life of a hormone** is a measure of the amount of time it remains active in the blood, and is defined as the **time it takes for half the hormone in the blood to be degraded. Hydrophilic** hormones have half-lives of **minutes,** while **hydrophobic** hormones have half-lives of **hours.**

Challenge Questions

37. Only cells with **receptors specific to the hormone** can/will respond to the hormone.

38. Hydrophobic chemical messengers must be synthesized on demand since they easily diffuse through cell membranes so they can't be stored in vesicles and will immediately leave the cell upon being synthesized. Thus they must be synthesized only when needed.

39. No, paracrines and neurotransmitters only affect cells near the site of release because they are **quickly degraded/inactivated** once in the interstitial fluid. Therefore there is no time for them to diffuse to more distant cells before being inactivated, and they generally don't enter the blood so aren't transported to other cells in that way.

Clinical Questions

40. Histamine stimulates inflammation, which causes capillary dilation and increased capillary permeability in the area affected. Capillary dilation results in increased blood flow to the area, making it red and warm, and increased capillary permeability results in the leakage of fluid from the blood, which will result in a runny/stuffy nose if it occurs in the nasal cavity. Histamine can also cause bronchial constriction, resulting in wheezing or coughing.

Histamine induces these effects when it binds to H_1 receptors on affected cells. Antihistamines are H_1 antagonists, and will compete with histamine for these binding sites, preventing histamine from binding. Therefore, **antihistamines should alleviate** (at least partially), **redness** (e.g. redness of the eyes), **swelling and fluid leakage** (stuffy, runny nose), **and wheezing or coughing if the allergen is inhaled. Antihistamines don't cure the allergy**, because they don't prevent the release of histamine in the first place (which is what triggers the allergic reaction). Antihistamines can only alleviate allergy symptoms.

41. Cyclooxygenase is the first enzyme in the pathway leading to the synthesis of prostacyclins and thromboxanes. These are both **important to the process of blood clotting**, and if they are not synthesized in the absence of cyclooxygenase, the blood will not clot normally.

SIGNAL TRANSDUCTION MECHANISMS

Completion

42. a. cytosol **b.** nucleus **c.** synthesis **d.** plasma membrane **e.** activity **f.** long, **g.** short

Matching

43. a. TK **b.** C, D, cAMP **c.** AC, PC

Multiple Choice

44. e   **45.** e   **46.** c   **47.** a   **48.** d   **49.** a
50. b   **51.** a   **52.** d   **53.** e

True/False

54. T

55. F The presence of an antagonist will **decrease** the likelihood that a chemical messenger will bind to the target cell and produce a response.

56. T   **57.** T

58. F Down-regulation makes a target cell **less responsive** to a chemical messenger.

59. F The effects of lipophilic messengers usually occur quite **slowly.**

60. T

61. F Enzyme-linked receptors function as both enzymes and receptors.

62. F Calcium exerts its effect as a second messenger by binding to a cytosolic protein called calmodulin.

Short Answer

63. Specificity means **each** type of target cell **receptor will bind only one** type/class of **chemical messenger.**

64. A **cascade** is a **series of sequential reactions**, which, in the case of signal amplification, **progressively increases in magnitude.**

65. When activated, **G proteins also act as enzymes that hydrolyze GTP.** As soon as GTP is hydrolyzed to GDP, the G protein is inactivated.

Labeling

66. a. regulated protein **b.** lipophobic messenger **c.** alpha unit of the G protein **d.** GDP **e.** GTP **f.** G protein-linked receptor **g.** plasma membrane **h.** extracellular fluid **i.** cytosol

GDP → GTP activates the G protein

Sequencing

67. e, f, b, h, a

Challenge Questions

68. The **magnitude** of a target cell's response will **increase as the concentration of messenger increases** because the more messenger that's present, the greater the proportion of target cell receptors that will be bound to messenger. This **response will** only **continue** as messenger concentration increases **until saturation is reached** (messenger is bound to all available receptors). At this point, the target cell will be responding maximally.

69. Ligand-gated channels are ion channels that open or close in response to the binding of a messenger to a receptor that is part of the channel. **Fast channels** are proteins that function as both receptors and ion channels. Binding of a messenger to the channel causes it to **open**, allowing ions to move into or out of the cell.

Slow channels are channels in which the receptor and channel are separate proteins linked by a G protein. When a messenger binds to the receptor, the G protein is activated which will either **open or close** the channel. **Fast channels** open rapidly but close again very rapidly (within seconds). **Slow channels** are slower to open or close, but stay opened or closed for minutes.

Clinical Questions

70. An **alpha antagonist** such as phenoxybenzamine will **block norepinephrine from binding to alpha receptors** on blood vessels, which will prevent them from constricting, resulting in a decrease in blood pressure.

71. Calcium has a number of effects on the body, one of which is that it **serves as an important second messenger** in regulating a variety of intracellular processes. The reason it is such an effective second messenger is that it is normally present in very low concentrations within the cells, so that the entry of just a small amount of calcium into the cell will trigger a cellular response. In **hypercalcemia**, both blood levels and intracellular levels of calcium will increase. This will **interfere with calcium's role as a second messenger**, which will disrupt the cellular processes affected. Disruption of cellular activity can lead to weakness, lethargy, and fatigue.

72. Caffeine, in high concentrations, can **act as a stimulant by inhibiting cAMP phosphodiesterase activity within cells**. This results in increased levels of cAMP in cells, which produces many of the effects of caffeine, including increased heart rate and blood pressure, and increased alertness.

Concept Maps

73. a. first **b.** G protein **c.** alpha subunit **d.** adenylate cyclase **e.** cAMP phosphodiesterase **f.** protein kinase A **g.** phosphoprotein phosphatase **h.** protein phosphorylation

74. a. G protein **b.** phospholipase C **c.** protein kinase C **d.** calcium **e.** protein phosphorylation **f.** protein kinase

LONG-DISTANCE COMMUNICATION VIA THE NERVOUS AND ENDOCRINE SYSTEMS

Short Answer

75. Neurotransmitters generally communicate with target cells by **opening and closing ion channels** in the cell membrane. **Hormones** communicate by **altering protein synthesis or activating G proteins** within target cells.

76. The **nervous system controls movements and allows us to perceive** the world around us and activities requiring rapid cellular communication. The **endocrine system coordinates metabolic activities among organ systems**, which can be accomplished using slower, but longer-lasting, methods of communication.

77. The **nervous system rapidly transmits signals**, but its effects are generally of **short duration**. The **endocrine system transmits signals more slowly**, but its effects are generally of **longer duration**.

ENDOCRINE GLANDS

Matching

78. a. I **b.** E **c.** M **d.** CRH **e.** O **f.** T_3 and T_4 **g.** TSH

Labeling

79. a. pineal gland **b.** hypothalamus **c.** pituitary gland **d.** thyroid gland **e.** parathyroid glands **f.** thymus **g.** adrenal gland **h.** pancreas **i.** ovaries **j.** testes **k.** heart **l.** stomach **m.** liver **n.** kidneys **o.** small intestine **p.** skin

True/False

80. F Epinephrine is secreted by the **adrenal medulla**.

81. F Follicle stimulating hormone (FSH) is secreted by the **anterior pituitary gland**.

82. T

83. F Antidiuretic hormone (ADH) is secreted by the **posterior pituitary gland**.

84. F Glucagon is secreted by the **pancreas**.

85. T

86. F The inhibition of a hypothalamic tropic hormone by the anterior pituitary hormone whose secretion it stimulates is called **short loop negative feedback**.

87. T

Multiple Choice

88. f **89.** c **90.** d **91.** a **92.** b **93.** c
94. b **95.** b **96.** e

Sequencing

97. c, a, d, e, b

Completion

98.

Anterior Pituitary Hormone	Hypothalamic Tropic Hormone(s)	Stimulatory (+) or Inhibitory (−) Effect
Growth hormone	GHRH	+
	GHIH	−
*ACTH	Corticotropin releasing hormone	+
*Thyroid stimulating hormone	Thyrotropin releasing hormone	+
*Follicle stimulating hormone	Gonadotropin releasing hormone	+
*Luteinizing hormone	Gonadotropin releasing hormone	+
Prolactin	Prolactin releasing hormone	+
	Prolactin inhibiting hormone	−
Posterior Pituitary Hormone	**Release Stimulus**	
Antidiuretic hormone	nerve impulses	
Oxytocin	nerve impulses	

Challenge Questions

99. Hypothalamic tropic hormones are present **in the blood at high concentrations** when they affect the target cells of the anterior pituitary because **they proceed directly to the anterior pituitary through the portal capillary system. Anterior pituitary hormones are quite diluted** by the time they reach their target cells since **they travel through the general circulation**. The lower the concentration of messenger stimulating a target cell, the less the effect.

100. The **placenta is only present during pregnancy** and is **only considered an endocrine organ at that time.** It is considered an endocrine organ because it **secretes estrogens and progesterone.**

101. <u>Glucose</u>

insulin

glucagon

glucocorticoids (cortisol)

growth hormone

glucose-dependent insulinotropic peptide (GIP)

epinephrine

<u>Calcium</u>

parathyroid hormone

calcitonin

cholecalciferol

Clinical Questions

102. Oversecretion of growth hormone would result in the child being **taller than normal with very long arms and legs, a large skull, and large internal organs.**

103. Assuming your friend is a non-pregnant female or is a male, the **main hormone** affected would be **ADH.** ADH will continue to be synthesized in the hypothalamus but **will be blocked from entering the posterior pituitary,** so it will not be secreted in the blood. This will **result in a large output of very dilute urine,** which will cause your friend to become dehydrated. Fortunately, this can be treated by administering ADH. (Oxytocin secretion would be affected in the same way, but this hormone is of particular importance to pregnant and lactating females.)

104. Hypothyroidism would result in **weight gain, fatigue, feeling cold all the time, dry skin, and possibly depression.**

Concept Map

105. a. corticotropin releasing hormone from hypothalamus **b.** ACTH from anterior pituitary **c.** raises blood glucose, adapts body to stress, promotes catabolism of proteins and fats **d.** long loop negative feedback **e.** short loop negative feedback

HORMONE ACTIONS AT THE TARGET CELL

Matching

106. a. AE **b.** A **c.** ER **d.** O **e.** PSD **f.** P **g.** SSD **h.** SE

Multiple Choice

107. d **108.** c **109.** d **110.** e **111.** b **112.** d **113.** c

True/False

114. T **115.** T

116. F When hormones are transported in the blood bound to carrier proteins, the hormone binds to the receptor **in its unbound state.**

117. T **118.** T

Short Answer

119. Antagonistic hormone pairs include:

parathyroid hormone and calcitonin

or

glucagon and insulin

Completion

120. a. elevated **b.** potassium **c.** cortex **d.** kidney **e.** blood/plasma

Challenge Questions

121. Steroid and thyroid hormones are stored temporarily in fatty tissue, and are transported bound to carrier proteins. **This provides a "storage" pool from which these hormones can be released if the free hormone concentration in the blood falls.** If the rate of hormone secretion is elevated for awhile and then returns to normal, the body may respond by releasing hormone from the pool.

122. Thyroid hormone is essential to the synthesis of the receptors on bronchiole cells to which epinephrine binds. Therefore, if there is no thyroid hormone there will be no receptor synthesis, which means the cells will be unable to respond to epinephrine.

Clinical Questions

123. The **thyroid gland would decrease output of thyroid hormone** which, due to reduced negative feedback, would result in **an increase in TRH secretion,** which would **increase TSH secretion.**

124. The **secondary hypersecretion would be the result of increased secretion of TSH** by the anterior pituitary. Increased TSH would **increase the secretion of thyroid hormones by the thyroid gland.** The elevated thyroid hormone level would negatively feed back to the hypothalamus, resulting in **decreased secretion of TRH.**

CHAPTER 6

OVERVIEW OF THE NERVOUS SYSTEM

Matching

1. a. CNS **b.** PNS **c.** AD **d.** ED **e.** EO, CNS, INS **f.** ANS, INS

Completion

2. a. central nervous system **b.** brain **c.** afferent **d.** central nervous system **e.** efferent **f.** somatic nervous system **g.** autonomic nervous system **h.** glands **i.** parasympathetic

Short Answer

3. Motor neurons regulate skeletal muscle contractions.

4. Effector organs in the **somatic nervous system** move skeletal muscles. Effector organs in the autonomic nervous system move smooth muscles such as those found in the digestive tract and cardiac muscle. Other effector organs of the autonomic nervous system include glands that secrete substances either into the bloodstream, into body cavities, or onto the surface of the skin.

Multiple Choice

5. e   **6.** b   **7.** a   **8.** e   **9.** b

True/False

10. T

11. F Sensory information is sent from **sensory receptors to the brain**.

12. F The peripheral nervous system is divided into the **afferent and efferent divisions**. The parasympathetic and sympathetic divisions make up the autonomic nervous system.

13. T   **14.** T   **15.** T

Clinical Questions

16. The brain mediates emotions and other complex functions. Psychotropic drugs alter mood by acting on the brain, which is part of the **central nervous system**.

17. Neurons in the afferent nervous system transmit information from sensors to the brain. Lidocaine operates on the **afferent nervous system**, thus blocking sensory information and the sensation of pain.

18. The **autonomic nervous system** regulates the rate of heart contractions and also innervates blood vessels.

Challenge Questions

19. This is an example of a reflex response. Afferent nerves of the **peripheral nervous system** sent a signal to the spinal cord, which integrated the information and sent a signal to the effector organs (muscles) by way of efferent nerves of the somatic nervous system. Your muscles responded by quickly pulling your hand off of the hot stove.

20. The **peripheral nervous system** sends the signal that the stomach is full via stretch receptors in visceral organs, such as the stomach, to the **central nervous system**. The brain interprets the information and informs you that you are full.

Concept Map

21. a. Spinal cord **b.** Sensory **c.** Sensory organs **d.** Efferent **e.** Somatic **f.** Skeletal muscles **g.** Parasympathetic **h.** Glands

CELLS OF THE NERVOUS SYSTEM

Matching

22. a. GC **b.** CB **c.** D **d.** SC **e.** C **f.** AH **g.** O **h.** AT **i.** O **j.** SC

Completion

23. a. neurons **b.** electrical **c.** glial **d.** structural **e.** efferent **f.** afferent **g.** visceral **h.** interneurons

Short Answer

24. An **action potential** is a rapid change in the **membrane potential** in nerve cells. The inside of the cell temporarily becomes positively charged relative to the outside.

25. Action potentials are initiated at the **axon hillock** of a neuron.

26. **Leak channels** are always open and contribute to the resting membrane potential. **Ligand-gated channels** open or close in response to the chemical messengers that bind to them. **Voltage-gated channels** open or close in response to changes in the neuron's membrane potential.

27. **Interneurons** are the integrators of the central nervous system. Higher level brain processing occurs at the interneurons.

Multiple Choice

28. c   **29.** e   **30.** c   **31.** b   **32.** a   **33.** a

True/False

34. F Visceral receptors send information to the brain from the interior of the body. Motor neurons send information from the brain to skeletal muscles.

35. T

36. F A ganglion is a cluster of cell bodies located in the peripheral nervous system. Clusters of cell bodies in the central nervous system are known as nuclei.

Sequencing

37. b, d, c, a, e

Clinical Question

38. Guillian-Barre syndrome is the loss of **myelination** in peripheral motor nerves leading to skeletal muscles. Because these nerves cannot transmit impulses effectively, the muscles they serve fall into disuse and become weak.

Challenge Questions

39. In the central nervous system, cell bodies are grouped into **nuclei** and the axons are grouped into bundles called **pathways**, **tracts**, or **commissures**. In the peripheral nervous system, cell bodies are grouped together into clusters called **ganglia** and the axons travel together in bundles called **nerves**.

40. **Schwann cells** produce the myelin around the axons in the peripheral nervous system. **Oligodendrocytes** produce the myelin around axons in the central nervous system.

41. The association of so many **dendrites** with one cell body **allows for an increase in the surface area of multipolar neurons** upon which synapses with other nerves can form. This increase in the number of synapses in turn increases the number of nerve cells with which the multipolar neuron can communicate.

42. The increase in diameter of an axon increases the surface area around the **node**, which allows for an increase in sodium channels at these nodes. This, in turn, **speeds up the action potential** and allows for **faster communication between cells**.

ELECTRICAL SIGNALS IN NEURONS

Matching
43. a. PD **b.** MP **c.** GP **d.** SP **e.** RMP **f.** AP **g.** EP

Completion
44. a. negative **b.** ions **c.** Graded **d.** ion **e.** threshold **f.** action potential **g.** temporal **h.** spatial

Short Answer
45. Ions and most water-soluble compounds are not lipid-soluble, so they cannot pass easily through the plasma membrane's **lipid bilayer**. Therefore, the plasma membrane's lipid bilayer is very resistant to the flow of ions across it. Since the membrane is not very permeable to ions, the charges tend to remain separated from each other. Thus, the membrane acts as a capacitor.

46. Inhibitory graded potentials move the membrane potential away from the threshold; that is, they decrease the **cell membrane potential** and reduce the likelihood of achieving an action potential.

47. Hyperpolarization occurs when the membrane of a nerve cell becomes more negative. This happens when potassium channels open and potassium exits the cell. The loss of positive potassium ions from the interior of the cell makes the cell's potential more negative.

48. In a neuron at rest, Na^+ is in a high concentration on the outside, so the chemical driving force for Na^+ is into the cell. Because Na^+ is positively charged, it is attracted electrically to the negatively charged proteins inside the neuron. The net effect of these two forces drives sodium into the neuron. K^+, on the other hand, is in a high concentration on the inside of the neuron, so the chemical driving force for K^+ is out of the cell. The negative charges present inside the neuron attract K^+ to the inside of the cell, so the electrical force for K^+ is into the cell. However, the chemical driving force is greater than the electrical driving force and so some K^+ leave the cell.

Multiple Choice
49. b **50.** b **51.** e **52.** b **53.** a

True/False
54. F At rest, **net sodium leaks into the cell** and **net potassium leaks out of the cell**.

55. T

56. F Plasma membranes are good **capacitors**; they keep charges separated.

57. T **58.** T

59. F Ligand-gated channels open in response to **chemicals**, usually a neurotransmitter. Voltage-gated channels open in response to changes in membrane potential.

60. T **61.** T

Labeling
62. a. depolarization **b.** repolarization **c.** resting potential **d.** hyperpolarization

Sequencing
63. d, a, c, b

Clinical Questions
64. a) **Action potentials** would be affected because voltage-gated channels are necessary to conduct action potentials. b) The **peripheral afferent nerves** send sensory signals to the **central nervous system**. When these nerves are blocked, tingling may occur. c) If the **diaphragm** were paralyzed, breathing would become impossible and would eventually result in death.

65. Loss of potassium can lead to **hyperpolarization** of neurons. This loss decreases the ability of the neurons to generate action potentials and can cause muscle weakness and fatigue. Potassium supplements help to increase the levels of potassium in the body and restore the membrane potential of neurons.

Challenge Questions
66. The Na^+/K^+ pumps both establish and maintain the resting **membrane potential** of nerve cells. If these pumps were to fail, the membrane potential would decay to zero and, eventually, **the nerve would not be able to conduct an action potential**.

67. Excitatory and inhibitory graded potentials are similar in that they both produce small changes in membrane potential on the dendrites and cell body. They do not travel very far, and they can both be summed either through spatial summation or temporal summation. They differ in that **excitatory graded potentials** bring the cell closer to threshold and thus closer to an action potential, while **inhibitory graded potentials** move the membrane potential away from threshold and inhibit action potentials.

68. Because there would be equal stimulation by **EPSPs** and **IPSPs** at the same time, the membrane potential would not change and would be equal to the resting membrane potential.

Concept Map
69.

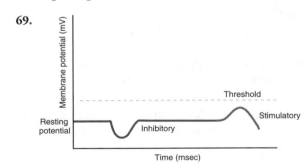

ACTION POTENTIALS AND THE BASIS OF NEURAL STABILITY

Matching

70. a. D **b.** AH **c.** R, AH **d.** R **e.** D **f.** D **g.** R, AH

Completion

71. a. axon hillock (trigger zone) **b.** axon terminal **c.** sodium **d.** enter **e.** sodium **f.** potassium **g.** exit **h.** potassium **i.** out

Short Answer

72. The **absolute refractory period** occurs during all of depolarization and most of repolarization. The **relative refractory period** occurs immediately after the absolute refractory period to the end of after-hyperpolarization.

73. Saltatory conduction describes the jumping of action potentials from node to node. This occurs because the action potential does not occur in the area covered by the myelin, but instead occurs only at the nodes.

74. The larger the diameter of an axon, the less resistance to longitudinal current flow there is down the axon. Therefore, larger-diameter axons have faster rates of conduction.

75. Myelinated axons conduct **action potentials faster** than those with no myelin. Myelin increases the resistance to the flow of ions across the membrane and therefore provides insulation to the axon. This decreases the resistance down the axon and results in a faster action potential.

76. During **depolarization**, sodium moves into the cell. During **repolarization**, potassium moves out of the cell. During **after-hyperpolarization**, potassium moves out of the cell.

Multiple Choice

77. c **78.** d **79.** d **80.** c **81.** a **82.** a
83. c **84.** d **85.** b **86.** b

True/False

87. F During depolarization the membrane potential changes from approximately −70 mV to +30 mV.

88. F **Saltatory conduction** is seen in myelinated axons.

89. T

90. F The membrane potential goes from approximately −70 mV to −85 mV.

91. F A **threshold stimulus** at the axon hillock is necessary to generate an action potential.

92. T

93. F Action potentials are **all-or-none** in their response. IPSPs and EPSPs are **graded** in their responses.

94. T   **95.** T

Sequencing

96. h, g, f, a, b, d, e, c

Clinical Question

97. Loss of **myelin** in afferent nerves leads to loss of sensation; loss of myelin in efferent nerves results in slower, uncoordinated muscle movements and eventually muscle paralysis. Loss of myelination in MS inhibits the ability of nerves to conduct **saltatory conduction**, which slows down the nerve impulse.

Challenge Questions

98. Local anesthetics keep sodium channels on the sensory neurons from opening. This block prevents action potentials in the sensory neurons, and sensory information is not sent to the brain. This lack of sensory information to the brain results in a lack of sensation of pain.

99. The neuron without K⁺ channel pumps would have a much longer action potential compared to a neuron with K⁺ channel pumps. This would occur because without K⁺ channel pumps, the cell would have to rely solely on passive processes to restore the membrane potential. This is a much slower process than the K⁺ channel pump-induced repolarization.

Concept Map

100.

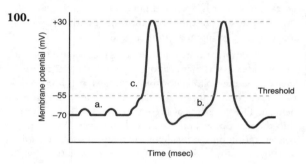

CHAPTER 7

TYPES OF SYNAPSES AND CHEMICAL SYNAPSES

Matching

1. a. ES **b.** SC **c.** PEN **d.** PON **e.** SC **f.** ADS **g.** ASS **h.** AAS **i.** SV

Completion

2. a. synapses **b.** chemical **c.** gap junctions **d.** neurotransmitter **e.** presynaptic **f.** synaptic cleft **g.** postsynaptic **h.** axon terminal **i.** calcium **j.** neurotransmitter **k.** exocytosis **l.** receptors

Short Answer

3. An **inhibitory synapse** is a synapse that causes **hyperpolarization** of the postsynaptic membrane, or stabilizes the membrane potential at the resting value. These synapses prevent action potentials from occurring in the postsynaptic neuron. An **excitatory synapse** is a synapse that causes **depolarization** of the postsynaptic membrane. These synapses bring the postsynaptic membrane closer to threshold and the production of an action potential.

4. Synaptic delay is a short period of time (1–5 msec) between the time the action potential in the presynaptic neuron reaches the axon terminal and the time a response is actually observed in the postsynaptic cell. This lag time is thought to be due to the time that it takes calcium to trigger exocytosis from the synaptic vesicles.

5. An **ionotropic receptor** is a ligand-gated receptor that opens an ion channel.

6. Neuromodulators are neurotransmitters that act through **G proteins** and generally produce long-lasting responses in postsynaptic neurons that affect other synaptic inputs.

7. Neostigmine counteracts muscle weakness by causing **sustained muscle contractions** because acetylcholine would not be cleared from the synaptic cleft. Acetylcholine would therefore continually be available to stimulate the skeletal muscles.

Multiple Choice

8. e   **9.** c   **10.** a or c   **11.** b   **12.** a
13. e   **14.** b

True/False

15. T

16. F Neurotransmitters are **cleared from the synaptic cleft** after they have exerted their effect.

17. T

18. F The process is reversible; the neurotransmitter is broken down by acetylcholinesterase.

19. T

20. F Movement of either **potassium ions** out of the cells or **chloride ion**s into the cell can cause an IPSP. An EPSP is caused by the movement of sodium into the cell.

Sequencing

21. g, a, d, b, e, c, f

Clinical Question

22. a. Muscle paralysis; relaxation **b.** Muscle paralysis; relaxation **c.** Sustained muscle contractions

Challenge Questions

23. When the neurotransmitter binds to the receptor on the postsynaptic membrane it causes **ligand-gated sodium channels** to open. As the channels open, sodium rushes into the cell at a faster rate than potassium leaves the cell, thus causing a depolarization.

24. The binding of a neurotransmitter to its receptor opens **ligand-gated potassium channels** in the postsynaptic membrane. When a neurotransmitter opens potassium channels, potassium rushes out of the cell and causes hyperpolarization.

25. 1) The neurotransmitter molecules may be degraded by **enzymes**, which are thought to be located on the postsynaptic or presynaptic neuron's plasma membrane, or on nearby cells. 2) The neurotransmitters may be **actively transported** back into the presynaptic neuron. 3) The neurotransmitters may **diffuse** out of the cleft.

Concept Map

26.

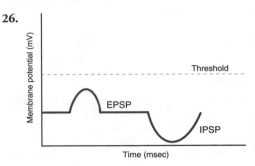

NEURAL INTEGRATION AND PRESYNAPTIC MODULATION

Matching

27. a. TS **b.** SS **c.** SS
28. a. B **b.** B **c.** PF **d.** B **e.** PI

Completion

29. a. Neural integration **b.** axon hillock **c.** threshold **d.** action potential **e.** depolarization **f.** action potentials

30. a. axoaxonic **b.** neurotransmitter **c.** postsynaptic **d.** facilitation **e.** inhibition

Short Answer

31. During **presynaptic facilitation** the amount of neurotransmitter is **increased**.

32. Summation for **neural integration** occurs if the membrane potential at the axon hillock reaches **threshold** and an action potential is generated. If threshold is not reached, an action potential does not occur.

Multiple Choice

33. c   **34.** e   **35.** e

True/False

36. T

37. F Presynaptic facilitation occurs when the release of a neurotransmitter is **increased**. Inhibition of the release of a neurotransmitter is synaptic inhibition.

38. F Axodendritic and axosomatic neurons **affect transmission nonselectively**.

39. F Presynaptic inhibition can occur at either excitatory or inhibitory synapses.

40. T

41. F Both **EPSPs** and **IPSPs** can be summed.

42. F Frequency coding affects the **frequency** of action potentials.

Labeling

43. Graph A represents **temporal summation** because two or more postsynaptic potentials are being generated in rapid succession **at the same synaps**e. Graph B represents **spatial summation** because two or more postsynaptic potentials are being generated **from different synapses at approximately the same time**.

Sequencing

44. c, d, b, a, e

Challenge Questions

45. Temporal and spacial summation are similar in that they both occur on the postsynaptic neuron. Further, the axon hillock integrates the signals coming in from presynaptic neurons, a process called neural integration or summation. **They are different** in the way that they carry out the summation. When two or more postsynaptic potentials are generated in rapid succession at the same synapse it is called temporal summation. By contrast, when two or more postsynaptic potentials are generated by different synapses at approximately the same time it is called spatial summation.

46. Frequency coding occurs when an increase in the strength of the threshold stimulus (suprathreshold stimulus) causes an increase in the frequency of action potentials. The end result is an increase in the amount of neurotransmitter released.

Concept Map

47. a. postsynaptic **b.** the presynaptic neuron releases a neurotransmitter **c.** axon hillock **d.** the presynaptic neurotransmitter induces a change in the amount of calcium that enters the postsynaptic axon **e.** the amount of neurotransmitter released from the postsynaptic neuron is altered

NEUROTRANSMITTERS: STRUCTURE, SYNTHESIS, AND DEGRADATION

Matching

48. a. NO **b.** GLU **c.** END **d.** END **e.** CAT **f.** HIS **g.** GLY **h.** ACH **i.** P

49. a. DOP **b.** EPI **c.** ACH **d.** EPI **e.** ACH **f.** ACH

Completion

50. a. Acetylcholine **b.** serotonin **c.** epinephrine **d.** dopamine **e.** amino acids **f.** nitric oxide

Short Answer

51. Choline acetyl transferase (CAT) catalyzes the synthesis of acetylcholine.

Multiple Choice

52. c   **53.** b   **54.** a   **55.** e   **56.** a   **57.** d

True/False

58. T   **59.** T

60. F Catecholamines generally produce slow responses through G proteins.

61. F Amino acid neurotransmitters are the most abundant neurotransmitter in the central nervous system.

62. F The two classes of adrenergic receptors are alpha and beta. Muscarinic and nicotinic receptors are examples of cholinergic receptors.

63. T

Clinical Questions

64. The heart and skeletal muscle have two different types of receptors. Skeletal muscle has **nicotinic cholinergic receptors** that respond to acetylcholine by stimulating the effector organ. By contrast, the heart has **muscarinic cholinergic receptors** that respond to acetylcholine by slowing heart rate.

65. By blocking **acetylcholinesterase** activity the acetylcholine is not degraded and remains in the synaptic cleft. Therefore, acetylcholine interacts with the postsynaptic membrane, causing continued stimulation. The muscles that regulate breathing, most notably the diaphragm, are continually stimulated and cannot be used for breathing.

Challenge Question

66. They are both similar in that they respond to the neurotransmitter **acetylcholine**. They differ however in their locations and effects on the postsynaptic cell. **Nicotinic cholinergic receptors** occur throughout the peripheral nervous system, especially in the autonomic nervous system and on effector organs innervated by somatic motor nerves. They also occur, though less frequently, in the central nervous system. Nicotinic receptors are ionotropic. Muscarinic receptors are metabotropic and act through a G protein. They are the most prominent cholinergic receptor in the central nervous system, but also occur in the peripheral nervous system.

Concept Map

67. a. acetyl CoA **b.** synaptic vesicles **c.** exocytosis **d.** cholinergic receptor **e.** the choline is taken back into the presynaptic neuron; the acetate diffuses away into bloodstream **f.** acetylcholinesterase

CHAPTER 8

GENERAL ANATOMY OF THE CENTRAL NERVOUS SYSTEM

Matching

1. a. CSF **b.** CR **c.** MN **d.** VC **e.** BBB **f.** BR

Completion

2. a. brain **b.** spinal cord **c.** cranium **d.** meninges **e.** blood-brain barrier **f.** cerebrospinal **g.** gray **h.** White **i.** bodies **j.** dendrites **k.** terminals **l.** axons **m.** Glial

Short Answer

3. The blood-brain barrier is a **physical barrier** made up of **special capillaries** with **tight junctions** that exist **between the blood and cerebrospinal fluid**. This barrier **restricts the passage of some materials** from the blood capillaries into brain tissue.

4. Ependymal cells line the **insides of the ventricles** and the **central canal**. In some ventricles these cells **help to form the choroid plexus**, which produces cerebrospinal fluid. Astrocytes **help to form the blood-brain barrier** by stimulating endothelial cells to develop tight junctions.

Multiple Choice

5. b   **6.** c   **7.** a   **8.** a   **9.** e   **10.** b

True/False

11. T   **12.** T

13. F Gases and other hydrophobic molecules penetrate through endothelial cells by **simple diffusion**.

14. T

15. F The thin layer of gray matter that covers the cerebrum is called the **cerebral cortex**. The blood-brain barrier is a physical barrier between the blood and the CSF.

16. T

Sequencing

17. b, c, d, g, a, f, e

Clinical Question

18. Most of the **penicillin travels through the bloodstream bound to albumin** and, by definition, **substances bound to albumin (hydrophobic substances) will not cross the blood-brain barrier**. In addition, there are **no carrier proteins in the blood-brain barrier** to assist in its transport.

Challenge Questions

19. Both of these regions **occur in the CNS** and **have both neural tissue and support (glial) cells** associated with them. They differ in that **gray matter** contains cell bodies, dendrites of neurons, and axon terminals that form synapses with them. Synaptic transmission and neural integration occurs in the gray matter. **White matter** is composed of myelinated axons and its function is to transmit the information in the form of action potentials.

20. CNS tissue has a **very high rate of metabolic activity** (even under resting conditions) compared to most other tissues in the body (except the kidney). This high rate of metabolic activity **demands rapid and continuous delivery of oxygen and glucose to CNS** tissue. In addition, as indicated earlier, **no storage of energy or oxygen occurs in brain** tissue, so a constant supply of blood to the brain is required.

21. Both types of fibers are composed of white matter in the CNS and are organized into tracts that connect one region of gray matter with another. **Commissural fibers** connect regions of the cerebral cortex with corresponding cortical regions on the opposite side. **Association fibers** connect one area of the cerebral cortex to another area of the cortex on the same side of the brain.

THE SPINAL CORD

Matching

22. a. VR **b.** DRG **c.** MN **d.** DR **e.** AT **f.** DH **g.** DT **h.** VH

Completion

23. a. afferent **b.** efferent **c.** ascending **d.** descending **e.** brain **f.** gray matter **g.** dorsal **h.** dendrites **i.** efferent neurons **j.** axon terminals **k.** afferent neurons **l.** interneurons

Short Answer

24. Ascending tracts transmit information from the spinal cord to the brain; **descending tracts** transmit information from the brain to the spinal cord.

25. Dermatomes **map out the body's surface** into various sensory areas. They allow clinicians to **determine the approximate location of damage to the spinal cord or spinal nerves**.

26. Cervical nerves emerge from the neck area. **Thoracic spinal nerves** emerge from the chest region of the spinal cord. **Lumbar nerves** emerge from the lower back, and **sacral nerves** emerge from the region of the tailbone. There is a single **coccygeal nerve** that emerges from the tip of the coccyx.

Multiple Choice

27. b   **28.** c   **29.** a   **30.** a

True/False

31. F Signals from the brain travel along descending tracts to efferent neurons in the **ventral** horn.

32. T

33. F The white matter of the spinal cord consists of **ascending and descending tracts**; interneurons are present in the gray matter.

34. F Descending tracts also **modulate sensory information**.

Labeling

35. Afferent division: a. afferent axon **b.** dorsal root ganglion **c.** cell body of afferent neuron **d.** dorsal root **e.** axon terminal of afferent neuron

Efferent division: **f.** cell body of efferent neuron **g.** ventral root **h.** efferent axon **i.** axon terminals of efferent neuron

Clinical Question

36. Julie likely has **spinal cord damage in the cervical region** and therefore cannot use motor neurons distal to the damage on the spinal cord. Sven probably has **spinal cord damage in the lumbar or sacral area**, as spinal nerves above that area appear to be functioning normally.

Challenge Question

37. Both terms describe communication between the brain and spinal cord. The most common mode of communication in the body is **contralateral**, where the ascending and descending tracts cross over and communicate on the opposite side of its origin. Less frequently, **ipsilateral** communication occurs where a pathway remains on the same side of its origin.

Concept Map

38. a. gray matter **b.** white matter **c.** Interneurons **d.** ventral horn **e.** ventral root **f.** axon terminals of afferent neurons synapse with interneurons **g.** carries afferent axons **h.** spinal nerves

THE BRAIN

Matching

39. a. T **b.** B **c.** OL **d.** TL **e.** H **f.** L **g.** PL **h.** FL

Completion

40. a. brainstem **b.** diencephalon **c.** medulla oblongata **d.** cerebrum **e.** basal nuclei **f.** limbic system **g.** diencephalon **h.** thalamus **i.** cortex **j.** endocrine **k.** nervous

Short Answer

41. The **right cerebral cortex** is generally more involved in spatial perception, artistic and creative activities, and is better at spatial perception. It also controls movement and sensory input on the left side of the body. The **left cerebral cortex** processes sensory input and controls motor functions from the right side of the body. The left cerebral cortex tends to excel in logic and analytical abilities.

42. The **limbic system** functions in learning, emotions, and basic survival drives such as fear. It is considered evolutionarily a more primitive part of the brain.

Multiple Choice

43. b **44.** c **45.** a **46.** a **47.** d **48.** c
49. b **50.** e

True/False

51. F Association areas of the cerebral cortex are directly involved with **complex processing and integrating information**; the hypothalamus regulates some hormones.

52. T

53. F Circadian rhythms are regulated in the **hypothalamus**; the thalamus is a relay between sensory information and the cerebral cortex.

54. F Cranial nerve VII is the facial nerve and contains **both sensory and motor nerves** of the face and tongue.

55. T

Clinical Questions

56. The stroke most likely occurred on the **right side of the brain** and may be located in the **primary motor cortex**.

57. Shining light into one eye can distinguish between damage to **CN II (the optic nerve)** and damage to **CN III (the oculomotor nerve)**. The optic nerve controls the direct pupillary light reflex, which means that shining light into one eye causes the pupil in that same eye to constrict. The oculomotor nerve, on the other hand, controls the consensual pupillary light reflex, which means that shining light into one eye causes the pupil in the opposite eye to constrict. In a healthy patient, shining light into either eye should cause both pupils to constrict; abnormalities in these reflexes are indicators of possible damage to the cranial nerves or to the brainstem itself.

Challenge Questions

58. The cerebral cortex is composed of valleys and hills called sulci and gyri, respectively. The sulci and gyri form convolutions that **greatly increase the surface area** and thus room for more neurons and glial cells in the brain.

59. Individuals may have **wide mood swings** and **erratic behaviors**, and **difficulty in controlling hormone secretion or production**. In addition, **body temperature, sleep cycles, and autonomic responses may not be well regulated.**

INTEGRATED CNS FUNCTION: REFLEXES

Matching

60. a. CR, AU, IN, PO **b.** SP, SO, IN, MO **c.** CR, AU, IN, PO **d.** CR, AU, CO, PO **e.** SP, SO, IN, PO

Completion

61. a. reflexes **b.** spinal cord **c.** autonomic **d.** innate **e.** muscle spindle stretch reflex **f.** pupillary light **g.** autonomic **h.** pupil

Short Answer

62. This reflex is an example of an **autonomic, innate, polysynaptic, cranial reflex.**

Multiple Choice

63. c **64.** a **65.** d **66.** b

True/False

67. F Reflexes are **patterned, automatic responses** that are some of the **simplest actions** of the nervous system.

68. F The withdrawal reflex involves skeletal muscle and so is a good example of a **somatic** reflex.

69. T **70.** T

Sequencing

71. d, e, b, c, a

Clinical Questions

72. The clinician is testing a spinal stretch reflex. By tapping the patellar tendon the **quadriceps muscle is stretched**. This stretch **stimulates muscle spindles** that send **signals via afferent neurons** to the spinal cord. These afferent neurons make **direct excitatory synaptic connections with** efferent neurons that **innervate the quadriceps muscle to contract**. At the same time, the **hamstring muscles** in the back of the leg **relax through reciprocal innervation**.

73. The action causes the toes to move, showing that **skeletal muscles are stimulated via spinal neurons**. In addition, if this reflex was never tested for previously in this individual, then it would also be considered an innate reflex.

Challenge Questions

74. The spinal and cranial reflexes are **similar** in that they **operate through reflex arcs**. These reflex arcs have sensors that transmit information to the CNS via afferent neurons, and the CNS responds to the effector organs by way of efferent neurons. The **difference** between the two is that **spinal reflexes are processed in the spinal cord**, whereas in **cranial reflexes the brain is the integrating center**.

75. The crossed-extensor reflex is important because it **assists in stabilizing** one's **weight and balance during reflexive actions**. In particular, it counteracts the effects of the withdrawal reflex. It causes extension of one leg when the other leg is withdrawn in response to a painful stimulus. This reflex also functions in gait when walking and running.

Concept Map

76. a. nociceptors **b.** afferent neurons **c.** efferent motor neurons **d.** afferent neurons **e.** spinal cord
f. interneurons **g.** muscles opposing the reflex relax
h. interneurons **i.** efferent motor neurons **j.** efferent neurons **k.** efferent neurons **l.** withdraw from stimulus
m. support body during withdrawal reflex

INTEGRATED CNS FUNCTION: VOLUNTARY MOTOR CONTROL

Matching

77. a. UMN **b.** BN **c.** RF **d.** EPT

Completion

78. a. cerebral cortex **b.** pyramidal tracts **c.** motor neurons **d.** spinal cord **e.** basal nuclei

Short Answer

79. The thalamus **relays information** between various parts of the CNS. **Information travels through the thalamus** into and out of the cerebral cortex.

80. The cerebellum **functions in coordination of skeletal muscles and balance**. It receives sensory information from various parts of the CNS and then communicates with the cortex so that the cortex can make the appropriate adjustments.

Multiple Choice

81. d   **82.** a   **83.** c   **84.** e   **85.** b

True/False

86. T

87. F Parallel processing is **common in both efferent and afferent pathways of the CNS**.

88. T

89. F The basal nuclei send output to the cortex through the **thalamus**.

90. T

Clinical Question

91. Since the basal nuclei are involved in providing feedback to the cortex for the development of motor strategies and smooth muscle movement, disruption of this communication by an **overproduction of dopamine can result in explosive, uncontrolled episodes of motor activity**.

Challenge Questions

92. Parallel processing occurs in both motor and sensory neurons. It is the **simultaneous transmission of the same type of information along separate neural pathways**. It is important because it **allows for at least partial recovery of damage to the pyramidal system**. The extrapyramidal system can partially compensate for lost motor and sensory function.

93. The **pyramidal tracts control the fine, delicate movements** of the surgeon's hands, arms, and fingers, while the **extrapyramidal tracts control the larger muscle groups** involved in gross movements and posture of the trunk, neck, and legs.

Concept Map

94. a. cortex **b.** brainstem **c.** cerebellum **d.** provide feedback to the cortex **e.** extrapyramidal tracts **f.** Provide feedback to the cortex for development of smooth muscle movement

INTEGRATED CNS FUNCTION: LANGUAGE AND SLEEP

Matching

95. a. REM **b.** REM **c.** SWS **d.** REM **e.** SWS

Completion

96. a. Wernicke's area **b.** Broca's area **c.** aphasia
d. receptive aphasia **e.** expressive aphasia

97. a. EEG **b.** Slow-wave sleep **c.** REM

Short Answer

98. While awake and alert the brain **produces EEG beta waves that are high-frequency and low-amplitude in nature**. While awake but resting the brain shows **alpha waves that are a pattern of lower-frequency and higher-amplitude.**

Multiple Choice

99. e　　**100.** a　　**101.** c　　**102.** e　　**103.** b

True/False

104. T

105. F **REM** dreams are more likely to be remembered.

106. T

107. F **Beta** waves are present while you are awake and alert; alpha waves are present when you are awake but resting.

Clinical Questions

108. This condition is called **expressive aphasia**. The most likely area damaged is **Broca's area**, located in the frontal lobe. When **damage to Broca's area occurs** it can result in the ability to **understand spoken or written words, but an inability to respond to the words.**

109. Sleep is important in many ways for the health of an individual. For example, **sleep may help us to conserve energy for activity during the day**. Sleep is also **beneficial to consolidate new, learned information** and **facilitate long-term memory storage**. In addition, research in animals suggests that sleep is important in **maintaining a well-operating immune system**. By not getting enough sleep the students **may be depriving themselves of mounting an appropriate immune response.**

Challenge Question

110. **Both** areas are devoted to language. **Wernicke's area** is located in the temporal and parietal lobes and is involved in language comprehension. **Broca's area** is located in parts of the frontal lobes and is involved in language expression.

INTEGRATED CNS FUNCTION: EMOTIONS AND MOTIVATION, LEARNING AND MEMORY

Matching

111. a. NL **b.** AL **c.** AL

112. a. PM **b.** DM **c.** PM

Completion

113. a. limbic system **b.** sensory input **c.** cortex **d.** autonomic **e.** Motivation

114. a. Learning **b.** memory **c.** long-term potentiation **d.** synapse

Short Answer

115. Emotions are how an individual **feels** about a particular situation or event. **Motivation** is the **impulse that drives our actions** in response to emotions.

116. Learning is the acquisition of **new information or skills**, while **memory** is the **retention of information or skills.**

Multiple Choice

117. b　　**118.** d　　**119.** a

True/False

120. F Repetition is **not** necessary, especially if the experience is perceived as important.

121. T　　**122.** T

123. F **Sensitization** is an increase in response to a repeated stimulus. Habituation is a decrease in response to a repeated stimulus.

Clinical Question

124. Since his procedural memory is intact, the damage is probably not to the cerebellum. Since his declarative memory is not operational, he **may have damage to his hippocampus**.

Challenge Question

125. Several areas of the brain are involved in this response. The **cerebral cortex integrates** your thoughts and communicates with the limbic system. The **limbic system creates the emotion** and it is transmitted to the cortex where you perceive it. Simultaneously, the **limbic system communicates with the hypothalamus** and it responds with hormones that raise heart rate, breathing rate, etc. The **hypothalamus communicates with the brainstem**, which **induces sympathetic nervous responses** at effector organs such as the heart, blood vessels, sweat glands, etc., which also lead to the outward expression of your emotions.

Concept Map

126. a. cortex association areas **b.** hypothalamus **c.** motor cortex **d.** autonomic responses

CHAPTER 9

GENERAL PRINCIPLES OF SENSORY PHYSIOLOGY

Matching

1. a. MR **b.** CR **c.** PR **d.** CR **e.** MR **f.** TR **g.** CR

Completion

2. a. sensory receptors **b.** cerebral cortex **c.** receptor **d.** pathway **e.** frequency coding **f.** population coding **g.** receptive fields **h.** lateral inhibition

3. The function of **sensory receptors** is **sensory transduction. Receptors convert** the **energy of a sensory stimulus into receptor potentials.** Sensory receptors are specialized neurons that detect energy from either the internal or external environment. These sensory receptors convert the energy of a sensory stimulus into changes in membrane potential called **receptor potentials.** The receptor potentials convey the information about the stimulus to the CNS where the information is integrated and perceived.

Multiple Choice

4. e **5.** b **6.** c **7.** a

True/False

8. T

9. F Receptive fields **vary widely in their sizes.**

10. F **Each sensory modality has its own labeled line.**

Labeling

11. a. cerebral cortex **b.** third-order neuron **c.** thalamus **d.** second-order neuron **e.** spinal cord or brain stem **f.** first-order neurons **g.** receptors

Challenge Questions

12. The **area of the index finger is innervated by afferent neurons with extensive branching and small receptive fields.** On the other hand, **the skin on the calf is innervated by afferent neurons with relatively few branches,** therefore, this area of the body has large receptive fields. This means that your sense of touch is more sensitive in the areas where the receptive fields are small and there are many afferent neurons that branch extensively.

13. By **overlapping receptive fields** lateral inhibition may occur. That is, afferent neurons in nearby receptive fields are inhibited, thus increasing the likelihood that the stimulus' location can be perceived correctly. Furthermore, localization can occur because receptive fields overlap, so that any stimulus that occurs within the region of overlap will activate both receptive fields.

14. Both frequency and population coding are methods of sensory coding that identify the type, strength, and location of a stimulus. **Frequency coding** senses a stimulus' intensity by the frequency of action potentials, sending more signals per unit time, whereas **population coding** senses a stimulus' intensity by the number of receptors stimulated.

THE SOMATOSENSORY SYSTEM

Matching

15. a. FNE **b.** RE **c.** HFR **d.** PC

Completion

16. a. somesthetic sensations **b.** proprioception **c.** free nerve endings **d.** thalamus **e.** dorsal column-medial lemniscal pathway **f.** pain **g.** thalamus **h.** spinothalamic tract **i.** primary somatosensory cortex

Short Answer

17. The pain response is the result of **two types of afferent neurons.** The **initial sharp, fast pain is localized pain** and is transmitted by $A\delta$ **fibers.** The latter pain is transmitted by C **fibers** and is perceived as a **more prolonged, less localized, aching pain.**

18. Referred pain is **activation of nociceptors in the viscera** (a body cavity). This pain is perceived, however, as if it occurred in other areas of the body. For example, the pain of a heart attack is often reported as being felt in the left arm or in the jaw.

Multiple Choice

19. b **20.** c **21.** a **22.** a **23.** c **24.** e

True/False

25. F Merkel's disks have **small** receptive fields and sense pressure in the skin.

26. T

27. F Warm thermoreceptors in the skin are **nonspecialized free nerve endings.**

28. F Polymodal receptors respond to a **number of different stimuli, including intense heat, cold, pain, and chemicals released from damaged tissue.**

Labeling

29. 1. dorsal column-medial lemniscal pathway

1a. proprioceptors or mechanoreceptors

1b. first-order neuron

1c. dorsal columns

1d. medial lemniscus

1e. medulla oblongata

1f. second-order neuron

1g. thalamus

1h. third-order neuron

2. spinothalamic tract

2a. nociceptors or thermoreceptors

2b. first-order neuron

2c. anterolateral quadrant

2d. Lissauer's tract

2e. medulla oblongata

2f. second-order neuron

2g. thalamus

2h. third-order neuron

Sequencing

30. d, a, c, b

Clinical Question

31. Since the man has damage to the spinal cord, **the spinothalamic tract would be damaged** and **information about temperature of the skin and pain could not be transmitted** along its pathways. Since the damage was done on the **left side of his spinal cord before it crosses over in the brainstem, the damage would affect sensations on the left side of the body.**

Challenge Question

32. This method of pain relief works due to the **gate-control theory of pain modulation**, which states that **somatic signals from nonpainful sources (the rubbing) can inhibit signals of pain (hitting his thigh into the fence)**. Interneurons in the spinal cord can act to inhibit second-order neurons that transmit pain information. When these interneurons are active, pain signals are suppressed and the sensation of pain is reduced.

VISION

Matching

33. a. EO **b.** PO **c.** AS **d.** HO **e.** MO

Completion

34. a. optic nerve **b.** optic chiasma **c.** right visual field **d.** left visual field **e.** optic tract **f.** lateral geniculate body **g.** thalamus **h.** visual cortex **i.** occipital

Short Answer

35. Depth perception requires input from two sources: your two eyes. To perceive depth, each eye must sense the same information from a different angle. The brain takes the different input from each eye to construct a three-dimensional image of what each eye sees separately. **When the brain receives input from only one eye it cannot provide depth to the image.**

36. In **parallel processing, visual inputs are segregated into many different, but parallel, pathways, and information delivered by each pathway is dealt with by different parts of the brain.** The brain integrates and makes "sense" of this different information.

Multiple Choice

37. b **38.** c **39.** a **40.** d

True/False

41. F Rods provide for **black and white** vision during low light intensities, while the cones provide for color vision.

42. T **43.** T

44. F The inner layer of the retina contains **ganglion cells**. The **middle layer** contains the bipolar cells and the rods and cones are present in the outer layer.

Clinical Questions

45. The patient is suffering from **glaucoma**, which is an increase in the volume of the aqueous humor that raises the pressure in the anterior cavity of the eyeball.

46. The child's lens is too strong for clear distance vision. To correct this problem, she will need a **concave** lens that will diverge the light rays before they reach her eye.

Challenge Questions

47. Your pupils dilate to **increase the amount of light** reaching the eye, thus **increasing visual acuity and making vision sharper**. To accomplish this, sympathetic fibers stimulate radial muscles that are arranged like spokes of a wheel. When the radial muscles of the iris contract, the pupil dilates or increases in diameter.

48. Lions have a **large proportion of rods in their eyes** that helps them to hunt under dim light conditions. These **rods offer increased night vision**, but some **sacrifice in visual acuity** is experienced. Since lions hunt relatively large prey at close distances, visual acuity is not necessary. **Eagles**, on the other hand, have an **abundance of cones** that allows for vision during the day in bright light. They have **very acute vision**, which is necessary for seeing small prey from long distances.

Concept Map

49. a. outer segment **b.** sodium **c.** depolarized **d.** inner segment **e.** calcium **f.** exocytosis

THE EAR AND HEARING

Matching

50. a. EA, ME **b.** IE **c.** ME **d.** EA **e.** EA **f.** IE

Completion

51. a. hearing **b.** external ear **c.** cochlea **d.** organ of Corti **e.** inner ear **f.** stereocilia **g.** potassium **h.** cochlear nerve **i.** thalamus **j.** auditory cortex

Short Answer

52. First, the **ossicles amplify the vibrations** from the tympanic membrane; second, the much **larger diameter of the tympanic membrane** than that of the oval window **also amplifies the sound**.

Multiple Choice

53. a **54.** a **55.** d **56.** e **57.** a

True/False

58. F The fluid in the scala vestibuli is called **perilymph**. Endolymph is located in the scala media.

59. F In the organ of Corti, **stereocilia** bend, causing receptor potentials in the hair cells.

60. T **61.** T

Sequencing

62. i, e, f, h, g, c, d, b, a, k, j

Clinical Question

63. The **hair cells in the basilar membrane of the cochlea** may be affected. In particular, the region closer to the oval and round windows, which activates hair cells located in the region in response to high-frequency sounds.

Challenge Question

64. Elephants have a spiral organ of Corti that is elongated at the helicotrema end, whereas **in dogs the proximal end of the spiral organ is stiffer** so that higher frequencies are required to excite the hair cells at that end.

THE EAR AND EQUILIBRIUM

Matching

65. a. K **b.** U **c.** A **d.** C **e.** S

Completion

66. a. semicircular canals **b.** saccule **c.** stereocilia **d.** ampullae **e.** brainstem **f.** thalamus

Short Answer

67. The **saccule** detects changes in linear vertical acceleration.

Multiple Choice

68. d **69.** a **70.** c

True/False

71. T

72. F At rest, hair cells release **minimal amounts of neurotransmitter** that communicates with afferent nerves of the vestibular nerve.

Clinical Question

73. These are all symptoms that the **vestibular apparatus** is not functioning properly.

Challenge Question

74. When the head begins to rotate, the **endolymph lags behind** and actually **moves in the direction opposite** of the rotation. When this action **bends the stereocilia in** the direction opposite of the **kinocilium, the hair cell is hyperpolarized** and the **frequency of action potentials in the afferent neuron declines.** When the head rotates and causes the stereocilia to bend toward the kinocilium, the **hair cells are depolarized** and the **frequency of action potentials in the afferent neuron increases.**

TASTE AND OLFACTION

Matching

75. a. ORC **b.** SC **c.** ORC **d.** BC

Completion

76. a. taste buds **b.** tastants **c.** transduction mechanism **d.** three cranial nerves **e.** medulla **f.** thalamus

Short Answer

77. Olfactory binding proteins **carry odorant molecules** to the receptor on the cilia; the binding of the odorant molecule to the receptor **initiates olfactory signal transduction.**

Multiple Choice

78. e **79.** a **80.** c

True/False

81. T

82. F Receptors for bitter flavors are most highly concentrated toward the **back** of the tongue. The tip of the tongue is most highly concentrated in sweet receptors.

Challenge Question

83. An odorant molecule binds to membrane receptor, which activates G_{olf}, which activates adenylate cyclase, which catalyzes the formation of cAMP. cAMP binds to calcium and sodium channels thus allowing these ions to flow into the cell and causing depolarization. In addition, chloride channels also open, allowing chloride to exit the cell thus increasing the depolarization of the receptor cell. Once the receptor cell is depolarized to threshold, action potentials are transmitted along the receptor's axons to the olfactory bulb located in the brain, where they communicate with second-order neurons (mitral cells). These mitral cells form the olfactory tract, which leads to the olfactory tubercle to the thalamus and on to the olfactory cortex. The other pathway transmits the information from the mitral cells to the hypothalamus, amygdala, and other portions of the limbic system.

Concept Map

84. a. potassium **b.** sodium **c.** depolarized **d.** calcium **e.** gustatory nucleus

CHAPTER 10

THE AUTONOMIC AND SOMATIC NERVOUS SYSTEMS

Matching

1. a. S **b.** P **c.** P **d.** S **e.** P

2. a. β_2 **b.** α_2 **c.** α_1 **d.** α_2 **e.** β_1 **f.** α_1

3. a. NJ **b.** TB **c.** MEP **d.** MN **e.** MF **f.** EPP **g.** MU

Completion

4. a. autonomic nervous system **b.** somatic nervous system **c.** parasympathetic **d.** sympathetic **e.** cardiac **f.** glands **g.** dual innervation

5. a. motor neuron(s) **b.** skeletal muscles **c.** ventral horn **d.** motor unit **e.** neuromuscular junction **f.** acetylcholine **g.** terminal bouton **h.** nicotinic cholinergic **i.** end-plate potential

6. a. yes **b.** yes **c.** no **d.** yes **e.** yes **f.** yes **g.** no

Short Answer

7. Autonomic ganglia contain the **axon terminals of preganglionic neurons and cell bodies** and dendrites of postganglionic neurons.

8. Nicotinic receptors are found on **postganglionic cell bodies, chromaffin cells of the adrenal medulla, and skeletal muscle cells**. The receptors always induce an **excitatory effect** on the effector organs by opening sodium channels. **Muscarinic receptors** are found on **effector organs of the parasympathetic nervous system** and can induce either an **excitatory or inhibitory effect, depending on which type of channel is opened** in response to the neurotransmitter.

9. A **visceral reflex** is an automatic change in the functions of visceral organs in response to changes that occur in the body. An example is the **release of gastric secretions** in response to food entering the stomach.

10. Collateral ganglia are **sympathetic ganglia separate from the sympathetic chain** and are situated **anterior to the spinal column**.

11. Varicosities are located on the **neuroeffector organs in the autonomic nervous system. Neurotransmitters are stored and released from them**.

12. The **hypothalamus** initiates the sympathetic effect in response to increased levels of activity. It also controls water balance, body temperature, and food intake. The **pons** and **medulla oblongata** function in controlling heart rate, blood vessel and bronchiole diameter, and breathing rate.

13. Latroxin, a toxin from the black widow spider, **stimulates the release of acetylcholine** from the motor neuron. This continued release of acetylcholine causes repeated end-plate potentials at the motor end plate. These repeated end-plate potentials continue to stimulate the skeletal muscle cells and cause muscle spasms and rigidity due to prolonged tetanic contractions. When the muscles in breathing are involved, death will occur because the muscles are continually stimulated and cannot relax. **Crotoxin**, a toxin from rattlesnake venom, **inhibits the release of acetylcholine**, causing muscle paralysis. Since acetylcholine is inhibited from being released from skeletal muscle terminal boutons, end-plate potentials do not occur and the skeletal muscles become paralyzed because the signal to contract never reaches the muscle. If the muscles in breathing become involved, they will not contract and death will occur.

Multiple Choice

14. b	**15.** c	**16.** e	**17.** a	**18.** c	**19.** d
20. c	**21.** b	**22.** d	**23.** b	**24.** b	**25.** c
26. b	**27.** c				

True/False

28. T

29. F Neurons that release norepinephrine are referred to as **adrenergic**. Neurons that release acetylcholine are referred to as cholinergic.

30. F Skeletal muscle cells contain **nicotinic** cholinergic receptors. Muscarinic cholinergic receptors are found on organs such as the heart, smooth muscles of the eye, and digestive tract.

31. T

32. F Nerves of the autonomic nervous system contain **both efferent and afferent fibers**.

33. T

34. F The autonomic nervous system is sometimes called the **involuntary** nervous system. The voluntary nervous system is the somatic nervous system.

35. T

Labeling

36. a. blood pressure decreases **b.** the cardiovascular control center in the medulla is stimulated **c.** increased sympathetic activity **d.** blood pressure increases

37. a. Preganglionic neuron (cholinergic) **b.** ACh **c.** nicotinic cholinergic receptors **d.** epinephrine **e.** nicotinic cholinergic receptor **f.** postganglionic neuron (adrenergic) **g.** Ach **h.** Ach **i.** cholinergic receptor

Sequencing

38. d, a, c, b

39. b, d, h, a, c, e, f, g

Clinical Questions

40. Epinephrine can stimulate any of the adrenergic receptors. Epinephrine has the desired effect of stimulating adrenergic β_2 receptors. This causes the bronchial muscles to relax, which permits the person to breathe easier. However, epinephrine may also cause increased heart rate by stimulating β_1 receptors on the heart. Increased sweating is caused by stimulation of α_1 receptors in the skin.

41. Beta blockers compete with epinephrine for the β_1 receptor sites on the heart and thus interfere with the action of epinephrine. Since epinephrine cannot stimulate the heart, it beats less forcefully and lowers blood pressure.

Challenge Questions

42. Symptoms might include **increased heart** rate and **vasoconstriction, leading to increased blood pressure**. Other symptoms might be increased sweating and dilated pupils.

43. β_1 **adrenergic receptors** are on the SA node of the heart and increase heart rate. β_1 **adrenergic receptors** are on cardiac muscle cells and make the heart beat more forcefully. α_1 **adrenergic receptors** are present on most blood vessels and cause the vessels to constrict.

44. The pupils are dually innervated. The **parasympathetic receptors that cause the pupil to constrict are muscarinic cholinergic receptors that are stimulated by the neurotransmitter acetylcholine. The sympathetic receptors that cause the pupil to dilate are** α_1 **adrenergic receptors that are stimulated predominantly by norepinephrine.**

Concept Maps

45. a. Preganglionic **b.** Ventral root **c.** White ramus **d.** Sympathetic ganglion **e.** sympathetic chain **f.** Spinal nerve

46. a. NE or EPI **b.** G protein activated **c.** Phospholipase C **d.** PIP$_2$ **e.** IP$_3$ **f.** calcium **g.** DAG **h.** Phosphorylation of protein

CHAPTER 11

SKELETAL MUSCLE STRUCTURE

Matching

1. a. S **b.** T **c.** MF **d.** TM **e.** MY **f.** F **g.** SR **h.** TT **i.** M **j.** A

Completion

2. a. sarcomere **b.** Z lines **c.** A band **d.** I band **e.** M line **f.** H zone

Short Answer

3. A **crossbridge** is the association of the myosin head with the active site on actin.

4. The **head groups** contain **an actin binding site that binds to actin**, and **an ATP-ase site that hydrolyzes ATP.**

Multiple Choice

5. a   **6.** a   **7.** c   **8.** b

True/False

9. F The cell membrane is known as the **sarcolemma**. The sarcomere is the area between Z lines.

10. F The sarcoplasmic reticulum covers the **myofibrils present inside of the cell membrane.**

11. T   **12.** T

13. F Each sarcomere extends from **Z line to Z line.**

Labeling

14. a. myofibril **b.** Z line **c.** M line **d.** A band **e.** I band **f.** H zone

The I bands **shorten** and the **light bands become thinner**. The A band **stays the same length**, which means that the **width of the dark area does not change**. The M line **remains stationary**, while the Z lines **move toward each other**, and the H zones **shorten.**

Clinical Question

15. Muscle fiber degeneration leads to **muscle weakness** and **inability to use the muscles** affected. Strength is lost from the large muscles first. When an affected child falls, he is noticed to be pulling himself up on something sturdy, much like a one-year-old child learning to walk.

Challenge Questions

16. Actin is composed of **three protein subunits**. The actin monomers are composed of G actin, each containing an active site for binding with myosin crossbridges. Two regulatory proteins, **tropomyosin and troponin**, are involved in starting and stopping muscle contractions.

Tropomyosin is a long fibrous molecule that blocks the myosin-binding sites. Troponin is a complex made up of three components, each having its own function. One troponin component attaches to the actin filament, one binds to tropomyosin, and the third binds to calcium ions.

17. Troponin and tropomyosin are similar in that they are **both actin regulatory proteins**; they enable muscle contractions to begin and end. They **differ because tropomyosin's function is to cover the active sites while the muscle is relaxed**, thus preventing binding to the myosin crossbridges. Just prior to a muscle contraction, tropomyosin shifts and exposes the active sites, allowing the myosin crossbridges to make contact with the active sites. The **role of troponin is to bind with calcium ions**, which helps cause the tropomyosin to shift and expose the active sites.

THE MECHANISM OF FORCE GENERATION IN MUSCLE

Matching

18. a. PS **b.** R **c.** B **d.** C **e.** U

Completion

19. a. ATP **b.** actin **c.** ATP **d.** ADP and Pi **e.** myosin **f.** energy **g.** P$_i$ from the ATPase **h.** energy **i.** low energy **j.** actin **k.** actin **l.** myosin **m.** ATP **n.** thin (actin)

Short Answer

20. Acetylcholine is released from the motor neuron where it **diffuses across the synaptic cleft and lands on specific receptors on the motor end plate of the muscle cell by opening sodium channels, allowing depolarization of the motor end plate.** This binding triggers depolarization and causes a change in membrane permeability of the muscle cell. This change causes an action potential in the muscle cell, which propagates down the T tubules where it triggers the release of calcium from the sarcoplasmic reticulum. Calcium serves as the signal that initiates the crossbridge cycle. After calcium is released from the sarcoplasmic reticulum it binds to the troponin complex, which causes the tropomyosin to shift out of its resting position. This shift exposes the myosin-binding sites of the actin monomers, which allows the crossbridge cycle to occur.

21. Creatine phosphate donates a phosphate to ADP to form ATP. This form of ATP synthesis (an example of substrate-level phosphorylation) is especially important during the first few seconds of active muscle contractions.

Multiple Choice

22. b   **23.** c   **24.** d

True/False

25. F Titin is associated with the **thick** (myosin) filaments.

26. F Creatine phosphate is the primary energy source for **short** bursts of activity.

Sequencing

27. c, b, a, d

Challenge Question

28. 1. Acetylcholine is released from the axon terminal of a motor neuron, which causes an end-plate potential in the muscle cell.

2. The action potential travels across the sarcoplasmic reticulum and down the T tubules.

3. The action potential triggers the release of calcium ions from the sarcoplasmic reticulum.

4 Calcium ions bind to troponin thus exposing the myosin-binding sites on the actin monomer.

5. Crossbridge cycling occurs (muscle contracts).

6. Calcium is transported back into the sarcoplasmic reticulum by active transport.

7. Troponin blocks the myosin-binding sites (muscle relaxes).

29. a. Muscles use stored glycogen for ATP production during the first few seconds of exercise. The pathway is glyconeogenesis and glycolysis.

b. In heavy exercise, such as lifting heavy weights, substrate-level phosphorylation (glycolysis) is the predominant pathway that synthesizes ATP.

c. When a muscle is exercised at a moderate rate such as a light jog, most of the ATP is supplied by oxidative phosphorylation. The fuel source is likely to be triglycerides.

Clinical Question

30. Acetylcholine is responsible for depolarizing the motor end plate of skeletal muscles, which leads to muscle stimulation. The lack of acetylcholine receptors means that, while acetylcholine may be produced by motor neurons, the skeletal muscles fail to depolarize to threshold because too few sodium channels open. This leads to lack of stimulation of the muscles and the inability of these muscles to generate forces, causing the weakness.

THE MECHANICS OF SKELETAL MUSCLE CONTRACTION

Matching

31. a. RP **b.** CP **c.** CP **d.** LP **e.** RP **f.** LP

Completion

32. a. crossbridges **b.** myosin **c.** actin **d.** decreases **e.** actin **f.** myosin **g.** lengthen **h.** actin

Short Answer

33. A **muscle twitch** is the **mechanical response of an individual motor unit to a single action potential.**

34. Recruitment is the **ability of a muscle to vary the muscular tension**, depending on the number of motor units activated. By stimulating more motor units within a muscle, the muscle can generate more force.

Multiple Choice

35. d   **36.** b   **37.** d   **38.** a   **39.** e

True/False

40. T

41. F A motor unit is the **motor neuron and all of the muscle fibers that it innervates**.

42. T   **43.** T

Sequencing

44. d, b, a, c

Clinical Question

45. Since barbiturates decrease acetylcholine release, the motor end plate of skeletal muscle cells cannot be stimulated to produce end-plate potentials. This inhibits action potentials in skeletal muscles and causes **muscle weakness and/or paralysis**. The diaphragm may also be affected, which can cause **shallow breathing or even death** if the diaphragm becomes totally paralyzed.

Challenge Questions

46. For fine motor control, as in threading a needle, just a few motor units are needed. When larger forces are needed, as when a person lifts 20 pounds, the nervous system activates more motor units, which induces more muscles fibers to participate in the activity. This process is called **recruitment**.

47. When **muscles are excessively stretched**, the **crossbridges cannot form** because actin and myosin do not overlap enough. When this occurs, sliding cannot be generated and the muscle contracts weakly. When muscles are **strongly contracted, the myofilaments touch and interfere with sliding** thus preventing any further shortening.

Concept Map

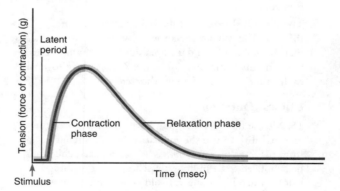

48 a. The **latent period** is the short time between when the motor neuron stimulates the muscle and the twitch occurs. **b.** The **contraction phase** occurs when the muscle is contracting and shortening, which causes an increase in muscular tension. **c.** During the **relaxation phase** tension slowly decreases as the muscle relaxes.

TYPES OF SKELETAL MUSCLE FIBERS

Matching

49. **a.** GF **b.** GF **c.** OF **d.** GF

Completion

50. **a.** fast oxidative **b.** slow oxidative **c.** ATP
d. glycolysis **e.** oxidative phosphorylation **f.** myosin
g. slow

Short Answer

51. **Glycolytic muscle fibers** have high cytosolic concentrations of glycolytic enzymes and therefore can generate ATP rapidly via anaerobic glycolysis. Since these fibers do not rely on oxygen, they tend to be larger in diameter, have few capillaries supplying them, and tend to lack myoglobin. **Oxidative fibers** are rich in myoglobin and mitochondria and can produce ATP via oxidative phosphorylation. These fibers tend to be smaller in diameter and well supplied with capillaries in order to deliver a consistent oxygen supply. When well conditioned, these fibers consume calories rapidly and successfully burn fat as a fuel source.

Multiple Choice

52. c   53. b   54. e

True/False

55. T

56. F When high-intensity exercise is stressed in a muscle the aerobic performance of the muscle is **hindered**.

Sequencing

57. b, c, a

Clinical Question

58. Fast-twitch muscles contract quickly and are used by the body for quick movements. Slow-twitch muscles contract slowly and work as antigravity muscles. On Earth, the combined use of these muscles makes it possible to walk comfortably. **In space, slow-twitch muscle takes on the characteristics of fast-twitch muscle.** Fast-twitch muscle fibers fatigue rapidly because the fibers use massive amounts of ATP and lack the capillaries necessary to supply oxygen to the muscle cells. Astronauts don't notice the change in space, but then experience difficulty with walking once back on Earth because they **no longer have the combination of fibers needed to walk comfortably**.

Challenge Question

59. The weight lifter experiences fatigue sooner than the marathon runner because the **weight lifter is engaging in high-intensity exercise**, which stimulates the muscles at high frequency and with larger forces on the muscles than the marathon runner. In high-intensity exercise, glycolytic muscle fibers are recruited, and these fibers have a tendency to generate lactic acid because of their low oxidative capacity. This causes a rapid buildup of lactic acid in the muscles and leads to fatigue sooner than in the marathon runner, who is recruiting far fewer glycolytic fibers. **Fatigue occurs more slowly in the marathon runner due to depletion of glycogen stores in the muscles.** A number of other factors also contribute to fatigue, including a relative deficit of ATP, a drop in pH in the muscle, and inactivation of the Na^+/K^+ pumps.

SKELETAL MUSCLES AT WORK AND OTHER MUSCLE TYPES

Matching

60. **a.** C, SK **b.** C, SM **c.** SK **d.** C, SM **e.** SM
f. C, SM **g.** C **h.** SM **i.** SK

Completion

61. **a.** pulls **b.** origin **c.** insertion **d.** antagonistic

62. **a.** striations **b.** calmodulin **c.** myosin kinase **d.** head
e. phosphatase **f.** phosphate

63. **a.** gap **b.** broad **c.** summation **d.** sinoatrial
e. atrioventricular

Short Answer

64. The origin of a muscle is defined as the point of attachment of a muscle that is stationary, and the insertion is the point of attachment that moves. Since the radius is moved toward the humerus when the brachioradialis contracts, the **radius is the insertion point and the humerus is the origin**.

65. **Calcium ions bind with calmodulin to cause smooth muscle contractions.** Once calcium is bound to calmodulin, the enzyme myosin kinase is activated, which breaks down ATP and initiates the smooth muscle contraction.

66. Pacemaker potentials are generated by cells of the **sinoatrial node of the heart**. These potentials are generated spontaneously and cause the heart to spontaneously depolarize. Pacemaker potentials are **less commonly found in smooth muscle** cells of the gastrointestinal tract.

67. Since the heart can beat on its own, the signal must originate within the heart muscle itself; this is known as **myogenic control**. However, **neurogenic control** occurs when the heart rate is controlled by nerves, and so by the brain.

Multiple Choice

68. e   69. e   70. d

True/False

71. F Smooth muscle is under **involuntary** control. Only skeletal muscle is strictly under voluntary control.

72. T   73. T

Sequencing

74. f, a, b, d, e, c

Clinical Question

75. Calcium channel **blockers inhibit the movement of calcium** across the sarcoplasmic reticulum of the smooth muscles in the walls of coronary arteries. **Calcium cannot bind to calmodulin** and cause the smooth muscle to contract. Thus the coronary arteries dilate and blood flow to the heart muscle tissue increases.

Challenge Question

76. Antagonists can oppose or reverse the movement of other muscles. Antagonistic muscles can help to **regulate the action of other muscles by contracting to provide resistance**, thus **preventing muscles from overshooting**. In addition, this arrangement protects muscles from overstretching and helps to stabilize the joint.

CHAPTER 12

AN OVERVIEW OF THE MAJOR COMPONENTS OF THE CARDIOVASCULAR SYSTEM AND THEIR FUNCTIONS

Completion

1. a. chordae tendinae **b.** right atrioventricular valve/ tricuspid valve **c.** systemic circuit **d.** interventricular septum **e.** veins **f.** aortic semilunar valve

Matching

2. a. PLAS **b.** PLAT **c.** L **d.** H **e.** E

Sequencing

3. d, c, a, b, e

Multiple Choice

4. c   **5.** e   **6.** a   **7.** c

True/False

8. F The right atrium receives blood from the **superior and inferior venae cavae**; the left atrium receives blood from the pulmonary veins. The ventricles receive blood from the atria.

9. T   **10.** T

11. F The left AV valve is also known as the **bicuspid or mitral valve**. The right AV valve is also known as the tricuspid valve.

12. T

Short Answer

13. The **three components** of the cardiovascular system and their **functions** are:

Blood – transports substances to and from the cells

Blood vessels – conduits through which the blood flows

Heart – pumps blood through the blood vessels

Challenge Questions

14. In bulk flow, molecules move as a stream in the same general direction. Since the predominant molecular motion is nonrandom, bulk flow is capable of rapidly transporting molecules from one location to another within the cardiovascular system.

15. Capillary walls are thin because capillaries are the **site at which substances are exchanged between the blood and the interstitial fluid** (e.g., oxygen leaves the blood, carbon dioxide enters the blood). The thin (one cell layer thick) capillary wall allows for quick, efficient molecular exchanges. **Arteries have thick walls because they must withstand the pressure of blood being pumped into them from the heart.**

16. Ventricular muscle is thicker than atrial muscle because the **ventricles must have the strength to pump blood great distances against resistance through the vasculature**, while the atria pump blood against little resistance into adjacent ventricles, which requires much less force. As the ventricles pump blood against the resistances within the systemic and pulmonary circuits, cardiac muscle develops and strengthens and the myocardium thickens in proportion to the force necessary to move blood through each circuit.

17. The **myocardium of the left ventricle is thicker than** that of the **right ventricle** because the **left ventricle pumps blood through the systemic circuit** while the **right ventricle pumps blood through the pulmonary circuit**. The systemic circuit is a much longer and more extensive vasculature than the pulmonary circuit, and therefore generates a greater resistance to blood flow (see Chapter 13). Because of this, the **left ventricle must generate more force to pump blood through the systemic circuit than the right ventricle needs to generate to pump blood through the pulmonary circuit**. The thicker myocardium of the left ventricle is necessary to generate the amount of force needed.

Clinical Questions

18. Longer than normal chordae tendinae would affect the function of the **atrioventricular valves**. These **valves may prolapse** (be pushed back into the atria) during a heart beat, which would allow some of the **blood in the ventricles to be pushed back into the atria** during ventricular contraction rather than moving forward into the pulmonary trunk or aorta. This would result in **less ejection of blood from the heart than normal**, resulting in a decreased cardiac output.

19. A ventricular septal defect (VSD) would decrease **the level of oxygenation of the blood**. A VSD would allow **deoxygenated blood from the right ventricle to move directly into the left ventricle, bypassing the lungs**. This deoxygenated blood would mix with the oxygenated blood in the left ventricle, **reducing the oxygen level of the blood being pumped into the systemic circuit.**

Matching

20. a. D **b.** D **c.** O **d.** O **e.** O **f.** D

Multiple Choice

21. b   **22.** c   **23.** a

True/False

24. T

25. F Arteries branching off the aorta are part of the **systemic** circuit.

26. T

27. F Blood leaving the pulmonary capillaries is **oxygenated**.

28. T

29. F The pulmonary arteries carry **deoxygenated blood.** All other arteries carry oxygenated blood.

Completion

30. left atrium   **31.** away from   **32.** deoxygenated

Short Answer

33. No, deoxygenated blood is not completely without oxygen. It **contains a relative lack of oxygen** since it is the blood returning to the heart after the cells have extracted the oxygen they need from oxygenated blood. Systemic venous (deoxygenated) blood typically has a P_{O_2} of about 40 mm Hg, while arterial (oxygenated) blood typically has a P_{O_2} of about 100 mm Hg.

34. The **pulmonary circuit** consists of all the blood vessels within the lungs and the blood vessels connecting the heart to the lungs. The **systemic circuit** is composed of all other blood vessels in the body (those that carry blood from the heart to all the tissues of the body except the lungs and back to the heart again).

Challenge Question

35. Oxygenated blood is usually illustrated in red and deoxygenated blood in blue for the following reasons. In reality, oxygenated blood is bright red, while deoxygenated blood is a darker red. **Because deoxygenated blood imparts a bluish color to the superficial veins, it is traditionally illustrated in blue, while the brighter red oxygenated blood is designated red.**

Clinical Questions

36. Mitral valve stenosis would **inhibit blood flow** through the **left** atrioventricular valve.

37. Mitral valve stenosis often **leads** to the **backup of blood in the pulmonary circuit** since the inhibition of flow between the left atrium and left ventricle will lead to incomplete emptying of the left atrium, which will inhibit the flow of blood from the pulmonary circuit into the left atrium. As blood backs up in the pulmonary circuit, the pressure in the pulmonary circuit will increase, resulting in pulmonary congestion.

Sequencing

38. pulmonary CAPILLARIES, PULMONARY VEINS, LEFT ATRIUM, LEFT AV VALVE, LEFT VENTRICLE, AORTIC SEMILUNAR VALVE, AORTA, SYSTEMIC ARTERIES, SYSTEMIC ARTERIOLES, SYSTEMIC capillaries, systemic venules, systemic veins, superior and inferior vena cavae, right atrium, right av valve, right ventricle, pulmonary semilunar valve, pulmonary arteries

ELECTRICAL ACTIVITY OF THE HEART

Multiple Choice

39. b   **40.** b   **41.** d   **42.** c   **43.** b   **44.** c

True/False

45. T   **46.** T

47. F Cells of the conduction system of the heart are specialized to initiate and/or conduct **action potentials.**

48. T

49. F Conduction fibers transmit action potentials at a **faster** rate than other cardiac muscle fibers.

50. T   **51.** T   **52.** T   **53.** T

Short Answer

54. Cardiac impulses are delayed in the AV node to allow the atria enough time to empty before the ventricles contract.

55. A pacemaker potential is the **automatic, slow depolarization** of the membrane of cardiac pacemaker cells that follows each action potential.

56.

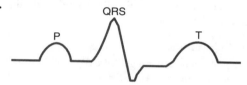

Completion

57. pacemaker   **58.** autorhythmicity

59. atrioventricular bundle

Matching

60. a. 1 **b.** 0 **c.** 3 **d.** 4 **e.** 2

Sequencing

61. d, b, g, e, f, a, c

Labeling

62.

	Phase	Depolarization/ repolarization/ plateau/rest	Primary ion movement(s)
a.	4	rest	—
b.	0	depolarization	**increased sodium influx**
c.	1	slight repolarization	**increased calcium influx, decreased sodium influx,** decreased potassium efflux
d.	2	plateau	**increased calcium influx,** decreased potassium efflux
e.	3	repolarization	**increased potassium efflux,** decreased calcium influx
f.	4	rest	—

Challenge Questions

63. **Sympathetic stimulation increases the action potential frequency** in cardiac pacemaker cells because it **causes a more rapid depolarization** of the pacemaker cell membrane following each action potential than would otherwise occur. This causes the membrane potential to **reach threshold more quickly, which decreases the time between action potentials** increasing the heart rate.

64. **The AV node rarely initiates cardiac contractions for two reasons.** As action potentials travel from the SA node to the AV node, they cause the **cells of the AV node to go into a refractory period in which they are incapable of generating their own action potentials.** Also, because the **SA node fires more frequently than the AV node** (70 beats per minute v. 50 beats per minute) it "beats the AV node to the punch," preventing it from initiating action potentials.

65. Repolarization of the atria is not visible on an ECG because it is **obscured by the QRS complex,** which occurs simultaneously due to ventricular depolarization. Atrial muscle, since it is thinner and has less muscle mass than ventricular muscle, generates a weaker sum electrical signal, which is obscured by the sum electrical signal produced by the ventricles.

Clinical Questions

66. If the **SA node is damaged,** the **AV node will take over as the pacemaker** of the heart and the heart will continue to beat so the affected person may not die. The **heart rate** will be **slower than normal,** however, as the AV node can only pace the heart at about 50 beats per minute. This can interfere with a person's ability to perform physical activities.

67. Increased duration of time between the P wave and QRS complex on an ECG indicates that the **time between atrial contraction and ventricular contraction is longer than normal.** This is probably the result of cardiac action potentials being delayed for too long a period of time in the AV node, a condition referred to as a **heart (or conduction) block.**

THE CARDIAC CYCLE

Matching

68. a. VF **b.** VE **c.** VF, VE, IR **d.** VF **e.** IR **f.** IC **g.** IR, IC

Completion

69. a. end-systolic volume **b.** end-diastolic volume **c.** stroke volume **d.** ejection fraction

70. a. QRS complex **b.** ventricular ejection **c.** T wave **d.** isovolumetric relaxation **e.** P wave **f.** ventricular filling

Multiple Choice

71. d **72.** e **73.** b **74.** c **75.** e **76.** a
77. b **78.** d **79.** c **80.** d

True/False

81. T **82.** T **83.** T **84.** T

85. F When a ventricle contracts, it ejects about **70 ml of blood. 60–65 ml remain in the ventricle.**

Short Answer

86. Aortic pressure begins to rise during **ventricular ejection.**

87. Ventricular diastole is almost twice as long as ventricular systole at rest. (Ventricular diastole takes up 65% of a heart beat; systole 35%.) This ensures there will be **adequate time to complete ventricular filling,** and **helps prevent fatigue** of the myocardium.

Sequencing

88. e, h, d, c, a, f, g, b, i

Challenge Questions

89. Blood flows fairly continuously through the vasculature despite the fact that it is pumped in spurts from the heart because the elastic walls of the aorta allow it to serve as a pressure reservoir. Some of the energy generated by the heart is stored by the aorta when its elastic walls expand as blood enters it. **During diastole, the walls of the aorta recoil, releasing the stored energy and pushing blood through the vasculature.** Therefore, blood moves through the vasculature during both systole and diastole, resulting in the continuous flow of blood.

90. The **dicrotic notch** in the aortic pressure curve is **generated when the aortic semilunar valve closes. Blood** in the aorta flows backward toward the left ventricle, **bouncing off the closed aortic semilunar valve,** producing a slight increase in pressure known as the dicrotic notch.

91. All four valves of the heart are closed during isovolumetric relaxation, which occurs at the beginning of ventricular diastole, because, as the ventricles begin to relax, the **pressure in the ventricles is lower than the pressure in the aorta/pulmonary trunk,** which keeps the semilunar valves closed; it **is greater than the pressure in the atria,** however, which keeps the atrioventricular valves closed.

Clinical Question

92. Blood pressure readings estimate aortic pressure. They **are taken with the person in a sitting position with his/her arm elevated to chest height because this places the brachial artery** (in which the pressure is actually being measured) **near the level of the aorta,** which produces a fairly accurate estimate of aortic pressure. Placing the patient in a sitting position also ensures that positional effects (as might occur if the patient stood up or laid down) will not influence the blood pressure reading.

CARDIAC OUTPUT AND ITS CONTROL

Completion

93. preload **94.** ventricular contractility **95.** afterload

96. a. vagus **b.** SA **c.** AV **d.** sympathetic cardiac **e.** SA **f.** AV **g.** myocardium **h.** heart rate **i.** decrease

Matching

97. a. D, DFT **b.** I, IL **c.** D, AF **d.** D, DAP **e.** I, VC

Multiple Choice

98. b **99.** d **100.** c **101.** e **102.** a **103.** d **104.** e

True/False

105. F As mean arterial pressure rises, afterload **increases**.

106. F Cardiac output will increase as the result of an increase in heart rate **and/or** an increase in stroke volume.

107. T **108.** T **109.** T

110. F Ventricular contractility is influenced by sympathetic stimulation **and hormones such as epinephrine, insulin, and glucagon**.

111. T

Short Answer

112. The average adult's **heart rate is slower than the "natural" frequency** (100 action potentials per minute) **of the SA node** because the SA node normally **receives parasympathetic stimulation, which slows the action potential frequency** of the pacemaker cells to about 70 per minute.

113. The **three primary factors that affect stroke volume** are **ventricular contractility, end-diastolic volume**, and **afterload**.

Challenge Questions

114. Starling's Law of the Heart says that the heart will automatically adjust its outflow to match venous return. This phenomenon occurs as a result of the Starling effect. The **Starling effect** is that the **force of ventricular contraction is proportional to the degree of stretch of the cardiac muscle fibers**. As end-diastolic volume increases, cardiac muscle is stretched more, which increases the force of ventricular contraction, resulting in an increased stroke volume and cardiac output. Likewise, as end-diastolic volume decreases and the cardiac muscle fibers aren't stretched as much, the force of ventricular contraction decreases, resulting in a decrease in stroke volume and cardiac output. **By adjusting stroke volume so cardiac output matches venous return, accumulation of blood in the heart is prevented and the heart is able to regulate its own size.**

115. Increased sympathetic stimulation will decrease the duration of systole because sympathetic stimulation increases the speed with which action potentials are conducted through the myocardium, decreasing the delay of impulse conduction between the atria and the ventricles. Therefore, ventricular contraction starts sooner after atrial contraction and proceeds more rapidly, which decreases the duration of systole.

116. Intrinsic control mechanisms of cardiac function are those that **originate within the heart** itself. The **Starling effect** on stroke volume is a major intrinsic influence on cardiac function.

Extrinsic control mechanisms of cardiac function are those that **originate outside the heart**. These include **autonomic control of heart rate, the effect of sympathetic stimulation on ventricular contractility, and hormonal influences on heart rate and contractility**.

Clinical Questions

117. Heart failure refers to the failure of the heart to maintain adequate circulation of blood as the result of inadequate cardiac output. It is most commonly, though not always, the result of decreased ventricular contractility, which leads to a decreased stroke volume and decreased cardiac output.

118. As a result of left-sided heart failure, blood would accumulate in the chambers of the left side of the heart, which would prevent blood in the pulmonary circuit from flowing normally into the left atrium. **Blood would back-up in the pulmonary circuit, increasing the pressure in the pulmonary vasculature, resulting in pulmonary congestion.**

119. In order to try to maintain a normal cardiac output, the patient's **heart rate would increase** to attempt to **compensate for the decrease in stroke volume** that would accompany heart failure.

Labeling

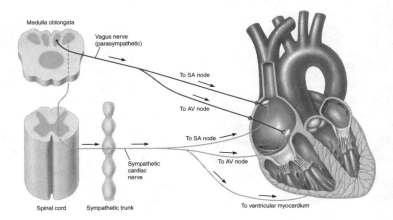

120. The vagus nerve releases **acetylcholine** at target cells, the sympathetic cardiac nerve releases **norepinephrine**.

Concept Map

121. a. ↓ heart rate **b.** ↑ afterload **c.** ↓ ventricular contractility **d.** ↓ preload **e.** ↓ filling time **f.** ↓ atrial pressure **g.** ↑ parasympathetic stimulation **h.** ↓ venous return **i.** ↓ force of atrial contraction

CHAPTER 13

THE COMPOSITION OF BLOOD

Matching

1. a. F b. B c. A d. G e. E

Multiple Choice

2. b   3. d   4. c   5. e   6. a

True/False

7. F The concentration of proteins in the plasma is **greater than** the concentration of proteins in the interstitial fluid.

8. T   9. T

10. F Each hemoglobin molecule binds a maximum of **four** molecules of oxygen.

11. T   12. T

13. F **Some leukocytes** are mobile and can migrate through tissues. **Erythrocytes** remain in the vasculature.

Completion

14. megakaryocytes   15. erythrocyte

16. red bone marrow   17. B_{12} 18. 5 liters

Short Answer

19. The **formed elements** of the blood and their **functions** are:

Erythrocytes – transport oxygen and carbon dioxide in the blood

Leukocytes – participate in defense against pathogens and other foreign materials

Platelets – involved in the process by which blood clots form

Challenge Question

20. The **hematocrit** is the **percentage of blood volume** composed of **erythrocytes**. The hematocrit of the blood sample described would be **52%**. This would be **normal for a man** (normal range 40–54%), but would be high for a woman (normal range 37–47%).

Clinical Questions

21. The runner's **hematocrit would be higher than normal** as he would be **dehydrated**. Dehydration would decrease his plasma volume, resulting in an increase in the proportion of erythrocytes in his blood compared to volume.

22. **Anemia** is a condition in which there is a **reduction in the oxygen-carrying capacity of the blood. Symptoms** include, but are not limited to, c**hronic fatigue, shortness of breath on exertion, and pale skin.** Anything that decreases the hemoglobin content of red blood cells or decreases the number of red cells in the blood can produce an anemia. Some of the more common **causes include** a **lack of iron in the diet**, which results in decreased hemoglobin production (iron deficiency anemia), a **lack of**

vitamin B_{12} **in the diet** (pernicious anemia) which interferes with the production of erythrocytes, **hemorrhage**, or **accelerated erythrocyte destruction**.

PLATELETS AND HEMOSTASIS

Multiple Choice

23. a   24. d   25. c   26. e

True/False

27. T   28. T   29. T

Short Answer

30. The **intrinsic coagulation pathway is activated by vascular damage**. Damage to a vessel exposes subendothelial collagen and phospholipids to the blood. When **factor XII** (Hageman factor) in the blood comes into contact with collagen and phospholipids, it is activated. Activated factor XII begins a coagulation cascade that culminates in the formation of a fibrin blood clot.

The **extrinsic pathway is activated by tissue damage**. Damaged tissue releases **tissue factor** (factor III), which enters the blood plasma and begins a coagulation cascade that culminates in the formation of a fibrin blood clot.

Challenge/Clinical Questions

31. **TPA (tissue plasminogen activator) is administered in the early stages of a heart attack because it converts plasminogen to plasmin. Plasmin enzymatically breaks down the fibrin in blood clots, dissolving the clot.** By administering TPA early in a heart attack, the hope is that it will stimulate dissolution of the clot in the coronary artery, restoring blood flow to the myocardium and preventing or minimizing damage to the heart.

32. Because the **formation of a blood clot results from a cascade of reactions, each of which depends on the one that comes before it, the loss or deficiency of even one coagulation factor will prevent the blood from clotting normally.** Without adequate factor VIII, the coagulation cascade cannot proceed to the end, the fibrin clot will not form, and excessive bleeding following injury will occur.

THE STRUCTURE AND FUNCTION OF BLOOD VESSELS

Completion

33. arteries   34. capillaries

35. metarterioles   36. peripheral, central

Multiple Choice

37. b   38. e   39. c   40. d   41. b   42. d

True/False

43. T   44. T

45. F Arteries carry blood **away** from the heart, while veins carry blood **toward** the heart.

46. T

47. F Substances that can easily cross continuous capillaries include oxygen, steroid hormones, and **carbon dioxide**. Proteins can more easily cross fenestrated capillaries, but only do so in certain organs.

Matching

48. a. M **b.** AS **c.** VL **d.** C **e.** AR **f.** VN

Short Answer

49. Structural differences between continuous and fenestrated capillaries include the following: **Continuous capillaries** are composed of **endothelial cells without pores** that are **joined tightly together**, while **fenestrated capillaries** are composed of **endothelial cells that contain large pores** called **fenestrations** and that, in some cases, **have gaps in between them.**

50. Fenestrated capillaries are **more permeable** to **large molecules** than continuous capillaries.

Challenge Questions

51. Fenestrated capillaries are not found in most of the brain vasculature. The **blood brain barrier**, which prevents pathogens and toxins from gaining access to brain tissue, is the **result of decreased permeability of the brain capillaries** as compared to capillaries elsewhere in the body. Since fenestrated capillaries are highly permeable, it would be counterproductive to have them present in the brain vasculature. (The only locations in which fenestrated capillaries might be present would be specialized areas of the brain without blood-brain barrier protection, such as capillaries connecting the hypothalamus and anterior pituitary.)

52. The **low compliance of arteries** combined with their **elasticity** allows them to serve as **pressure reservoirs**. This means that they can **store the pressure generated by the heart as blood is pumped into them, and then release that pressure during diastole to keep blood flowing smoothly through the vasculature.** The **high compliance of veins** allows them to serve as **volume reservoirs**. Their ability to stretch without much change in internal pressure allows them to **store blood** until a situation arises in which it is needed to help maintain adequate cardiac output.

Clinical Questions

53. Because the **veins serve as volume reservoirs**, as blood is lost during a slow **hemorrhage**, **some/most of it is replaced by blood stored in the veins** that is forced toward the heart, so it contributes to cardiac output. Since veins have a high compliance, blood can leave the volume reservoir with little decrease in venous pressure, so cardiac output can be maintained at an adequate level.

54. If the veins had a lower compliance than they do, they would not be able to serve the role described in Question 53. If they had a lower compliance, veins would **not be able to store blood as effectively.** When stored blood moved out of the veins, there would be a fairly **large decrease in venous pressure**, which would result in a decreased stroke volume and cardiac output. This would

be counterproductive to the desired effect of maintaining adequate cardiac output.

PATTERNS OF BLOOD FLOW WITHIN THE CARDIOVASCULAR SYSTEM

Short Answer

55. Series flow occurs **between** the **pulmonary and systemic circuits**. In this flow pattern, **blood at any point in the vasculature must pass sequentially through each circuit before returning to its starting point.** Blood flow **within** the systemic and pulmonary circuits travels in a **parallel flow** pattern. In this situation, **blood flows simultaneously to numerous organs** in the systemic circuit and **travels simultaneously throughout individual organs** of the systemic and pulmonary circuits. Parallel flow is possible because of the branched arrangement of the vasculature.

56. Advantages of parallel flow within the systemic circuit are as follows.

1. Since each organ is fed by a separate artery, **each receives fully oxygenated blood** instead of blood that has already been used by another organ.

2. **Blood flow to organs can be independently regulated** to match the metabolic needs of the organs.

3. There is less resistance to blood flow in a parallel flow arrangement as compared to a series flow arrangement.

Labeling

57.

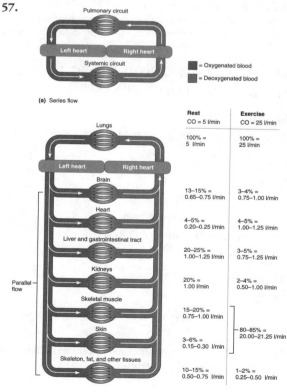

(a) Series flow

(b) Parallel flow

True/False

58 F The heart muscle receives most of its nourishment via the blood that flows through the **coronary arteries.**

59. T   **60.** T

61. F The distribution of blood flow to organs and within organs is **adjusted to meet the metabolic needs of the organs at any given point in time.**

Multiple Choice

62. a   **63.** a

Completion

64. distribution   **65.** arterioles

Sequencing

66. a, h, d, g, e, f, c, e, i, b, a

Challenge Question

67. Blood flow to the skeletal muscles increases during exercise in order to provide the **oxygen they need to aerobically generate the amount of ATP** necessary to support their metabolic needs during increased activity. **Blood flow** to the **skin increases** to meet the **metabolic and fluid needs of the sweat glands** as they produce sweat to cool the body during exercise. Increased blood flow to the skin directly helps **cool the body** by allowing **heat to radiate off** the body's surface. In order to allow blood flow to the skin and skeletal muscles to increase during exercise, blood flow to some other organs must decrease. **Since the activities of the liver and gastrointestinal tract are not critical during exercise, their level of metabolic activity and blood flow decreases. This allows the distribution of blood to be shifted** so that more flows to the skin and skeletal muscles.

PHYSICAL LAWS GOVERNING BLOOD FLOW AND BLOOD PRESSURE

Multiple Choice

68. e   **69.** b   **70.** c   **71.** d   **72.** b

Completion

73. 90, 0

74. pulmonary arteries, pulmonary veins, 15

75. vasodilation, vasoconstriction

76. total peripheral resistance (TPR)

77. vasoconstriction

True/False

78. T

79. F As vessel radius decreases, resistance **increases.**

80. T

81. F The largest pressure drop in the cardiovascular system occurs along the **arterioles.**

82. T

Matching

83. a. I **b.** D **c.** D **d.** D

Short Answer

84. The **four factors that affect resistance** within the vasculature are **vessel radius, vessel length, blood viscosity, and manner of flow.** Of these, **vessel radius has the biggest impact** on changes in vascular resistance on a minute-to-minute, day-to-day basis.

85. The **equation** that designates the **relationships among pressure, resistance, and flow** in the **systemic circuit is CO = MAP/TPR** (cardiac output = mean arterial pressure divided by total peripheral resistance). **Cardiac output (CO) is equivalent to flow.**

Challenge Questions

86. The total length of the pulmonary vasculature is much less than the length of the systemic circuit, so **the resistance within the pulmonary circuit is much less.** Therefore, **a lower pressure gradient in the pulmonary circuit can generate the same flow as a higher pressure gradient in the systemic circuit** (since flow = $\Delta P/R$).

87. The **rate of blood flow in both vessels A and B would be identical**, since the pressure gradients and resistances would be identical.

A. Pressure gradient = 50 mm Hg – 25 mm Hg = 25 mm Hg

B. Pressure gradient = 200 mm Hg – 175 mm Hg = 25 mm Hg

Clinical Questions

88. Obesity often leads to the development of hypertension because, as fat content in the body increases, the **number of capillaries in the systemic circuit increases** as more capillaries are required to supply blood to the additional adipose tissue. Increasing the number of capillaries will **increase the overall length of the systemic vasculature**, which will **increase total peripheral resistance, increasing the mean arterial pressure** (MAP = CO × TPR). Also, the pressure of the excess weight tends to compress vessels, increasing peripheral resistance and MAP.

89. Arteriosclerosis might interfere with the flow of blood to organs in the following ways. The **buildup of plaque** will **decrease the vessel radius**, which will **increase vessel resistance, decreasing blood flow**, and will create turbulent flow within the vessels, which will also increase resistance and decrease blood flow. **Stiffening of the arterioles** will **decrease their ability to vasodilate**, which will **increase vessel resistance, decreasing blood flow.** Complete vessel blockages can lead to the growth of new vessels that bypass the blockage (called **collateral circulation**), which **increases vessel length, increasing resistance and decreasing blood flow.**

90. Blood doping will increase peripheral resistance by **increasing blood viscosity** and blood volume as it will result in an increase in the number of red blood cells present in the blood. This will adversely impact cardiac function because the **heart will have to work much harder to maintain an adequate cardiac output** in the face of the increased peripheral resistance. Blood doping is a dangerous practice.

Concept Map

91. a. decreased **b.** increased **c.** mean arterial pressure (MAP) **d.** increased **e.** increased **f.** decreased **g.** increased **h.** decreased **i.** increased

FACTORS AFFECTING FLOW AND DISTRIBUTION OF BLOOD TO ORGANS

Sequencing

92. C, A, B

Short Answer

93. The **distribution of blood flow to organ B would decrease**, while the proportion of blood flowing to **organs A and C would increase**.

Multiple Choice

94. b   **95.** d   **96.** a

True/False

97. T

98. F If the resistance in individual organs remains constant but mean arterial pressure increases, the blood flow to **all** organs will increase.

99. F Mean arterial pressure is equivalent to cardiac output multiplied by total peripheral resistance. **MAP = CO × TPR**.

100. F The vascular resistance of an organ is altered primarily by the **vasodilation and vasoconstriction of the small arteries and arterioles** that supply that organ with blood.

Matching

101. a. I **b.** I **c.** I **d.** D **e.** D **f.** D

HOW CHANGES IN CENTRAL VENOUS PRESSURE AFFECT BLOOD FLOW TO ORGANS

Completion

102. increases, skeletal muscle pump

103. pressure gradient, abdomen, thoracic cavity

104. venomotor tone

105. venous pooling

Multiple Choice

106. e   **107.** c   **108.** d   **109.** a

True/False

110. T

111. F Neurons that generate venomotor tone are called **venoconstrictor** neurons.

112. T   **113.** T

Matching

114. a. D **b.** I **c.** I **d.** D **e.** D

Short Answer

115. The **skeletal muscle pump** helps push blood through the peripheral veins as the result of the **alternate contraction and relaxation of the leg muscles. Contraction of the muscles squeezes the veins**, increasing the pressure within them. This closes the distal valves, preventing blood from being pulled backward by gravity, and opens the proximal valves so that blood moves forward toward the heart. When the muscles relax, the venous pressure decreases, causing the proximal valves to close, which prevents the blood that just flowed past them from being pulled back down by gravity, and the distal valves open so blood can enter the veins from below.

Challenge/Clinical Questions

116.

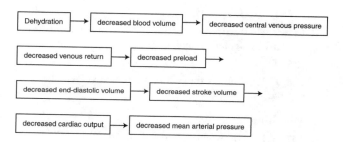

117. Cracked ribs might decrease a person's central venous pressure and cardiac output in the following way.

Cracked ribs → painful breathing → decreased depth of breathing → decreased pressure gradient between the abdominal and thoracic cavity → decreased movement of blood from the peripheral to the central veins → decreased central venous pressure → decreased end-diastolic volume → decreased stroke volume → decreased cardiac output

118. The patient probably **fainted** because **standing increases the pressure in the leg veins, causing them to expand**. This increases the amount of blood located in the veins (venous pooling), which will decrease central venous pressure, venous return, and cardiac output. The decreased cardiac output will **decrease mean arterial pressure**. Normally the heart can compensate for this and maintain adequate blood flow to the vital organs, but in this case the patient had congestive heart failure and his heart couldn't compensate. Therefore, **when the patient stood up, blood flow to his brain decreased due to the decreased mean arterial pressure** (orthostatic hypotension), and he fainted. When he fell to the floor and was **lying down, the blood in his legs was able to move toward his central veins**, which increased his central venous pressure, **increasing** venous return, cardiac output, and **mean arterial pressure. Blood flow to his brain then increased, allowing him to regain consciousness.**

MOVEMENT OF FLUID ACROSS CAPILLARY WALLS

Completion

119. filtration **120.** absorption

121. oncotic **122.** edema

Multiple Choice

123. b **124.** e **125.** c **126.** d **127.** e

True/False

128. T **129.** T

130. F Filtration and absorption often **occur at different locations in the same capillary.**

131. F When the sign of the net filtration pressure is positive, **filtration** will occur. Negative net filtration pressure results in absorption.

132. T **133.** T

134. F Fluid within the lymphatic system is returned to the **cardiovascular system.**

135. T

136. F Fluid enters the lymphatic system via lymphatic **capillaries.**

Matching

137. a. DA, IF **b.** DA, IF **c.** DF, IA **d.** IF, DA

Short Answer

138. Three factors assist the flow of lymphatic fluid through the lymphatic system. Contraction of the skeletal muscles, particularly in the legs, compresses the lymphatic vessels, causing lymph to move forward. **Contraction of the smooth muscle in the walls of lymph ducts** also helps force the fluid forward, and **valves in the lymph ducts** close behind the lymph so gravity does not pull it backward.

139. Lymphatic capillaries connect on only one end to lymphatic vessels, while **blood capillaries are connected at both ends** to other blood vessels (a venule and arteriole). **Lymphatic capillaries have larger pores** than fenestrated blood capillaries.

Challenge Question

140. Prolonged standing in one position, as occurs in bridesmaids/groomsmen participating in long wedding ceremonies, **decreases the activity of the skeletal muscle pump.** The effect of gravity leads to **venous pooling,** which **increases the hydrostatic pressure** in the capillaries of the legs, **increasing the rate of filtration.** This results in a **decrease in circulating blood volume,** which **decreases central venous pressure, cardiac output,** and

mean arterial pressure. Decreased mean arterial pressure may **reduce blood flow to the brain,** which would result in the bridesmaid or groomsman **fainting.**

Clinical Questions

141. Congestive heart failure (which technically refers to left-sided heart failure) eventually **results in right-sided heart failure** because the right side of the heart is unable to eject all of its normal stroke volume into the pulmonary circuit due to the elevated pressure within the pulmonary vasculature. Once right-sided heart failure occurs, since the right ventricle is retaining some of its normal stroke volume, **the right atrium is not able to completely empty and blood backs up into the systemic veins. This increases venous pressure, which increases the hydrostatic pressure in the capillaries, which results in increased filtration and decreased absorption, producing peripheral edema. The increased venous pressure and congestion of blood within the liver will cause it to enlarge.**

142. Two pathways by which kidney disease or damage could result in the development of edema are illustrated by the concept maps below.

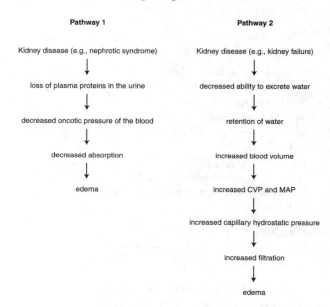

CHAPTER 14

EXTRINSIC CONTROL OF CARDIOVASCULAR FUNCTION: REGULATION OF MEAN ARTERIAL PRESSURE

Completion

1. medulla oblongata **2.** parasympathetic, sympathetic

3. baroreceptor **4.** hypertension

5. beta **6.** pressor

7. angiotensin converting enzyme (ACE)

Matching

8. a. D **b.** I **c.** D **d.** D **e.** D **f.** I **g.** D

9. a. B **b.** B **c.** B **d.** B **e.** B **f.** B **g.** B

10. a. EH, AII, ADH **b.** EL, EH **c.** AII **d.** EL **e.** ADH **f.** EL, EH **g.** EL, EH

Multiple Choice

11. b	**12.** b	**13.** e	**14.** c	**15.** d	**16.** c
17. e	**18.** b	**19.** e	**20.** e	**21.** d	**22.** b
23. b	**24.** c	**25.** a	**26.** e	**27.** b	**28.** d
29. c					

Labeling

30.

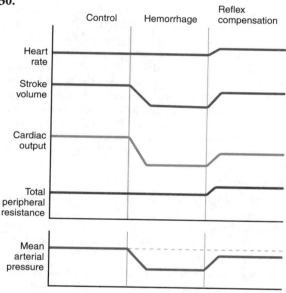

True/False

31. T   **32.** T

33. F In response to a decrease in mean arterial pressure, the baroreceptor reflex produces physiologic responses that increase heart rate and stroke volume and **increase** total peripheral resistance.

34. F A baroreceptor reflex can be triggered in response to **either a decrease or an increase in mean arterial pressure**. The responses generated by the reflex in these two cases will be the opposites of each other.

35. F Increased parasympathetic stimulation will decrease the heart rate. **It has no effect on the arterioles**.

36. T

37. F The regulation of mean arterial pressure is an example of **extrinsic** control. Local changes in organ blood flow in response to changes in the metabolic activity of the organ would be an example of intrinsic control.

38. F When arterial baroreceptors notify the central nervous system of a decrease in mean arterial pressure, the responses produced include an **increase** in sympathetic nervous system activity and a **decrease** in parasympathetic nervous system activity.

39. T

40. F Arterial baroreceptors and volume receptors trigger the **same type of sympathetic responses**.

41. T   **42.** T

43. F Angiotensin-converting enzyme is located primarily on the **inner surface of blood vessels in the lungs**.

44. T

45. F Increased sympathetic stimulation of the adrenal gland will **increase** the secretion of epinephrine.

46. T   **47.** T   **48.** T

Short Answer

49. It is **advantageous** to the body **that arterial baroreceptors are located in the aortic arch and carotid sinuses** because the **pressure in the aorta affects blood flow to all organs in the systemic circuit, and the pressure in the carotid arteries affects blood flow to the brain**. The ability to detect pressure changes in these locations ensures that responses can quickly be generated to maintain adequate blood flow to all systemic organs, especially the brain.

50. High and low concentrations of epinephrine have opposite effects on most vascular beds in the body **because of differences in alpha and beta adrenergic receptors** in terms of their **affinity for epinephrine** and their **distribution throughout the vasculature. Most arterioles have more alpha receptors than beta receptors**, but **beta receptors have a higher affinity for epinephrine than alpha receptors**, so at low epinephrine concentrations beta receptors will be stimulated and vasodilation will occur. At higher epinephrine concentrations, both alpha and beta receptors will be stimulated, and since alpha receptors predominate, vasoconstriction will occur.

51. Venous and cardiac baroreceptors, located in the walls of systemic veins and the heart, are often referred to as volume receptors because they monitor venous pressure, which is determined to a large extent by the volume of blood in the veins (since most of the body's blood volume is located in the veins).

Sequencing

52. c, i, e, g, b, f, a, h, d

Challenge Questions

53. Vasodilation generally does not occur in all the arterioles in the body at the same time, as this would cause a large decrease in total peripheral resistance, resulting in a significant decrease in mean arterial pressure. In order to maintain mean arterial pressure and meet the metabolic needs of organs at the same time, the arterioles in the vascular beds of the most active organs are dilated while the arterioles in the vascular beds of less active organs are constricted. When the activity levels/metabolic needs of the organs change, the pattern of vasodilation/vasoconstriction changes as well, so the blood flow needs of all organs are met by "trading off" vasodilation and vasoconstriction amongst vascular beds. Local intrinsic control mechanisms will override general extrinsic control mechanisms to ensure that the metabolic needs of organs are met.

54. The mean arterial pressure (MAP) is maintained at a slightly lower than normal level following hemorrhage until blood volume is restored. The reason for this is that, **as long as blood volume remains low, the compensatory mechanisms of the baroreceptor reflex must continue to be active in order to maintain MAP. If the baroreceptor reflex brought the MAP back to its original level, the stimulus (lower than normal MAP) triggering the baroreceptor reflex would be removed and the compensatory mechanisms would stop resulting in an undesirable decrease in MAP.**

55. The goal of a baroreceptor reflex that occurs in response to a decrease in mean arterial pressure (MAP) is to increase the MAP enough to maintain adequate blood flow to the heart and brain. The baroreceptor reflex accomplishes this in part by increasing sympathetic stimulation of the arterioles in most locations throughout the body, which results in vasoconstriction, increasing the total peripheral resistance and MAP. However, **the arterioles of the brain and heart are affected very little by sympathetic stimulation, so they remain dilated during the baroreceptor reflex. In this way blood flow to the brain and heart is maintained, but at the expense of blood flow to other organs.**

56. It is advantageous to the body for the arterioles in **cardiac and skeletal muscle to have more beta than alpha receptors while arterioles elsewhere have more alpha than beta receptors because of the physiologic responses generated during the fight-or-flight response.** The purpose of the fight-or-flight response is to prepare the body to perform intense physical activity in the face of a perceived danger. One of the major features of this response is the secretion of epinephrine from the adrenal glands. **Since the binding of epinephrine to beta receptors produces the vasodilation of arterioles while the binding of epinephrine to alpha receptors results in vasoconstriction, the abundance of beta receptors in the resistance vessels of the heart and skeletal muscles allows blood flow to increase to those organs to meet their metabolic needs during the fight-or-flight response; the abundance of alpha receptors in less essential organs (such as those of the GI tract) will generate vasoconstriction, making more blood available to the heart and skeletal muscles.**

Clinical Questions

57. His blood pressure remained fairly stable during the first 45 minutes after his blood loss due to the compensatory mechanisms (including arteriolar vasoconstriction) triggered by the baroreceptor reflex that helps maintain mean arterial pressure (MAP). However, if blood volume is not restored within an hour or so following hemorrhage, **intrinsic control mechanisms that seek to increase blood flow to the organs begin to override the arteriolar vasoconstriction induced by the baroreceptor reflex. These intrinsic control mechanisms will generate vasodilation** in response to the decreased oxygen and increased carbon dioxide levels in the tissues (among other triggers), which will decrease vascular

resistance, resulting in a decrease in MAP and possible circulatory shock. At this point, blood flow to the brain will decrease, resulting in loss of consciousness.

58. The baroreceptor reflex doesn't keep arterial blood pressure within "normal limits" in people who have hypertension because the gradual increase in arterial pressure that occurs with this disorder causes the baroreceptors to become desensitized to the higher pressure, essentially resetting them to a higher "normal." Therefore, the **baroreceptors perceive the hypertension as the homeostatic set point.**

59. She fainted because the pressure of her tight collar on the carotid sinuses caused the baroreceptors there to perceive that an increase in the MAP was occurring. The baroreceptors then increased the frequency of action potentials sent to the medulla oblongata, which responded by increasing parasympathetic output and decreasing sympathetic output to the cardiovascular system. This resulted in a decreased cardiac output and decreased total peripheral resistance, which **decreased the mean arterial pressure and blood flow to the brain, resulting in loss of consciousness. By loosening her collar, pressure on the carotid baroreceptors was alleviated and the now low MAP could be accurately detected. This allowed a baroreceptor reflex to be triggered, which increased the MAP** and restored adequate blood flow to the brain, allowing your co-worker to regain consciousness.

Another possible explanation for your co-worker's loss of consciousness would be that the tight collar inhibited blood flow through the carotid arteries, decreasing blood flow to the brain and therefore, the brain's oxygen supply, resulting in unconsciousness.

60. Excessive secretion of antidiuretic hormone (ADH or vasopressin) will cause vasoconstriction of the arterioles, which will **increase the MAP,** and will also cause the retention of fluid by the kidneys. This will **increase blood volume,** increasing central venous pressure and cardiac output, which will increase the MAP.

Concept Maps

61. a. I **b.** I parasympathetic activity **c.** D sympathetic activity **d.** D **e.** D contractility **f.** D
g. D vasoconstriction **h.** I **i.** D venous pressure
j. D **k.** D heart rate **l.** D **m.** D **n.** D

62. a. D **b.** D **c.** D **d.** D **e.** D **f.** D **g.** D **h.** I **i.** D
j. I **k.** I **l.** I **m.** I **n.** I **o.** D **p.** I **q.** I **r.** I **s.** I **t.** I **u.** I
v. I **w.** I

INTRINSIC CONTROL OF CARDIOVASCULAR FUNCTION: REGULATION OF BLOOD FLOW DISTRIBUTION TO ORGANS

Completion

63. ischemia
65. myogenic
67. reactive hyperemia
69. stretch

64. active hyperemia
66. autoregulation
68. perfusion

Multiple Choice

70. c **71.** e **72.** a **73.** b **74.** d **75.** e
76. c **77.** c **78.** a **79.** d

Matching

80. a. D **b.** D **c.** D **d.** C **e.** D **f.** C **g.** D **h.** D **i.** C

True/False

81. F Vasodilation of organ arterioles will lower the organ resistance, which will **increase** blood flow to the organ.

82. T **83.** T

84. F An increase in the metabolic activity of an organ will result in an **increase** in the tissue carbon dioxide concentration.

85. T

86. F A falling metabolic rate usually leads to a **rising** tissue oxygen concentration.

87. F Blood flow to an organ will increase as the tissue concentration of carbon dioxide **increases**.

88. T **89.** T

90. F In systemic organs, perfusion pressure is equivalent to **mean arterial pressure**.

91. T

92. F In active hyperemia, blood flow to the organ **increases**.

93. T

Sequencing

94. g, c, e, a, d, b, f

95. a, d, c, e, b

Challenge Questions

96. It is difficult to tell whether local changes in organ blood flow occur in response to a change in pressure within the arterioles or is due to a change in the metabolic activity of the organ, because both processes are interconnected and cause arteriolar responses that occur in the same direction. For example, a decrease in perfusion pressure will decrease blood flow to the tissues, resulting in a decreased tissue oxygen concentration and an increased tissue carbon dioxide concentration—the same metabolic changes that would occur due to increased metabolic activity of the organ. Regardless of the cause, the decrease in oxygen and increase in carbon dioxide will stimulate local vasodilation. In addition, the myogenic response generated by a decrease in perfusion pressure will also cause vasodilation. Therefore, it would be difficult to determine the initial cause of the vasodilation.

97. Extrinsic and intrinsic controls of organ resistance are not equally important in all organs, because organ arterioles vary in their response to sympathetic and local stimuli. The blood vessels of some organs have numerous sympathetic synaptic connections (such as the skin and GI tract) while those of other organs are relatively unaffected by sympathetic stimulation (e.g., the brain and heart). Also, the sensitivity of vascular smooth muscle to stretch or vasoactive chemicals varies from organ to organ.

For example, arterioles in the skin are very sensitive to bradykinin, while arterioles in the kidneys are stretch sensitive.

Clinical Question

98. Inflamed tissues are red because histamine, a chemical released from damaged tissue cells, **causes vasodilation**. Histamine stimulates the synthesis of nitric oxide, which causes vasodilation of the arterioles in the inflamed tissue, **resulting in increased blood flow to the tissue, which causes the tissue to redden.**

OTHER CARDIOVASCULAR PROCESSES

Short Answer

99. Sinus arrhythmia is the rhythmic variation in heart rate that occurs with respiratory movements. It is especially pronounced in children. For reasons not entirely understood, **during inspiration an increase in sympathetic stimulation of the SA node causes the heart rate to increase, while during expiration an increase in parasympathetic stimulation of the SA node causes the heart rate to decrease.**

100. Sweat glands help cool the body in a couple of ways. **Perspiration released onto the surface of the skin cools the body by evaporation. The sweat glands also secrete bradykinin, which stimulates local arterioles to vasodilate. This increases the blood flow to the skin, allowing heat to leave the body by radiation.**

Multiple Choice

101. d **102.** b **103.** a **104.** e **105.** c **106.** a
107. c **108.** d

True/False

109. T

110. F During exercise, blood flow to cardiac and skeletal muscle and the skin can increase to about **90%** of cardiac output.

111. T **112.** T

Challenge Questions

113. Venous return increases during exercise because of increased activity of the **skeletal muscle pump and respiratory pump**, as well as an **increase in venomotor tone**, resulting from increased activity of the sympathetic division of the nervous system.

114. During exercise, blood flow to the skin, heart, and skeletal muscles increases while blood flow to most other organs (except the brain) decreases. Blood flow to the skin increases during exercise primarily to **help the body dissipate heat** (it also helps meet the increased metabolic needs of the sweat glands.) **Blood flow to the heart and skeletal muscles increases during exercise to meet the increased metabolic needs of these organs, while blood flow decreases to less essential organs such as the stomach and kidneys so more blood is available to the heart, skeletal muscles, and skin.**

115. Competitive marksmen pull the trigger during an exhalation because the **slowing of the heart rate that occurs during exhalation allows the marksman to try to shoot between heart beats, which will provide for a more stable, accurate shot.**

116. The **primary cardiovascular effects** that are produced when **chemoreceptors are stimulated** by a low arterial oxygen level are a **decrease in heart rate** and an **increase in total peripheral resistance. The decreased heart rate helps the heart conserve oxygen** under these conditions by decreasing the workload on the heart, but this results in a decrease in cardiac output, which results in a decrease in mean arterial pressure. **The increased total peripheral resistance offsets the effect of the decreased cardiac output, allowing MAP to be maintained** so that blood flow to the heart and brain is not compromised.

Clinical Question

117. The baroreceptor reflex might be ineffective in compensating for a severe blood loss on a hot day because, as soon as the person's body temperature starts to rise, **thermoregulatory responses will override the baroreceptor reflex.** At this time the arterioles in the skin will vasodilate, resulting in a decreased total peripheral resistance (which counteracts the baroreceptor reflex effect) and decreased mean arterial pressure.

CHAPTER 15

OVERVIEW OF RESPIRATORY FUNCTION AND ANATOMY OF THE RESPIRATORY SYSTEM

Matching

1. a. RZ **b.** RZ **c.** CZ **d.** CZ **e.** RZ **f.** CZ

Completion

2. a. internal **b.** oxygen **c.** carbon dioxide **d.** acid-base **e.** pathogens

Short Answer

3. Both terms refer to the **exchange of oxygen and carbon dioxide. Internal respiration** is the exchange of carbon dioxide and of oxygen in the **cells of the body with the blood**, whereas **external respiration** is the exchange of gases between the **body's tissues and the atmosphere.**

Multiple Choice

4. b   **5.** d

True/False

6. T   **7.** T

8. F Adjacent alveoli are **connected to each other by alveolar pores.**

9. F Cartilage is plentiful in the **trachea and bronchi.** The bronchioles have smooth muscle associated with them.

Sequencing

10. i, l, b, a, k, c, e, h, d, g, f, j

Clinical Question

11. Pleurisy can be caused by **decreased secretion of intrapleural fluid.** With a reduced volume of intrapleural fluid, the pleural surfaces become dry and rub together, causing a stabbing pain each time Anita breathes.

Challenge Question

12. Goblet cells line the larynx and trachea and secrete mucus, which traps foreign particles. **Ciliated cells** also occur in the larynx and trachea and serve to sweep mucus toward the glottis, where the mucus is then swallowed. **Macrophages** are cells in the bronchioles that engulf harmful particles in the interstitial space and on the surface of the epithelium. **Type I cells** occur in the epithelium of the alveoli and, together with the capillaries, form the respiratory membrane. Also located in the alveoli are **type II alveolar cells** that engulf harmful particles inhaled into the lungs and secrete pulmonary surfactant.

FORCES FOR PULMONARY VENTILATION

Matching

13. a. I **b.** E **c.** I **d.** E **e.** E **f.** E **g.** I

Completion

14. a. atmospheric **b.** lungs **c.** contraction **d.** external intercostal **e.** increase **f.** decreases **g.** expands **h.** atmospheric **i.** chest wall **j.** internal intercostal

Short Answer

15. The two factors that determine intra-alveolar pressure are the **quantity (in moles) of air** in the alveoli and the **volume of the alveoli themselves.**

16. Transpulmonary pressure is the **difference between the intrapleural pressure and the intra-alveolar pressure.** As the chest wall expands, the intrapleural pressure decreases, which in turn increases the transpulmonary pressure.

Multiple Choice

17. b   **18.** e   **19.** b

True/False

20. F During inspiration, the diaphragm contracts and moves **downward.** The diaphragm relaxes and moves upward during expiration.

21. F Boyle's law states that, as the volume of a container increases, the pressure exerted by the gas in that container **decreases.**

22. T

Labeling

23. a) **Intra-alveolar pressure (P_{alv})** is the pressure within the alveoli. b) **Intrapleural pressure (P_{ip})** is the pressure inside the pleural space. c) **Transpulmonary pressure** is the difference between the intra-alveolar pressure and the intrapleural pressure.

Concept Map

24. a. downward **b.** external intercostals **c.** increases **d.** intrapleural **e.** transpulmonary pressure **f.** expand **g.** alveoli **h.** atmospheric **i.** bulk flow **j.** recoil **k.** decreases **l.** intra-alveolar **m.** atmospheric **n.** functional residual capacity (FRC)

Clinical Question

25. At rest, intrapleural pressure is negative, and intra-alveolar pressure is zero. When the left pleural sac is prunctured, as in the case of a gunshot wound, the negative intrapleural pressure is lost when the atmospheric pressure (at 160 mm Hg) forces air into the pleural cavity. This pressure forces the left lung to collapse because the pressure in the pleural cavity is now greater than the intra-alveolar pressure.

Challenge Question

26. Each lung is contained within its own pleural sac. This compartmentalization helps to keep one lung inflated if the other collapses.

FACTORS AFFECTING PULMONARY VENTILATION

Matching

27.a. I **b.** I **c.** D **d.** D **e.** I **f.** I **g.** D

Completion

28. a. airway resistance **b.** compliance **c.** volume **d.** inspiration **e.** radius **f.** autonomic

Short Answer

29. Lung compliance is the **change in lung volume** as a **result of changes in transpulmonary pressure**.

30. The rate of airflow into and out of the lungs is determined by: 1) **the pressure gradient between the alveoli and the atmosphere**, and 2) **the airway resistance**. The greater the pressure difference between the atmosphere and the alveoli, the faster air flows into and out of the lungs. A decrease in airway resistance will also result in a more rapid rate of airflow.

Multiple Choice

31. b **32.** c

True/False

33. F As carbon dioxide increases, airway resistance is **decreased**. By increasing the diameter of the airways, the body is able to match airflow to blood flow.

34. T

35. F Removal of tractive forces during expiration reduces airway diameter and **increases** airway resistance.

Clinical Questions

36. Since little pulmonary surfactant is produced until the last two months of fetal development, babies born prematurely often have **too little surfactant to keep the alveoli inflated between breaths**. To remedy this, the baby will have to be kept on a positive-pressure ventilator to keep the lungs inflated all the time. (The baby may also be given a pharmaceutical to increase the production of surfactant). In addition, **fluid may need to be removed from the lungs**, because the infant's transition from fluid-filled lungs as a fetus to air-filled lungs may not yet be complete.

37. Jennifer has asthma, which causes the bronchioles to constrict and reduce airflow. **Epinephrine acts on β2 receptors of the smooth muscles** in the bronchioles, causing the bronchioles to dilate. The dilation decreases air resistance and allows the lungs to deliver more oxygen to the cells.

Challenge Question

38. Both asthma and COPDs increase airway resistance and decrease airflow into and out of the lungs. In the case of **asthma**, the **increase in airway resistance is acute** (short term): the smooth muscles of the bronchioles are constricted. Increased airway resistance, increased mucus production, and inflammation of the walls of the bronchioles cause decreased airflow. **COPDs**, by contrast, are associated with **chronic (long-term) increases in airway resistance**, which may be caused, for example, by emphysema or chronic bronchitis.

CLINICAL SIGNIFICANCE OF RESPIRATORY VOLUMES AND AIRFLOWS

Matching

39. a. V_T **b.** ERV **c.** RV **d.** FRC **e.** IRV **f.** IC **g.** VC **h.** TLC

Completion

40. a. capacities **b.** spirometry **c.** rate **d.** Minute ventilation **e.** Minute alveolar ventilation **f.** dead space

Short Answer

41. Lung volume is an individual measurement, while lung capacity is the sum of two or more lung volumes.

42. Obstructive pulmonary diseases involve increases in airway resistance. This condition results in increased residual volumes because an increase in resistance makes it harder to breathe. One result of an obstructive pulmonary disorder is an increase in functional residual capacity and an increase in total lung capacity. **Restrictive pulmonary disorders are often caused by damage to the lungs or chest wall**, resulting in a decrease in total lung capacity.

Multiple Choice

43. c **44.** a **45.** d **46.** b

True/False

47. F A normal FEV_1 value is approximately **85%**.

48. T

49. F Total lung capacity is the **volume of air in the lungs at the end of a maximum inspiration**. It is the sum of V_T + IRV + ERV + RV. Tidal volume is the volume of air that is normally exchanged with each breath.

Clinical Question

50. This man likely has a **restrictive pulmonary disorder**. In older patients, this may be due to deformities of the thorax, ossification of the costal cartilage, and/or possibly paralysis of the intercostal muscles. Any or all of these may hinder thoracic expansion and reduce vital capacity and total lung capacity.

Challenge Questions

51. Minute ventilation = tidal volume × respiration rate

5,200 ml = 400 mL × respiration rate, so solving for respiration rate = **13 breaths per minute**

52. IC = V_T + IRV, so 3,350 mL = 450 mL + IRV, solving for IRV = **2,900 mL**

IRV is the volume of air that can be inspired at the end of a normal inspiration.

VC = V_T + IRV + ERV, so 4,600 mL = 450 mL + 2,900 mL + ERV, solving for ERV = **1,250 mL**

ERV is the maximum volume of air that can be exhaled at the end of a normal exhalation.

FRC = ERV + RV, so FRC = 1,250 mL + 1,100 mL, solving for ERV = **2,350 mL**

FRC is the volume of air remaining in the lungs at the end of a normal exhalation.

TLC = V_T + IRV + ERV + RV, so TLC = 450 mL + 2,900 mL + 1,250 mL + 1,100 mL, solving for TLC = **5,700 mL**

TLC is the total volume of air in the lungs at the end of an inspiration.

Labeling

53. a. tidal volume (V_T) **b.** inspiratory reserve volume (IRV) **c.** residual volume (RV) **d.** expiratory reserve volume (ERV) **e.** vital capacity (VC) **f.** functional residual capacity (FRC) **g.** total lung capacity (TLC)

CHAPTER 16

OVERVIEW OF THE PULMONARY CIRCULATION AND DIFFUSION OF GASES

Matching

1. a. 250 mL/min **b.** 2,700 mL/min **c.** 1,000 mL/min **d.** 750 mL/min **e.** 2,500 mL/min **f.** 882 mL/min **g.** 200 mL/min

Completion

2. a. pulmonary **b.** oxygen **c.** blood/hemoglobin **d.** carbon dioxide **e.** left **f.** systemic **g.** oxygen **h.** carbon dioxide **i.** right

3. a. partial pressures **b.** total pressure **c.** solubility **d.** thirty

Short Answer

4. Partial pressure is the proportion of the pressure of the entire gas that is due to the presence of an individual gas.

P_{O_2} = 0.21 × 760 mm Hg = 160 mm Hg

P_{N_2} = 0.79 × 760 mm Hg = 600 mm Hg

P_{CO_2} = 0.0003 × 760 mm Hg = 0.23 mm Hg

5. P_{O_2} = 0.21 × 619 mm Hg = 130 mm Hg

P_{N_2} = 0.79 × 619 mm Hg = 489 mm Hg

P_{CO_2} = 0.0003 × 619 mm Hg = 0.18 mm Hg

6. Under water, pressure increases 760 mm Hg for every 30 feet of depth. So the total pressure 60 feet under water is 2,280 mm Hg.

P_{O_2} = 0.21 × 2,280 mm Hg = 479 mm Hg

P_{N_2} = 0.79 × 2,280 mm Hg = 1,801 mm Hg

P_{CO_2} = 0.0003 × 2,280 mm Hg = 0.68 mm Hg

7. If the cells of the body produce 225 mL/min of carbon dioxide, then the rate of alveolar ventilation of carbon dioxide is also 225 mL/min. This happens because, under most conditions, carbon dioxide moves into alveolar air from the blood at the same rate it is produced in the tissues.

Multiple Choice

8. c **9.** b **10.** e

True/False

11. T

12. F Carbon dioxide is about **30** times more soluble in water than oxygen.

13. F At equilibrium, the concentration of gas in the air above a liquid is **equal to** the concentration of gas dissolved in the liquid.

Labeling

14. a. 100 mm Hg **b.** 40 mm Hg **c.** 100 mm Hg **d.** 40 mm Hg **e.** 100 mm Hg **f.** 40 mm Hg **g.** 40 mm Hg **h.** 46 mm Hg **i.** 40 mm Hg **j.** 46 mm Hg **k.** 40 mm Hg **l.** 46 mm Hg

Sequencing

15. f, e, a, b, d, c

Clinical Question

16. A hyperbaric chamber can increase air pressures far above atmospheric pressure. This increase in pressure inside the hyperbaric chamber mimics the pressure that divers experience when going deep under water. After a long, deep dive, divers may experience the bends if they ascend too quickly. This occurs when nitrogen gas bubbles form in the blood as the pressure rapidly decreases. The bubbles cause joint pain, paralysis, or possibly air embolisms. To counteract the effects of the bends, divers may be placed in the hyperbaric chamber where the pressure is increased. The increase in pressure decreases the likelihood that nitrogen will come out of solution and thus decreases the nitrogen gas bubble formation. The pressure inside of the chamber is then decreased slowly so that nitrogen bubbles do not form in the blood.

Challenge Questions

17. When a gas mixture and a liquid are in contact with each other, gas molecules dissolve in the liquid until the system reaches equilibrium. At this point, gas molecules in both states are at the same partial pressure. Therefore, the partial pressure of the oxygen dissolved in water is also 140 mm Hg.

18. There is more carbon dioxide dissolved in the water because carbon dioxide is much more soluble in water than oxygen is and so goes into solution more readily.

EXCHANGE OF OXYGEN AND CARBON DIOXIDE

Matching

19. a. I **b.** I **c.** D **d.** I **e.** D

Completion

20. a. diffusion **b.** greater **c.** greater **d.** oxygen consumption **e.** increases **f.** hyperpnea

Short Answer

21. Alveolar gas pressures differ from atmospheric pressure because 1) exchange of gases occurs between the alveolar air and the capillary blood; 2) the atmospheric air, which is high in oxygen, mixes with the air in the dead space of the conducting zone, which is high in carbon dioxide; and 3) the air in the alveoli is saturated with water, while the air in the atmosphere is not. Each of these reasons decreases the P_{O_2} within the alveoli compared to atmospheric P_{O_2} values.

22. Mixed venous blood is the blood found in the pulmonary artery. It is called "mixed" because all of the venous blood from the various parts of the body mixes in the right atrium and is then pumped to the lungs by the right ventricle via the pulmonary artery.

Multiple Choice

23. c **24.** d **25.** a

True/False

26. F When you ascend a mountain to 10,000 feet, atmospheric P_{O_2} for oxygen **decreases**.

27. F Most of the gas exchange takes place in the **first one-third** of the alveolar capillary.

28. T **29.** T

Sequencing

30. d, b, c, a

31. a, c, b, d

Clinical Question

32. The patient is **hyperventilating** and is **"blowing off" the carbon dioxide at the alveoli**, which decreases the blood P_{CO_2} and increases the blood pH. In other words, alveolar ventilation is greater than the demands of the tissues, which increases the P_{O_2} to above 100 mm Hg.

Challenge Question

33. When alveolar ventilation decreases below the demands of the tissues, P_{CO_2} rises above 40 mm Hg and P_{O_2} drops below 100 mm Hg.

TRANSPORT OF GASES IN THE BLOOD

Matching

34. a. Both **b.** CO_2 **c.** CO_2 **d.** O_2 **e.** O_2 **f.** O_2 **g.** O_2 **h.** CO_2

Completion

35. a. hemoglobin **b.** Bohr **c.** carbamino **d.** carbon dioxide **e.** Haldane **f.** dissolved **g.** bicarbonate

Short Answer

36. $CO_2 + H_2O \leftrightarrow H_2CO_3 \leftrightarrow H^+ + HCO_3^-$

37. No. The **blood is already approximately 98% saturated with oxygen** when atmospheric oxygen is 21%. The increased oxygen concentration can only increase the amount bound to hemoglobin by a very small percentage.

Multiple Choice

38. c **39.** c **40.** b **41.** c **42.** a

True/False

43. T

44. F The carbon dioxide content of the blood **falls** as the P_{O_2} increases.

45. F In respiring tissues, the Haldane effect promotes the loading of **carbon dioxide**.

46. T

Challenge Question

47. Fetal hemoglobin has the ability to carry more oxygen at the same partial pressures compared to maternal hemoglobin. This means that the developing fetus is able to load more oxygen onto the hemoglobin and therefore deliver more oxygen to the developing tissues of its body. Because the fetus is growing at a much faster rate than is the mother, it needs to have an efficient way of delivering oxygen. In addition, the fetus is extracting oxygen from the maternal blood (which has a P_{O_2} of 100 mm Hg), compared to the mother, who is extracting oxygen from the environment (which has a P_{O_2} of 160 mm Hg). The fetal hemoglobin needs to be more efficient at extracting the oxygen from a source of lowered P_{O_2}.

Clinical Question

48. Case #1: **With hemolytic anemia, erythrocytes are ruptured prematurely.** This can happen with a mismatched blood transfusion, and leads to a decrease in the oxygen-carrying capacity of the blood **because there are fewer red blood cells to carry oxygen.**

Case #2: Iron-deficiency anemia can result from inadequate intake of iron-containing foods and impaired iron absorption. **The lack of iron means that the heme groups lack the element iron to bind to the oxygen.** In females, iron-deficiency anemia can also be caused by loss of blood through menstrual flow.

Case #3: In sickle cell anemia, the abnormal hemoglobin formed, hemoglobin S, becomes spiky and sharp when deprived of oxygen. This causes the red blood cells to become crescent-shaped when they unload oxygen molecules or during vigorous exercise. **These deformed erythrocytes rupture easily and can block small blood vessels and capillaries, thus reducing the oxygen delivery to tissues.**

Concept Maps

49. a. 90% **b.** 30% **c.** 20% **d.** 1 **e.** 3 **f.** 3 **g.** 2 **h.** 1
50. a. CO_2 **b.** erythrocytes **c.** hemoglobin **d.** carbaminohemoglobin **e.** carbonic anhydrase **f.** bicarbonate ions **g.** chloride ions

CENTRAL REGULATION OF VENTILATION AND CONTROL OF VENTILATION BY CHEMORECEPTORS

Matching

51. a. E **b.** I **c.** B **d.** I

Completion

52. a. brain stem **b.** dorsal respiratory group **c.** ventral respiratory group **d.** pontine respiratory group **e.** P_{O_2} **f.** P_{CO_2}
53. a. P_{CO_2} **b.** CO_2 **c.** hydrogen ions **d.** carotid bodies **e.** pH **f.** P_{O_2} **g.** medulla oblongata **h.** cerebrospinal fluid

Short Answer

54. During inspiration, VRG neurons increase action potentials gradually until a maximal number of action potentials occur at the peak of inspiration. By contrast, the DRG neurons have more complex patterns of activity that depend on the degree of stretch of the lungs.

55. In humans, central chemoreceptors are located in the medulla, while peripheral chemoreceptors are located in the carotid bodies.

Multiple Choice

56. b   **57.** c   **58.** a   **59.** b   **60.** b   **61.** e

True/False

62. F Chemoreceptors are sensitive to **changes in the chemicals such as H^+ concentration and P_{CO_2}** in the bloodstream and adjust the breathing rate accordingly.
63. T   **64.** T
65. F Peripheral chemoreceptors respond to changes in P_{O_2} (< 60 mm Hg), P_{CO_2}, or pH.

Clinical Questions

66. Strenuous hyperventilation can lower the blood P_{CO_2} so much that a lag period occurs before it rebounds enough to stimulate respiration again. The swimmers can hold their breath longer, but not because their lungs can hold more oxygen, but because of the loss of carbon dioxide. This practice however, can cause oxygen starvation to the brain and one can black out underwater and drown.

67. When Marie hyperventilates **she is expelling carbon dioxide at a faster rate than it builds up in the blood from the tissues.** This causes a decrease in H^+ concentration and increases the blood pH. By closing her mouth and breathing through her nose, Marie is forced to slow down her ventilation rate. This causes her to retain more carbon dioxide, which causes the H^+ concentration to increase and drops her blood pH back within the normal range.

Challenge Questions

68. A **decrease in blood pressure can cause an increased respiration rate.** This reflex is important because, **when blood pressure drops, less blood is delivered to the tissues** and therefore less oxygen is delivered to the tissues. The **increased breathing rate helps to compensate for the decreased delivery of oxygen.**

69. During hypoventilation, **carbon dioxide is produced by the tissues at a faster rate than ventilation can expel carbon dioxide from the body.** This causes carbon dioxide to build up in the blood, which causes an increase in H^+ concentration, which drops the pH of the blood. Central and peripheral chemoreceptors increase their activity and send signals to the medulla. The medulla responds by increasing ventilation, which rids the blood of carbon dioxide. This lowers the blood pH and the chemoreceptors are no longer stimulated.

Concept Map

70. a. chemoreceptors **b.** Pons **c.** medulla **d.** VRG **e.** DRG

LOCAL REGULATION OF VENTILATION AND PERFUSION AND THE RESPIRATORY SYSTEM IN ACID-BASE HOMEOSTASIS

Matching

71. a. AK **b.** AK **c.** AD **d.** AK **e.** AD

Completion

72. a. alveoli **b.** capillaries **c.** 1 **d.** vasoconstriction **e.** bronchoconstriction

73. a. 7.38 **b.** 7.42 **c.** Acidosis **d.** 7.35 **e.** alkalosis **f.** urinary **g.** P_{CO_2} **h.** carbonic acid **i.** alkalosis **j.** kidneys **k.** 20:1

Short Answer

74. Lisa has a **ventilation-perfusion mismatch**. Because her P_{O_2} is above normal and her P_{CO_2} is below normal, she has decreased perfusion. In other words, something is preventing blood from returning to the pulmonary capillaries and her perfusion is too low.

75 a. If the arterial blood [HCO3⁻] increases, there will more of this buffer in the blood to take H⁺ out of solution and the pH of the blood will increase (become more basic).

b. If the arterial blood [CO_2] increases, more H⁺ will be produced and the pH of the blood will decrease (become more acidic).

Multiple Choice

76. b   **77.** c   **78.** a

True/False

79. F The lungs regulate the concentration of **carbon dioxide**, whereas the kidneys regulate the concentration of **bicarbonate ions**.

80. T

81. F Hypoventilation can produce respiratory **acidosis**.

82. T

Clinical Question

83. Because of the blood clot, Mrs. Tyndall has a decreased perfusion to the lung, which causes an increased ventilation-perfusion ratio. The **clot causes the P_{O_2} to rise above normal and the P_{CO_2} to fall below normal.** In regions of the lung with high ventilation-perfusion ratios, the **increase in P_{O_2} and decrease in P_{CO_2} will cause bronchoconstriction and vasodilation to decrease the ventilation while increasing the perfusion.**

Challenge Question

84. Jerome has **decreased ventilation**, which causes the ventilation-perfusion ratio to fall below 1. This may be caused by some obstruction in the airway. This causes a lower P_{O_2} and a higher P_{CO_2} than normal. The **low P_{CO_2} causes bronchodilation** (to increase ventilation) and the **low P_{O_2} causes vasoconstriction** (to decrease perfusion).

CHAPTER 17

FUNCTIONS OF THE URINARY SYSTEM AND ANATOMY OF THE URINARY SYSTEM

Matching

1. a. RA **b.** VC **c.** GL **d.** AE **e.** RV **f.** PC **g.** EA **h.** IV

Completion

2. a. bladder **b.** nephrons **c.** renal corpuscle **d.** Bowman's capsule **e.** plasma **f.** proteins **g.** secretion **h.** water **i.** peritubular **j.** plasma **k.** filtrate

Short Answer

3. The kidneys are considered endocrine glands because **they synthesize and secrete at least one hormone**, erythropoietin, which is involved in the regulation of red blood cell production. The kidneys are also necessary for the activation of vitamin D_3.

4. Cortical nephrons, which make up the majority of nephrons in the kidneys, are located primarily within the **outer renal cortex. Juxtaglomerular nephrons** are less common and located in the **deeper medulla of the kidneys.** One major difference is the **length of their loops of Henle.** Cortical nephrons have relatively short loops, while juxtaglomerular nephrons have much longer loops.

5. In addition to the five primary functions listed on page 533 of the text, the kidneys also perform a number of secondary endocrine and endocrine-like functions. These functions include **producing the hormone erythropoietin**, which stimulates the production of red blood cells, and **producing renin**, which is an enzyme involved in regulating water and salt balance. The kidneys also activate vitamin D_3, which regulates levels of calcium and phosphate in the blood. In addition, during times of stress and periods of fasting, the kidneys can liberate molecules from the liver used to synthesize glucose.

Multiple Choice

6. b   **7.** b   **8.** d   **9.** c   **10.** d   **11.** a

True/False

12. T   **13.** T

14. F A person can function with **only one kidney** if that kidney is operating normally.

15. F The arcuate arteries are branches of the **renal arteries.** The **vasa recta** branch from efferent arterioles and run along the loop of Henle and collecting ducts.

Sequencing

16. b, i, k, g, h, e, l, f, c, j, a, d

Labeling

17. a. thin ascending limb of loop of Henle **b.** collecting duct **c.** thick ascending limb of loop of Henle **d.** distal convoluted tubule **e.** collecting tube **f.** afferent arteriole **g.** efferent arteriole **h.** renal corpuscle **i.** Bowman's capsule **j.** glomerulus **k.** proximal tubule **l.** proximal convoluted tubule **m.** proximal straight tubule **n.** descending limb of loop of Henle **o.** minor calyx

Clinical Questions

18. Glomerulonephritis means **inflammation of the glomerulus.** The inflammatory response damages the filtration membrane of the glomerulus, increasing its permeability. **Blood proteins and red blood cells begin to pass into the renal tubules and are lost in the urine.**

19. Cystitis is an inflammation of the bladder. Females are more susceptible than males because of their short urethra. Because the urethral opening is situated close to the anal opening, improper toilet habits can carry fecal bacteria into the urethra and up into the bladder.

Challenge Questions

20. The **juxtaglomerular apparatus is composed of an area of cells called the** *macula densa* **that responds to changes in the solute concentration of the filtrate in the tubule lumen.** The juxtaglomerular apparatus is also composed of granular cells that synthesize and secrete renin, which is involved in regulating blood volume.

21. With hypotension, the **GFR would be greatly reduced** and less filtrate would enter the renal tubules. With hypertension, the **GFR would be increased,** thus increasing the flow of filtrate.

BASIC RENAL EXCHANGE PROCESSES

Matching

22. a. BCHP **b.** BCOP **c.** GOP **d.** GCHP

Completion

23. a. hydrostatic **b.** Bowman's capsule **c.** oncotic **d.** Bowman's capsule **e.** 125 mL/min.

Short Answer

24. The kidneys have an average glomerular filtration rate (GFR) of 125 mL of plasma each minute, which means that the kidneys filter 7,500 mL of plasma each hour. Since there are 24 hours in a day, the kidneys filter 180,000 mL of plasma each day, which is 180 liters of plasma (there are 1,000 mL in each liter) of plasma filtered by the kidneys in a single day.

25. The filtration fraction is equal to the GFR divided by the renal plasma flow rate:

$$\frac{115 \text{ mL/min.}}{575 \text{ mL/min.}} = 20\%.$$

26. The glomerular membrane consists of three layers. A basement membrane is sandwiched between two cell layers. The inside cell layer is composed of capillary endothelial cells that are in contact with the lumen of the capillary on the inside and with the basement membrane on the other side. The outer portion of the glomerular membrane is composed of epithelial cells that are in contact with the basement membrane on one side and the Bowman's space on the other.

Multiple Choice

27. e   **28.** b   **29.** c   **30.** a   **31.** e   **32.** d

True/False

33. F Under normal blood pressure values when blood pressure rises, GFR **remains constant.**

34. F Myogenic regulation of GFR involves **intrinsic regulation of GFR.** Sympathetic stimulation of afferent and efferent arterioles in the kidneys is a result of extrinsic regulation.

35. F Mesangial cells are modified smooth muscle cells surrounding glomerular capillaries. The **granular cells** secrete renin.

36. T   **37.** T

Sequencing

38. d, g, a, e, b, f, c

Labeling

39. a. filtration **b.** reabsorption **c.** secretion **d.** excretion

Clinical Questions

40. A decrease in plasma proteins will cause the glomerular oncotic pressure to decrease, which will initially increase GFR. However, autoregulatory forces (myogenic regulation, tubuloglomerular feedback, and mesangial cell contraction) will eventually bring the GFR back within normal range.

41. Frank is taking a diuretic that will increase his fluid output.

Challenge Questions

42. A GFR of 144 liters/day means that the kidneys filter 144,000 mL/day (144 liters × 1,000 mL). So, kidneys filter 6,000 mL each hour (144,000 mL/24 hours), and 100 mL each minute (6,000 mL/60 min.).

43. Glucose is freely filtered at the glomerulus and eventually travels to the lumen of the proximal convoluted tubule. Glucose is actively transported across the apical membrane of epithelial cells of the proximal tubule by sodium-linked active transport (cotransported with sodium from the tubular lumen into the epithelial cell). Glucose is then transported by facilitated diffusion in the basolateral membrane into the peritubular fluid, where it diffuses into the plasma of the peritubular capillary.

Concept Map

44. a. Afferent arteriole **b.** GFR **c.** macula densa **d.** Constriction **e.** increases **f.** decreases

REGIONAL SPECIALIZATION OF THE RENAL TUBULES AND EXCRETION

Matching

45. a. S **b.** R **c.** B **d.** R **e.** S

Completion

46. a. water **b.** bloodstream **c.** distal tubule **d.** collecting duct **e.** plasma **f.** hormones

Short Answer

47. Signals from the stretch receptors that detect filling of the bladder transmit signals to the cerebral cortex indicating that the bladder is full. This signal also activates descending pathways that inhibit the parasympathetic neurons controlling the detrusor muscle, causing it to relax, and other descending pathways that excite the motor neurons that contract the external urethral sphincter.

48. Renal threshold is the plasma concentration above which a compound will show up in the urine.

Multiple Choice

49. b   **50.** c   **51.** a   **52.** e   **53.** a   **54.** c

True/False

55. F To estimate GFR one must know the **excretion rate** and the plasma concentration of a substance.

56. T

57. F Most (~70%) water reabsorption occurs in the **proximal tubule**. The ascending loop of Henle is impermeable to water.

58. T

Labeling

59. Top figure is proximal tubule, lower figure is distal tubule.

a. apical membrane **b.** "leaky" tight junction **c.** brush border **d.** microvilli **e.** mitochondria **f.** basolateral **g.** "leaky" tight junction

Clinical Questions

60. Glycosuria means that glucose is present in the urine. Glucose is filtered by the glomerulus and, under normal circumstances, 100% of it is reabsorbed back into the bloodstream. Glucose is reabsorbed via cotransport with sodium from the tubular lumen into the epithelial cell. A deficiency in sodium can lead to a decrease in glucose reabsorption and, therefore, glucose appearing in the urine.

61. Helen's urine output will increase. Glucose is normally reabsorbed from the kidney tubule. The presence of glucose in the glomerular filtrate osmotically draws water into the tubules and causes increased urine flow.

Challenge Questions

62. The proximal tubule is a mass absorber of filtered solutes and water, and though there is regulation in this tubule, it represents only a minor component of regulatory output. On the other hand, the distal tubule (and collecting duct) are specialized to allow regulation of reabsorption and secretion by various hormones, including aldosterone, ADH, and atrial natiuretic peptide. Regulation at the distal tubule has the most significant impact on renal output.

63. The micturition reflex begins when the bladder begins to stretch and stretch receptors send information to the CNS. Parasympathetic motor neurons send signals to the detrusor muscle via pelvic nerves, which produces sustained contraction of the urinary bladder.

Concept Map

64. a. basolateral membrane **b.** Na^+/K^+ pumps **c.** apical **d.** cotransport **e.** countertransport **f.** sodium **g.** chloride **h.** potassium

CHAPTER 18

THE CONCEPT OF BALANCE AND WATER BALANCE

Matching

1. a. IO **b.** EO **c.** IO **d.** OO

Completion

2. a. output **b.** use **c.** plasma **d.** cells **e.** fluid **f.** water **g.** food **h.** metabolism **i.** insensible water loss **j.** osmolarity

Short Answer

3. ADH regulates the permeability to water of the late distal tubule and collecting ducts. Under conditions where the body needs to conserve water, ADH is secreted from the posterior pituitary and acts to promote the reabsorption of water, thus increasing blood volume and decreasing urine volume. When the plasma has excess water, ADH secretion is decreased, which causes decreased reabsorption (and decreased blood volume), and more water is lost in the urine. Here, we see why the hormone is so named. It is an *anti diuretic*, that is, it prevents water loss at the kidneys.

4. The countercurrent multiplier **establishes a concentration gradient** that allows for the passive transport of water in the collecting ducts. The multiplier also **reabsorbs water and solutes** before the tubular fluid reaches the distal convoluted tubule. Thus, the countercurrent multiplier provides a way for the kidneys to both concentrate and dilute the urine.

Multiple Choice

5. b   **6.** b   **7.** d   **8.** a   **9.** e   **10.** b
11. b

True/False

12. T   **13.** T

14. F   Fluid entering the loop of Henle is **iso-osmotic** relative to extracellular fluid.

15. T

16. F   The collecting duct is controlled by **ADH**.

17. T

Sequencing

18. b, c, d, a, f, g, e

Clinical Questions

19. Diabetes insipidus is the lack of ADH production and/or secretion. Because of the decreased production of ADH, the kidneys do not reabsorb water at the distal tubule or at the collecting ducts. This leads to massive water loss in the urine (polyuria) and excessive thirst (polydipsia).

20. Mike is taking the diuretic to increase water loss in his tissues (especially his skin). He hopes to have more muscle definition by doing so. However, this practice can lead to dehydration, hypotension, cardiac arrhythmias, and even death.

Challenge Questions

21. Loop diuretics, like Lasix, act by inhibiting sodium reabsorption in the ascending limb of the loop of Henle. Because sodium is not reabsorbed into the vasa recta, water does not enter the vasa recta either. The water that is normally reabsorbed is now lost as urine. This lowers blood volume, which in turn lowers blood pressure.

22. ADH is an anti-diuretic and, as such, decreases urine output by increasing the permeability of the collecting ducts to water. This allows for more reabsorbtion of water into the bloodstream. By blocking the action of ADH, alcohol increases urine output and the individual becomes more dehydrated.

Concept Map

23. a. digestive tract **b.** Absorption **c.** Filtration **d.** Secretion **e.** excretion, feces **f.** Insensible **g.** excretion, urine

SODIUM, POTASSIUM, CALCIUM BALANCE, AND INTERACTIONS BETWEEN FLUID AND ELECTROLYTE REGULATION

Matching

24. a. Na^+ **b.** Na^+ **c.** K^+ **d.** Ca^{2+} **e.** K^+ **f.** Na^+

Completion

25. a. aldosterone **b.** atrial natriuretic peptide **c.** potassium **d.** volume **e.** sodium **f.** reabsorption **g.** digestive tract **h.** bone

Short Answer

26. Too little plasma sodium is called hyponatremia and is **associated with low blood volume and hypotension**. Too much plasma sodium (hypernatremia) leads to **high blood volume and hypertension**.

27. In the proximal tubule, potassium is reabsorbed through potassium channels. In the distal tubule, potassium is secreted through specific potassium channels located in the apical membrane of principal cells.

Multiple Choice

28. a   **29.** a   **30.** b   **31.** e   **32.** e   **33.** d
34. a   **35.** e

True/False

36. F   Aldosterone **increases** the synthesis of Na^+/K^+ pumps in the basolateral membrane of the renal tubules.

37. T

38. F   Regulation of potassium secretion occurs in the **late distal tubule and collecting duct**.

39. F   **High** plasma levels of potassium stimulate aldosterone secretion.

Labeling

40. a. Angiotensinogen **b.** Juxtaglomerular cells **c.** (ACE) Angiotensin converting enzyme **d.** Adrenal cortex **e.** Aldosterone

Clinical Questions

41. ACE inhibitors **block the conversion of angiotensin I into angiotensin II**. By doing so, they prevent the adrenal cortex from secreting aldosterone. Since the adrenal cortex does not secrete aldosterone, sodium and water are not reabsorbed in the kidneys as readily, lowering blood volume and hence blood pressure. The lowering of blood volume makes it easier for the failing heart to pump blood. In addition, because angiotensin I is not converted into angiotensin II, it does not stimulate the posterior pituitary to release ADH. The lack of ADH means that more tubular fluid is lost in the urine, thus decreasing blood volume. Furthermore, angiotensin II is not able to act as a vasoconstrictor and, therefore, does not increase total peripheral resistance.

42. Parathyroid hormone is secreted from the parathyroid glands. This hormone increases blood calcium levels, therefore, Jill will have hypercalcemia. Symptoms may include muscle weakness, sluggishness, hypertension, constipation, and nausea.

Challenge Questions

43. In response to hemorrhage, body systems work to conserve as much blood volume as possible. The posterior pituitary secretes ADH to help reabsorb water back into the bloodstream from the collecting ducts. ADH increases the permeability of the distal tubules and collecting ducts to water, thus water is able to move via the tubules and ducts into the peritubular space and the bloodstream.

In response to decreased blood pressure at the afferent arteriole, the granular cells of the juxtaglomerular apparatus release renin, causing the cascade of events of the renin-angiotensin-aldosterone system. The net effect of each step of this system is to increase blood pressure either by increasing blood volume or by increasing total peripheral resistance. Angiotensin II causes a number of effects that help to increase blood pressure including: 1) increasing ADH secretion; 2) constricting systemic arterioles; 3) increasing the thirst response; 4) stimulating the release of aldosterone from the adrenal cortex. Aldosterone increases sodium reabsorption at the kidneys, which, in turn, increases water reabsorption, which increases blood volume and blood pressure.

ANP release from the atria of the heart will decrease. ANP decreases blood pressure by decreasing sodium reabsorption. ANP also decreases the secretion of both renin and aldosterone.

44. Plasma calcium levels are increased by parathyroid hormone, which is synthesized and secreted from the parathyroid glands. Parathyroid hormone increases calcium reabsorption in the kidneys, which stimulates calcitriol (which in turn increases calcium absorption in the digestive tract), and stimulates the resorption of bone. Calcitonin is made and secreted from C cells of the thyroid gland. It decreases plasma calcium levels by increasing bone formation and decreasing resorption at the kidneys.

Concept Map

45. a. calcitonin **b.** Resorption **c.** Absorption **d.** Kidneys **e.** PTH **f.** calcitonin

ACID-BASE BALANCE

Matching

46. a. AD **b.** AD **c.** AK **d.** AD **e.** AD **f.** AD **g.** AK **h.** AK

Completion

47. a. 7.35 **b.** 7.45 **c.** acidosis **d.** alkalosis **e.** carbon dioxide **f.** carbonic acid **g.** carbonic anhydrase **h.** P_{CO_2} **i.** Metabolic alkalosis **j.** metabolic acidosis

Short Answer

48. Metabolic acidosis is caused by an increase in acids in the plasma from sources other than carbon dioxide. The causes are varied and may include a high-fat or high-protein diet, heavy exercise, excessive diarrhea, or kidneys that are not operating normally. **Respiratory acidosis is caused by an excess of carbon dioxide in the blood due to hypoventilation.**

49. Under severe acidosis, **glutamine helps to compensate by contributing more bicarbonate to the plasma.** Glutamine is transported into the epithelial cells of the proximal tubule from the peritubular fluid and the tubular fluid. Breakdown of glutamine results in bicarbonate ions.

These newly generated ions are cotransported with sodium, or countertransported with chloride ion, and move into the peritubular capillaries where they buffer the hydrogen ions.

50. As the blood becomes more **acidic** due to an increase in hydrogen ions, the **kidneys reabsorb and synthesize more bicarbonate ions.** In addition, the kidneys move H⁺ from the blood to be excreted into urine. If the blood becomes more **basic** due to a decrease in hydrogen ion concentration, the **kidneys decrease hydrogen ion secretion and bicarbonate reabsorption.**

Multiple Choice

51. a   **52.** c   **53.** a   **54.** a   **55.** c   **56.** c
57. b   **58.** e

True/False

59. F The nervous system is one of the systems of the body **most affected** by wide changes in plasma pH levels. The detrimental effects caused by changes in pH include tingling sensations, confusion, coma, and even death.

60. T

61. F Because proteins have a net negative charge associated with them, they **are** effective buffers, especially within the intracellular fluid. **Hemoglobin** is an important intracellular protein that acts as a buffer of hydrogen ions for red blood cells.

62. F The proximal tubule **reabsorbs 80–90% of the bicarbonate ions.** It secretes hydrogen ions.

63. T

Labeling

64. a. Plasma pH **b.** Acidity **c.** Ventilation **d.** Plasma pH

Clinical Questions

65. Because the child has been vomiting profusely, he is losing acids in the stomach. These acids are normally neutralized by alkaline secretions in the small intestine that come from exocrine secretions produced in the pancreas. Because the acids from the stomach are no longer being generated and the pancreas is still producing alkaline secretions, the plasma becomes more alkaline, resulting in metabolic alkalosis.

66. Because Susie's bicarbonate to carbon dioxide ratio is less than 20:1, she has acidosis. This can be caused by either a decrease in bicarbonate ion, or an increase in carbon dioxide. To determine whether she has metabolic or respiratory acidosis, we need to check her plasma bicarbonate and carbon dioxide levels.

If her bicarbonate is less than 24 mM, she has metabolic acidosis and she might be hyperventilating to get rid of carbon dioxide. If the cause of her problem is of respiratory origin, she will be hypoventilating, which causes the P_{CO_2} levels to be greater than 40 mm Hg. In this case, the kidneys compensate by increasing bicarbonate reabsorption, so plasma bicarbonate levels are greater than 24 mM.

Challenge Questions

67. Simple hydrogen ion buffering is the first line of defense against changes in plasma pH. Buffering can only limit the changes in plasma pH, it cannot reverse them. On the other hand, respiratory (and renal compensation) act via negative feedback to actually reverse changes in plasma pH.

68. Late stage emphysema inhibits the ability of gases to be exchanged between the lungs and the outside world. This means carbon dioxide may build up in the blood due to a decreased gradient across the respiratory membrane, which slows down diffusion and causes respiratory acidosis.

Concept Map

69. a. $[HCO_3^-] < 24$ mM **b.** Metabolic acidosis
c. Respiratory compensation **d.** $P_{CO_2} > 40$ mm Hg
e. Renal compensation **f.** $[HCO_3^-] > 24$ mM **g.** $P_{CO_2} > 40$ mm Hg **h.** $P_{CO_2} < 40$ mm Hg **i.** Respiratory alkalosis
j. Renal compensation

CHAPTER 19

OVERVIEW OF DIGESTIVE SYSTEM FUNCTION

Matching

1. a. S **b.** MD **c.** M **d.** CD **e.** A

Short Answer

2. It is essential that both mechanical and chemical digestion take place in the digestive system for the following reasons. **Most ingested nutrients** (carbohydrates, proteins, and fats) **can't be absorbed without first being broken down into smaller chemical subunits**, which is **the role of chemical digestion**. In order for chemical digestion to proceed efficiently, **digestive enzymes must have access to as much surface area of the ingested food as possible**, and **mechanical digestion** (which involves chewing and mixing movements in the digestive tract) **provides this increased surface area** by physically breaking down large particles of food into smaller particles. By breaking food down into smaller particles, **mechanical digestion also makes it easier for food to pass through the digestive tract.**

FUNCTIONAL ANATOMY OF THE DIGESTIVE SYSTEM

Completion

3. a. digestive tract **b.** passageway **c.** accessory glands
d. enzymes **e.** gastrointestinal (GI) tract

Matching

4. a. LES **b.** PS **c.** IS **d.** R **e.** P **f.** CL **g.** F **h.** E **i.** D
j. BB

Multiple Choice

5. b	**6.** c	**7.** b	**8.** e	**9.** b	**10.** a
11. d	**12.** c	**13.** e	**14.** c	**15.** d	**16.** b
17. e	**18.** c				

True/False

19. T **20.** T

21. F The **muscularis externa** is the layer of the GI tract primarily responsible for motility of the tract.

22. T **23.** T

24. F The mechanical and chemical digestion of food begins in the **mouth**.

25. T

26. F **Pepsinogen** is an inactive precursor of the enzyme pepsin. Intrinsic factor assists the absorption of vitamin B_{12}.

27. T **28.** T **29.** T

30. F Another name for the colon is the **large** intestine.

31. F The internal anal sphincter is composed of **smooth** muscle, while the external anal sphincter is composed of **skeletal** muscle.

32. T **33.** T

34. F Pancreatic juice is an **exocrine fluid** secreted into the **small intestine**.

35. F The gallbladder **stores and releases** bile. The **liver** secretes bile.

36. T

37. F The products of the exocrine pancreas are produced by the pancreatic **acini**.

Sequencing

38. mouth, pharynx, esophagus, stomach, duodenum, jejunum, ileum, ascending colon, transverse colon, descending colon, sigmoid colon, rectum

Labeling

39. a. microvilli **b.** brush border **c.** villi **d.** crypt of Leiberkuhn **e.** absorptive cells **f.** lacteal

Short Answer

40. Mucus is important to the digestive tract because it **protects the lining of the GI tract from abrasion as food moves through it; provides lubrication to ease the passage of food; and in the stomach forms the gastric mucosal barrier that prevents stomach acid from damaging the lining of the stomach. Mucus is secreted by exocrine cells known as goblet cells.**

41. The enteric nervous system is a network of nerve fibers located within the gastrointestinal tract that serves as an important regulator of GI function. It is **composed of the submucosal plexus**, located in the submucosa, and the **myenteric plexus**, located in the muscularis externa. It **receives input from autonomic and sensory neurons** located in the wall of the GI tract and **sends output to the effector cells of the GI tract.** Although its activities can be regulated by the CNS, **it can** also **act independently.**

42. Blood leaving the small intestine does not carry nutrients directly back to the general circulation, but first carries them to the liver through the hepatic portal vein. This is important as the **liver** removes many of the nutrients from the blood and **processes them before they enter the general circulation; it also removes any toxins** that may have been absorbed in the small intestine. From the liver the blood returns to the general circulation via the hepatic vein.

43. The exocrine pancreas is the digestive portion of the pancreas. It **secretes digestive enzymes** within pancreatic juice into the small intestine. Pancreatic juice is produced by the **acinar and duct cells** of the pancreas. The **endocrine pancreas** serves an endocrine function— the **secretion of hormones into the blood.** The **pancreatic islets** are the endocrine cells of the pancreas, and they produce a number of hormones of which **insulin and glucagon** are the best known. (Insulin is produced by pancreatic islet beta cells, while glucagon is produced by alpha cells.)

Challenge Questions

44. The acidity of the stomach is important physiologically for a number of reasons. The **acidic environment converts the inactive protease pepsinogen into active pepsin,** so protein digestion can begin in the stomach. The acidity also **assists protein digestion by denaturing some of the proteins in food,** and the acidic environment **helps protect the body against ingested pathogens by destroying some bacteria.** The low pH of the stomach doesn't damage the stomach lining because **the epithelial cells of the gastric mucosa secrete a thick, alkaline mucus referred to as the gastric mucosal barrier that protects the stomach from acid.**

45. The **mucosa of the small intestine is well adapted for efficient absorption** in a number of ways. **The mucosa is folded into numerous small projections called villi** that extend into the lumen of the small intestine and **increase the surface area available for absorption. Within each villus are blood capillaries and lymphatic capillaries (lacteals)** that allow absorbed nutrients immediate access to the circulatory system. Additional small projections known as **microvilli are located on the apical surface of the epithelial cells of the villi, which serve to further increase the surface area available for the absorption of nutrients** (and also serve as the site of the brush border enzymes).

46. Zymogens are the inactive proteases trypsinogen, chymotrypsinogen, and procarboxypeptidase, and are stored in zymogen granules in the acinar cells of the pancreas until use. These enzymes are activated to trypsin, chymotrypsin, and carboxypeptidase only when they are secreted in pancreatic juice and reach the duodenum. It is **critical that these enzymes be synthesized and stored in their inactive zymogen forms as the pancreas is made of protein and would be autodigested by the proteases if they were produced and stored in their active forms.**

Clinical Questions

47. Appendicitis means inflammation of the vermiform appendix, and is usually the result of a bacterial infection of the appendix. **Peritonitis refers to inflammation of the peritoneum. If the appendix ruptures during appendicitis, the released bacteria often cause severe peritonitis which can be fatal if not quickly treated with antibiotics.** Therefore, it is essential that appendicitis be quickly identified and the appendix removed before rupture to prevent the dangerous complication of peritonitis. **The pain of an appendicitis attack is most commonly epigastric, periumbilical, or in the right lower quadrant of the abdomen.** However, sometimes the abdominal pain is diffuse and hard to localize. A phenomenon known as rebound tenderness is often associated with appendicitis. In this phenomenon, the health care practitioner pushes on the abdomen over the painful area and then releases the pressure. If rebound tenderness is present, the patient will experience more pain during the rebound of the abdomen than during the application of pressure.

48. Heartburn is the result of gastroesophageal reflux, in which stomach contents back up into the esophagus through a relaxed lower esophageal sphincter. Since the esophagus does not have a protective mucosal barrier against stomach acid, the acid will irritate the esophagus, producing **sensations such as substernal burning or discomfort** especially after meals or when the person is lying down. Heartburn can be serious if it occurs persistently (a situation known as gastroesophageal reflux disease or GERD). In this situation the lining of the esophagus can be eroded, causing precancerous cellular changes to develop. Therefore, it is important for anyone with persistent heartburn to see his/her health care practitioner and be treated.

DIGESTION AND ABSORPTION OF NUTRIENTS AND WATER

Completion

49. a. starch **b.** glycogen **c.** sucrose **d.** lactose **e.** maltose **f–h.** glucose, fructose, and galactose **i.** monosaccharides

Matching

50. a. d,b **b.** d,c **c.** a,a **d.** f,c **e.** e,c **f.** a,c **g.** b,c **h.** e,c **i.** c,c

Multiple Choice

51. a **52.** e **53.** c **54.** d **55.** b **56.** d
57. e **58.** a

True/False

59. F Bile salts **emulsify** lipids.

60. F Chylomicrons enter **lacteals** (lymphatic capillaries) within the villi.

61. T **62.** T

63. F The digestion of most lipids begins in the **small intestine.**

64. T   **65.** T

Short Answer

66. Zymogen activation begins when pancreatic juice enters the duodenum and trypsinogen comes into contact with the brush border enzyme enterokinase. **Enterokinase catalyzes the conversion of trypsinogen to trypsin. Trypsin then catalyzes the conversion of chymotrypsinogen to chymotrypsin, and procarboxypeptidase to carboxypeptidase within the duodenum.**

67. Emulsification means the breakdown of fat globules into smaller fat droplets. The emulsification of fats occurs in the small intestine and is **performed by bile salts** (a component of bile). This is important to fat digestion because it **increases the surface area of fats exposed to lipases, and therefore increases the efficiency of fat digestion**.

Challenge Questions

68. A **very low-fat diet will have no effect on the absorption of water soluble vitamins** as their absorption depends on special transport proteins. However, this type of diet **will adversely affect the absorption of the fat soluble vitamins A, D, E, and K. These vitamins depend on fats to be absorbed**, as they dissolve in lipid droplets, micelles, and chylomicrons. Therefore, a very low-fat diet can result in insufficient absorption of fat soluble vitamins, leading to a vitamin deficiency.

69. Many enzymes are involved in carbohydrate digestion because carbohydrates must be broken down to monosaccharides in order to be absorbed, and carbohydrate digestion occurs in a couple of different locations in the body. **The amylases, found in saliva and pancreatic juice, break down carbohydrates to disaccharides. However, other enzymes must break down the disaccharides into monosaccharides, and specific enzymes break down specific disaccharides in the small intestine.** For example, sucrase breaks down sucrose to glucose and fructose, and lactase breaks down lactose to galactose and glucose.

Clinical Questions

70. Prilosec may decrease the efficiency with which proteins are digested to some degree, but will not adversely affect overall protein digestion. Since Prilosec decreases the acidity of the stomach, **there may be decreased conversion of pepsinogen to pepsin which will decrease the amount of protein chemically digested in the stomach. However, since proteases are secreted into the duodenum in pancreatic juice and are present in the small intestine as brush border enzymes, proteins will still be digested in the small intestine.**

71. Gastric bypass surgery will place a person at risk for developing pernicious anemia if they don't receive supplemental vitamin B_{12}. Vitamin B_{12} is necessary to synthesize hemoglobin, and if it is not absorbed in adequate amounts, pernicious anemia will develop due to a hemoglobin deficiency. **Intrinsic factor, produced by** the parietal cells of the stomach, is necessary for the absorption of vitamin B_{12}. Following gastric bypass, since such a small part of the stomach remains functional the amount of intrinsic factor produced decreases significantly and vitamin B_{12} absorption decreases considerably as well.** Therefore vitamin B_{12} supplementation is necessary following a gastric bypass.

GENERAL PRINCIPLES OF GASTROINTESTINAL REGULATION

Completion

72. a. osmoreceptors **b.** mechanoreceptors
c. chemoreceptors **d.** gastrointestinal wall **e.** enteric
f. central

Multiple Choice

73. d   **74.** e   **75.** a   **76.** e

True/False

77. T   **78.** T   **79.** T

80. F Effector cells in GI organs include smooth muscle cells, exocrine cells, and endocrine cells.

81. F Short reflex pathways **don't** involve the CNS, while long reflex pathways **do**.

Matching

82. a. S **b.** J, D **c.** J, D **d.** J, D

Challenge Question

83. Short-term regulation of food intake involves eating in response to hunger and stopping when full. Physiologic hunger is regulated by the hypothalamus, which is influenced by **satiety signals, physiologic signals that suppress hunger**. Satiety signals include insulin, which is released from the pancreas when a meal is ingested and signals the hypothalamus to decrease the sensation of hunger; CCK, which is released from the small intestine when chyme enters it and results in decreased hunger; and nerve impulses from mechanoreceptors and chemoreceptors in the wall of the GI tract.

Long-term regulation of hunger involves changes in food intake in response to changing metabolic needs of the body over an extended period of time. Leptin seems to play a role in the long-term regulation of hunger. **Leptin is a molecule that is secreted by adipose cells in response to fat deposition, and it signals the hypothalamus to decrease the sensation of hunger.** This makes sense, as fat deposition occurs when calorie intake exceeds the energy needs of the body.

Concept Map

84. a. long reflex pathway **b.** short reflex pathway
c. enteric nervous system **d.** central nervous system
e. sight, taste, smell of food

GASTROINTESTINAL SECRETION AND ITS REGULATION

Matching

85. a. S **b.** CCK **c.** G, H **d.** CCK **e.** CCK, S **f.** CCK, S

Multiple Choice

86. b **87.** e **88.** d **89.** b **90.** c **91.** a

True/False

92. T **93.** T **94.** T

95. F The secretion of pancreatic juice is controlled **primarily** by intestinal-phase stimuli, but is **also controlled by gastric-phase and cephalic-phase stimuli.**

96. F When CCK and secretin are both present at the same time, they **enhance each other's actions**, a phenomenon known as **potentiation**.

97. T

Challenge Questions

98. Gastric acidity increases as gastric emptying occurs because the proteins in the chyme, which have a buffering effect on the acid, leave the stomach. The increased acidity acts directly on G cells to suppress gastrin secretion. Since gastrin stimulates the secretion of H^+ from parietal cells, inhibiting its release will result in decreased acidity of the stomach.

99. The bicarbonate-rich pancreatic juice that enters the duodenum in response to secretin is very important as it buffers/neutralizes the acid chyme being received from the stomach. Since the **digestive enzymes that work in the small intestine are most effective at a slightly alkaline pH**, they would not work optimally were it not for the bicarbonate in pancreatic juice. Neutralizing the acid in chyme **also protects the lining of the small intestine from damage.**

Clinical Question

100. Bile emulsifies fats, which aids their digestion by increasing the surface area exposed to lipases. Since the liver is the organ that produces and secretes bile, a person without a gallbladder will still produce bile. However, functions of the gallbladder include concentrating bile and releasing fairly large amounts of bile into the duodenum when chyme is present, so **without a gallbladder less bile will enter the duodenum when chyme is present than usual. This may decrease the efficiency of fat digestion,** but the body will still be able to digest fat because lipases will still be present and active.

Concept Map

101. a. parasympathetic activity **b.** G cells **c.** parietal **d.** pepsinogen **e.** distension of stomach **f.** mechanoreceptors **g.** short and long reflexes **h.** gastrin **i.** gastrin **j.** parietal and chief cells

GASTROINTESTINAL MOTILITY AND ITS REGULATION

Completion

102. a. central **b.** ileogastric **c.** gastroileal **d.** intestino-intestinal **e.** colonocolonic **f.** gastrocolic

Matching

103. a. a,c **b.** a **c.** a **d.** b, d, e **e.** a **f.** b, c, e

Multiple Choice

104. a **105.** c **106.** e **107.** b **108.** c **109.** e **110.** d

True/False

111. T **112.** T

113. F Vomiting is a **reflex** process initiated by the vomiting center in the medulla oblongata.

114. T

115. F Substances that induce vomiting are known as **emetics**.

116. T **117.** T

118. F Receptive relaxation involves relaxation of the smooth muscle in the upper portion of the stomach, and is triggered by the **swallowing center**.

119. T **120.** T

121. F Electrical activity moves from one smooth muscle cell to another within the GI tract through structures called **gap junctions**.

122. T

Short Answer

123. The purpose of the epiglottis is to cover the glottis during swallowing, preventing food or liquid from entering the larynx and trachea.

124. A migrating motor complex is a series of intense muscular contractions within the stomach or small intestine that occurs between meals. Accompanied by relaxation of the pyloric and ileocecal sphincters, migrating motor complexes serve to **empty the stomach and small intestine of remaining chyme.**

Sequencing

125. c, f, b, g, e, a, d

Challenge Question

126. The rate of gastric emptying must be regulated so that the duodenum does not receive food too rapidly and become overdistended, and to allow adequate time for digestive activity to occur in the stomach and duodenum. The rate of gastric emptying is coordinated by gastric-phase and intestinal-phase stimuli (but can also be influenced by cephalic-phase stimuli). For example, distention of the stomach triggers the release of gastrin, which stimulates gastric motility, while distention of the duodenum inhibits gastric motility. Gastric motility is also inhibited by the actions of CCK, secretin, and GIP, which are released into the blood when chyme enters the duodenum. All of these activities ensure that chyme is pumped a little at a time from the stomach to the duodenum, at a rate the duodenum can handle.

Clinical Question

127. a. 1) Diarrhea often occurs as the result of excessive intestinal motility. Peristaltic waves occur much more rapidly, and sometimes more forcefully, than normal as a result of irritation of the intestine or emotional stimuli that increase the amount of parasympathetic stimulation received by the intestine. Since the chyme is rapidly propelled through the small and large intestines, little time is available for the digestion or absorption of nutrients (including water), resulting in feces with a large liquid content.

2) **Diarrhea can also be the result of ingestion of a substance that is nonabsorbable by the person.** The nonabsorbable substance draws water into the intestinal lumen by osmosis, resulting in diarrhea. Lactose has this effect on people who are lactase deficient, producing a condition known as lactose intolerance.

3) **The excessive mucosal secretion of fluid and electrolytes in the intestine, which can occur in response to bacterial enterotoxins, can also cause diarrhea.**

b. Prolonged diarrhea can be a problem because it can lead to dehydration and electrolyte imbalances, as well as nutrient deficiencies.

CHAPTER 20

AN OVERVIEW OF WHOLE BODY METABOLISM

Completion

1. a. hydrolysis **b.** substrate level **c.** oxidative **d.** ADP **e.** electron transport chain **f.** mitochondria

Short Answer

2. The **most important determinant** of the particular **metabolic pathways that are active** and the **direction in which they are occurring** at any given point in time is the **activity and number of the enzymes** involved in the metabolic pathways.

3. Two ways in which compartmentation occurs at the tissue level are:

1. **Particular enzymes are found only in the cells of certain tissues.**

2. **Particular hormone receptors are located only on the cells of certain tissues.**

Cellular compartmentation can be exemplified by the fact that **certain processes occur in specific locations within the cell.** For example, glycolysis occurs in the cytosol while the Krebs cycle occurs in the mitochondrial matrix.

4. Body cells require a continual supply of energy even when a person is not eating, so it is essential for the body to store some ingested nutrients for later use instead of using all ingested nutrients immediately. Between meals, these stored molecules are broken down into molecules that the cells use for energy.

Challenge Question

5. Carbohydrates and proteins can be used to produce energy or lipids because both of these molecules can be catabolized to acetyl CoA. Acetyl CoA can **either enter the Krebs cycle and be used to produce ATP**, or it can participate in an **anabolic metabolic pathway that will convert it to lipid.**

ENERGY INTAKE, UTILIZATION, AND STORAGE

Multiple Choice

6. c   **7.** a   **8.** d   **9.** b

True/False

10. F The two primary energy storage molecules in the human body are **triglycerides** and **glycogen.**

11. T   **12.** T

13. F Carbohydrate storage occurs primarily in the **liver and skeletal muscle.** Triglyceride storage occurs primarily in adipose tissue.

Completion

14. a. glycogen **b.** adipocyte **c.** disaccharides **d.** fatty acids and glycerol **e.** lipolysis **f.** amino acids

Concept Map

15. a. digested **b.** glucose transporters **c.** cells **d.** oxidized for energy **e.** provide substrates to other metabolic reactions **f.** glycogen **g.** glycogenolysis **h.** glucose

Sequencing

16. b, e, f, c, a, d

ENERGY BALANCE

Matching

17. a. CW **b.** EI **c.** MW **d.** EC **e.** MR

Completion

18. a. heat **b.** work **c.** 60 **d.** 40 **e.** ATP

Multiple Choice

19. c   **20.** e   **21.** a   **22.** b   **23.** d

True/False

24. F Most of the expenditure of energy accounted for by the basal metabolic rate is the result of metabolic activity within the **nervous system and skeletal muscles.**

25. T   **26.** T

Short Answer

27. The **pool of nutrients within the bloodstream** that cells use to generate energy can be **replenished** by **absorbing more nutrients into the bloodstream** from ingested food or by **mobilizing energy stores.**

28. Basal metabolic rate is estimated in humans by **measuring oxygen consumption** (which correlates with the rate of nutrient oxidation) **in a person who is awake, lying down, has fasted for 12 hours, and is physically and mentally relaxed.**

29. The body is in energy balance when energy input equals energy output.

Challenge Question

30. Basal metabolic rate is expressed as the rate of energy expenditure per unit body weight because basal metabolic rate increases as body weight increases. This is because a **larger mass of tissue requires the increased expenditure of energy** in order for its cells to be maintained. Therefore, in order to get an accurate estimate of the amount of energy being expended to meet the body's basic metabolic needs, weight must be taken into account.

Clinical Question

31. A negative energy balance is achieved when energy input is less than energy output. Your mom could achieve this by **decreasing energy input as a result of decreased food intake**, or **by increasing energy output through increased exercise**. The most effective way to achieve weight loss would be through a combination of both.

ENERGY METABOLISM DURING THE ABSORPTIVE AND POSTABSORPTIVE STATES

Multiple Choice

32. d   **33.** b   **34.** c   **35.** e   **36.** c   **37.** d

Matching

38. a. A **b.** A **c.** PA **d.** A **e.** PA

True/False

39. T   **40.** T

41. F The absorptive state is primarily **anabolic**, while the postabsorptive state is primarily **catabolic**.

42. T

43. F The amount of glycogen stored by skeletal muscle and liver cells is enough to supply the body with energy for a few **hours**.

44. T

45. F During prolonged fasting, cells of the central nervous system can use **ketones** for energy.

Completion

46. a. very-low-density lipoproteins **b.** lipoprotein lipase **c.** fatty acids **d.** diffusion **e.** energy **f.** triglycerides

Short Answer

47. Fats, amino acids, and excess glucose absorbed during the absorptive state are taken up by liver, muscle, and fat cells and converted to energy storage molecules (triglycerides, proteins, and glycogen). (Note that proteins are not typically energy storage molecules, but they will be catabolized to produce energy during starvation.)

48. It is critically important for plasma glucose levels to be maintained during the postabsorptive state because the cells of the central nervous system must have a continual supply of glucose in order to produce the energy they need to function since they don't store glycogen. If blood glucose levels drop, dizziness, confusion, loss of consciousness, or in extreme cases, even death, may occur.

Challenge Questions

49. Glucose formed from glycogenolysis within skeletal muscle cells can be used only within those cells because it cannot cross the plasma membrane and enter the blood. The reason for this is that glycogen is catabolized to glucose-6-phosphate, and **in order for glucose to cross the plasma membrane it must be unphosphorylated. The enzyme that removes the phosphate group from glucose, glucose-6-phosphatase, is not present in skeletal muscle cells.**

50. Storing energy as carbohydrate or protein would increase the body's weight more than storing that same amount of energy as fat, because triglyceride molecules can store more energy per gram than either carbohydrate or protein stores can. Triglycerides store 9 kcal/gm, carbohydrates store 4 kcal/gm, and proteins store about 5 kcal/gm. Therefore, if the body were storing 100 kcal of energy as triglyceride, it would weigh 11 gm, but would weigh 25 gm if stored as carbohydrate and 20 gm if stored as protein.

REGULATION OF ABSORPTIVE AND POSTABSORPTIVE METABOLISM

Completion

51. a. insulin **b.** beta **c.** pancreas **d.** glucagon **e.** alpha **f.** anabolic **g.** catabolic **h.** glucose

Multiple Choice

52. c   **53.** b   **54.** e   **55.** a   **56.** c

True/False

57. T

58. F The **increased** plasma glucose levels that occur during the absorptive state act directly on the beta cells of the pancreas to increase insulin secretion. Decreased plasma glucose levels during the postabsorptive state will act on alpha cells of the pancreas to increase glucagon secretion.

59. T

60. F If plasma glucose concentration decreases, glucagon secretion **increases**.

61. T

62. F **Glucagon** promotes the catabolism of energy stores and inhibits energy storage. Insulin opposes the catabolism of energy stores and promotes energy storage.

63. T   **64.** T

Matching

65. a. I **b.** I **c.** G **d.** I **e.** G **f.** I **g.** G

Short Answer

66. Since **exercise directly increases the number of glucose transporters in the plasma membranes of skeletal muscle cells, insulin has little effect on the glucose permeability of exercising skeletal muscle**. However, in **resting skeletal muscle** insulin is essential in increasing the glucose permeability of the cells, because **insulin triggers an increase in the number of GLUT 4 glucose transport proteins in cell plasma membranes.**

67. During the stress response, **sympathetic activity increases, which increases glucagon secretion from the alpha cells of the pancreas. The increased secretion of glucagon results in increased plasma glucose (due to increased gluconeogenesis and glycogenolysis), and increased plasma fatty acid and glycerol levels (due to increased lipolysis)**. These changes make energy more available to the cells during the increased metabolic activity characteristic of the stress-associated fight-or-flight response.

Challenge Questions

68. Following a **meal rich in proteins but low in carbohydrates**, the resulting increased plasma levels of amino acids will **stimulate the secretion of insulin** (which will increase amino acid uptake by cells), but will also stimulate an **increase in glucagon secretion**. This **increased secretion of glucagon is important as it offsets the effect of insulin on blood glucose, preventing the blood glucose concentration from falling. Therefore, following this type of meal, the blood glucose concentration should remain fairly stable.**

A **meal rich in both proteins and carbohydrates will initially raise the blood glucose level** because of the high carbohydrate intake. This will result in **a large increase in insulin secretion. Insulin release will also be triggered, along with glucagon secretion, as a result of the**

increased amino acid levels in the blood following a protein-rich meal. However, in this case, **so much more insulin than glucagon is secreted that glucagon does not offset the effect of insulin**, and the blood glucose level will eventually decrease as glucose is taken up by cells and is converted to glycogen for storage. **Therefore, following this type of meal, glucose levels initially rise but then fall back to normal.**

69. Since cells of the central nervous system (CNS) do not store glycogen, continual glucose uptake from the blood is essential to provide the cells a source of energy. **When plasma glucose levels are low, it is critical that the available glucose be able to efficiently enter the cells of the CNS. Since low blood glucose levels inhibit the secretion of insulin, if CNS cells were dependent on insulin to allow glucose to enter them, they would be unable to function normally due to a lack of energy any time plasma glucose levels dropped (as would occur during the postabsorptive state). Therefore, it is very important to brain function that glucose uptake by cells of the CNS does not require insulin.**

Clinical Questions

70. As mentioned above, cells of the CNS require a continual supply of glucose for energy because they don't store glycogen. **In hypoglycemia, blood glucose levels drop, and brain cells do not receive the energy supply they need in order to function normally. Symptoms associated with this condition include confusion, lethargy, dizziness, and loss of consciousness. Death may occur if the blood glucose level remains very low.** Hypoglycemia is what causes diabetics to lose consciousness during an insulin reaction.

71. The three classic symptoms of diabetes occur for the following reasons. Hyperglycemia will result in the **excretion of glucose in the urine, which makes it hyperosmolar. As the hyperosmolar urine forms in the kidneys, it attracts water, resulting in osmotic diuresis (the volume of urine increases, producing polyuria). Because more water enters the urine than normally would, the body becomes dehydrated, resulting in excessive thirst (polydipsia). Since glucose is unable to enter the cells, the cells starve, causing the body to feel hungry all the time (polyphagia).**

HORMONAL REGULATION OF GROWTH

Multiple Choice

72. c   **73.** e   **74.** b   **75.** d   **76.** d

Matching

77. a. osteoblasts **b.** osteoclasts **c.** osteoid **d.** deposition **e.** resorption **f.** osteocytes **g.** calcification

True/False

78. F Androgens cause the **hypertrophy** of skeletal muscle during puberty.

79. T

80. F Growth hormone levels usually **decrease** after puberty.

81. T

Completion

82. a. anterior pituitary **b.** growth hormone releasing hormone **c.** growth hormone inhibiting hormone (somatostatin) **d.** negative feedback

Short Answer

83. At **high concentrations, glucocorticoids inhibit growth** as they promote bone resorption and protein catabolism.

Challenge Questions

84. A growth spurt is seen during puberty followed by the cessation of growth in height because of the effects of the sex hormones on bones. **Sex hormones promote bone growth** by stimulating the secretion of growth hormone and IGF-1, as well as stimulating osteoblast activity; but they also **promote the closure of the epiphyseal plate,** which will cause bones to stop growing in length. Therefore, the actions of the sex hormones explain the growth pattern seen during adolescence.

85. Nutritional status is very important to growth. Hormones alone will not allow a person to grow to their genetically determined size potential, because **growth requires raw materials and fuel. These raw materials, such as proteins and calcium, and fuel, such as glucose, are obtained through the diet.** Therefore, a child or adolescent who is chronically malnourished will not grow to their full potential because their body will lack the raw materials and energy necessary to allow their soft tissues and bones to grow adequately.

86. A prolonged shortage of sleep during adolescence, over weeks or months, could affect a person's ultimate height, because growth hormone secretion increases during sleep and falls during the day. Continual sleep deprivation will result in lower than normal levels of growth hormone, which could decrease the rate of growth.

Clinical Question

87. Both **gigantism and acromegaly are the result of excessive secretion of growth hormone,** which often occurs as the result of an anterior pituitary tumor. The **difference between the two is the age at which the disorder develops. Gigantism is seen in children,** because if excessive growth hormone secretion occurs before the epiphyseal plates close, the **clinical manifestations produced will include a significant increase in height with a proportional increase in the size of soft tissues and organs.** The child will grow to be a "giant," as the name of the disorder implies. **Acromegaly occurs when growth hormone secretion increases in adulthood, after the epiphyseal plates have closed.** In this case, **no increase in height occurs, but bones increase in circumference and the size of the soft tissues**

increases. These changes are disproportionate to the person's height, and affected individuals develop such characteristics as a protruding jaw, large lips, large hands, and large limbs.

THYROID HORMONES

Multiple Choice

88. c **89.** d **90.** b **91.** a **92.** e **93.** b
94. d **95.** c **96.** a

Matching

97. a. H **b.** T **c.** T **d.** T **e.** APG

True/False

98. T **99.** T

100. F TRH secretion is **inhibited** by stress.

101. T

102. F Thyroid hormones increase the metabolic rate of most tissues of the body, but **not in the brain, spleen, or gonads.**

103. T

Sequencing

104. c, b, d, e, a

Short Answer

105. The **conversion of T_4 to T_3 in the plasma is known as activation,** and it is advantageous because **T_3 is four times more potent than T_4,** but more T_4 is initially synthesized in the thyroid gland than T_3. **By converting T_4 to T_3 in the plasma, the body ends up with a large amount of the most potent form of the hormone.**

GLUCOCORTICOIDS

Completion

106. a. adrenal cortex **b.** cortisol **c.** circadian rhythm **d.** stress **e.** general adaptation syndrome

Multiple Choice

107. e **108.** b **109.** c **110.** d

True/False

111. F Increased secretion of cortisol will **increase** the plasma glucose level.

112. F Increased secretion of cortisol will **weaken** the responses of the immune system.

113. T

Short Answer

114. Glucocorticoids are administered following organ transplants because they suppress the immune system. By doing so, they decrease the immune response against the foreign tissue, which **will decrease the likelihood that the organ will be rejected.**

Challenge Question

115. Glucocorticoids are necessary for survival during prolonged fasting because, without glucocorticoids, the cells would starve. The reason for this is that **glucocorticoids maintain the normal concentrations of the enzymes that are necessary for energy mobilization reactions** (e.g. those involved in gluconeogenesis, glycogenolysis, proteolysis, and lipolysis). Without glucocorticoids, enzyme levels would be too low to allow enough energy to be mobilized from storage to support the metabolic activities of the cells.

Clinical Question

116. Cushing's syndrome is the result of the hypersecretion of cortisol. Symptoms include, but are not limited to, fat deposition in the abdomen and face, hyperglycemia, weakness, a tendency to bruise easily, and muscle wasting.

Concept Map

117. a. hypothalamus **b.** corticotropin releasing hormone (CRH) **c.** anterior pituitary **d.** adrenocorticotropic hormone (ACTH) **e.** adrenal cortex **f.** glucocorticoids (cortisol) **g.** negative feedback

CHAPTER 21

AN OVERVIEW OF REPRODUCTIVE PHYSIOLOGY

Matching

1. a. SZ **b.** WD **c.** AG **d.** srY **e.** MIS **f.** MD **g.** TS **h.** SSC

Completion

2. a. fertilization **b.** parturition **c.** puberty **d.** secondary **e.** Males **f.** females **g.** menopause

Short Answer

3. Autosomes are chromosomes that determine traits *other* **than the sex of the individual. Sex chromosomes** are either X or Y chromosomes and they **determine an individual's sex.**

4. The testes are considered to have endocrine tissue because they **secrete hormones**, most notably testosterone. Testosterone helps to promote gametogenesis, growth, and the maintenance of secondary sex characteristics.

5. Gametes have a total of **23 unpaired, unduplicated chromosomes**. There are 22 autosomes and one sex chromosome (either an X or a Y). In zygotes, there are **46 total chromosomes composed of 22 pairs of homologous autosomes and a single pair of sex chromosomes** (either XX or XY).

Multiple Choice

6. c   **7.** b   **8.** d   **9.** c   **10.** d   **11.** a

True/False

12. T   **13.** T

14. F Egg and sperm cells do not fully mature until **during and after puberty.**

15. F The reproductive tract is present in **both males and females**, and is the system of accessory ducts through which egg and sperm are transported.

Sequencing

16. f, b, c, e, g, a, d

Clinical Question

17. An extra chromosome can occur in the zygote one of two ways. During meiosis I, homologous chromosomes should separate into different cells. If *both* homologous chromosomes move into one cell during meiosis I, then the resulting gamete will have both homologous chromosomes inside of it. During fertilization, this cell will acquire a single chromosome number 21 from the other parent, which will result in an extra copy of chromosome number 21. **Alternatively, meiosis I may be normal, but during meiosis II the two sister chromatids may fail to separate into two distinct cells.** This, too, can result in an extra copy of chromosome number 21. When this cell fuses with the other parent's gamete at conception, it will have three copies of chromosome number 21.

Challenge Questions

18. Both testosterone and Müllerian-inhibiting substance (MIS) are involved in sex differentiation of the fetus. **Testosterone acts on Wolffian ducts to promote the development of male reproductive organs, including external genitalia. MIS serves a different role in that it promotes the regression and disappearance of the Müllerian ducts.** When the fetus is destined to be a female, the absence of testosterone causes the Wolffian ducts to degenerate, while the absence of MIS allows the Müllerian ducts to form the female reproductive organs.

19. The testes in males continually produce sperm. **Males retain the ability to reproduce throughout their entire adult lives.** In females, reproductive capacity and ovulation is cyclic. **Females lose reproductive capacity at menopause.**

THE MALE REPRODUCTIVE SYSTEM

Matching

20. a. FSH **b.** LH **c.** GnRH **d.** TST **e.** INH

Completion

21. a. testes **b.** accessory glands **c.** seminiferous tubules **d.** Sertoli **e.** androgens **f.** anterior pituitary **g.** gonadotropin-releasing hormone (GnRH)

Short Answer

22. The blood-testis barrier is formed by tight junctions between the Sertoli cells. After puberty, this barrier prevents the membrane antigens of the developing spermatozoa from escaping through the basal lamina into the bloodstream. **This is important because the sperm are not formed until after puberty, well after the immune system has been programmed to recognize the body's own tissues early in life. Therefore, the sperm cells formed after puberty are not recognized by the body's immune system since they are produced after the immune system has been programmed.** In addition, meiosis produces sperm cells that are genetically distinct from all other cells of the body. **Without this barrier, the male's immune system would attack the newly formed, unrecognized sperm cells.**

23. Nitric oxide is released from parasympathetic neurons that innervate the penis. **Nitric oxide causes vasodilation of arteries, causing the erectile tissue of the penis to become engorged with blood.** Vascular spaces inside the tissue fill with blood and expand, which brings about an erection.

24. Sertoli cells help or "nurse" the developing spermatozoa. **In this role, Sertoli cells secrete luminal fluid, manufacture and secrete androgen-binding protein, and regulate the germ cell response to FSH and testosterone.**

Multiple Choice

25. b   **26.** a   **27.** c   **28.** a   **29.** e   **30.** c

True/False

31. T

32. F   FSH is produced in the **anterior pituitary.**

33. F   The bulbourethral glands produce secretions that aid in **lubrication.**

34. T   **35.** T

Sequencing

36. d, g, a, e, b, f, c

Labeling

37. a. Spermatogonia (2n) **b.** Primary spermatocytes (2n) **c.** Secondary spermatocytes (n) **d.** Spermatids (n) **e.** Spermatozoa (n)

Clinical Questions

38. The production of sperm is dependent on temperature. The scrotal sac lies outside of the body cavity in order to provide optimal temperatures that are just below normal body temperatures. **By wearing tight shorts during exercise and tight briefs during the day, Paul's testes may be experiencing higher than normal temperatures, causing sperm production to drop. This situation may be remedied by decreasing the temperature of the testes by wearing looser fitting clothing.**

39. A vasectomy is the ligation (or tying off) of the vas deferens. This procedure allows for spermatozoa to be produced, but prevents the spermatozoa from reaching the body exterior. **Most of the ejaculate volume is the result**

of secretions from the accessory glands (prostate gland, seminal vesicles, and bulbourethral glands). Spermatozoa make up a very tiny percentage of the ejaculate volume. Therefore the ejaculate volume will not be noticeably diminished.

Challenge Questions

40. Prolonged use of anabolic steroids in doses higher than normally experienced in the body can lead to decreased endogenous serum concentrations of LH, FSH, and testosterone. That is, the body decreases natural production of these hormones because the exogenous levels are so high. In males, the lack of FSH, LH, and testosterone leads to testis atrophy. **In females, muscle mass is increased, but so are other male-related secondary sex characteristics, including increased facial hair growth, deepening of the voice, and loss of hair on the head.**

41. The spermatogonia serve two functions in the male. **Once they undergo mitosis, one of the daughter cells undergoes meiosis to eventually become the functional spermatozoa. The other daughter cell, however, remains at the periphery of the seminiferous tubule to produce future spermatogonia. This process ensures that the total number of spermatogonia does not change and that there are always cells present to produce future spermatozoa.**

Concept Map

42. a. Anterior pituitary **b.** LH secretion **c.** Sertoli cells **d.** Testosterone secretion **e.** Inhibin secretion **f.** Maintenance of secondary sex characteristics **g.** Protein synthesis in skeletal muscle

THE FEMALE REPRODUCTIVE SYSTEM

Matching

43. a. FSH **b.** LH **c.** EST **d.** PRG

Completion

44. a. ovaries **b.** 28 **c.** pituitary **d.** menstruation **e.** germ **f.** birth **g.** fertilization

Short Answer

45. In the human female, primary oocytes enter meiotic arrest. **The chromosomes stop moving and meiosis is halted. This occurs when the female is a fetus and the primary oocytes remain in this suspended development until just prior to ovulation, when the primary oocyte undergoes meiosis I.**

46. The acidic environment in the vagina allows it to ward off pathogenic organisms (bacteria and fungi) that can enter the vagina from the external environment. This acid environment, produced by helpful bacteria that normally live in the vagina, does suppress the motility of some sperm. However, **the alkaline fluid produced in the seminal vesicles in males helps to temporarily neutralize this acid environment, ensuring that many of the sperm cells remain mobile.**

Multiple Choice

47. b **48.** c **49.** a **50.** e **51.** a **52.** c

True/False

53. F The proliferation phase of the menstrual cycle is marked by an **increase in endometrial tissue.** The secretory phase of the ovarian cycle is marked by menstruation.

54. T

55. F The **corpus luteum** helps to maintain the endometrium when implantation occurs. The *Graafian follicle* is the term used for the follicle just prior to ovulation.

Sequencing

56. d, g, a, e, b, f, c

Labeling

57. a. Primordial follicle **b.** Granulosa cells **c.** Antrum **d.** Corona radiata **e.** Corpus luteum

Clinical Question

58. During a female's reproductive years, estrogen levels remain high. These high levels of circulating estrogen aid in maintaining bone growth and strength (by mediating parathyroid hormone activity). Parathyroid hormone increases calcium levels in the bloodstream by stimulating osteoclasts to resorb bone, which causes calcium release from the bone matrix. Estrogen tempers the bone-wasting effects of parathyroid hormone. **During menopause, estrogen levels drop, which can lead to increased bone loss and osteoporosis. By taking estrogen replacement therapy, a woman can help ward off osteoporosis.**

Challenge Questions

59. The menstrual cycle begins on the day when menstruation begins, an obvious landmark in her cycle. Many of the other physiological changes that occur in the female's body (a rise in hormone levels or ovulation, for example) are not as obvious as menstruation, so physiologists and clinicians use the first day of a woman's period as the beginning of the menstrual cycle.

60. Sperm cells begin meiosis when males reach puberty, and the process continues throughout their life. For a single sperm cell, it takes about 70 days from the beginning of meiosis until the end of meiosis. In human females, the ovaries have primary oocytes, which enter meiotic arrest and begin meiosis just prior to ovulation. Meiosis is completed only if fertilization occurs. This means that, in ovaries, the time span between the beginning of meiosis and the end may be as short as a few days or, alternatively, many years. If the egg is never fertilized, it will never complete meiosis.

Concept Map

61. a. GnRH secretion **b.** LH and FSH secretion **c.** Estrogen secretion **d.** Progesterone secretion increases **e.** Positive feedback

FERTILIZATION, IMPLANTATION, AND PREGNANCY, AND PARTURITION AND LACTATION

Matching

62. a. hCG **b.** PRL **c.** PLG **d.** OXT **e.** PRL **f.** PRG **g.** EST, OXT

Completion

63. a. uterine tube **b.** blastocyst **c.** endometrium **d.** placenta **e.** progesterone **f.** mammary **g.** anterior pituitary **h.** secretory

64. a. Parturition **b.** cervix **c.** placenta **d.** mammary glands **e.** prolactin **f.** production **g.** oxytocin **h.** milk ejection

Short Answer

65. When sperm are initially deposited in the vagina they are incapable of penetrating an oocyte. **Capacitation is the process by which the membrane surrounding each sperm cell becomes more fragile so that the hydrolytic enzymes in their acrosomes can be released.** As a result of capacitation, sperm also change their pattern of tail movement, which permits them to swim faster.

66. Estrogen directly promotes the growth of fatty deposits and duct tissue in the breasts. Estrogen also indirectly stimulates breast growth by promoting the release of prolactin from the anterior pituitary. Finally, estrogen stimulates the growth of the uterine smooth muscle and increases the responsiveness of the uterine smooth muscle to oxytocin.

67. A breech birth is when the legs or hips of the fetus attempt to pass through the birth canal before the head. **This position can lead to a compression of the umbilical cord between the fetus and the uterine wall, thus cutting off the blood supply to the fetus. This type of birth is also difficult for the mother and may cause maternal fatigue or even death.**

Multiple Choice

68. b **69.** c **70.** a **71.** e **72.** a **73.** c

True/False

74. F During the **first trimester** of pregnancy, estrogen and progesterone are secreted from the corpus luteum. During the last six months, these hormones are produced by the placenta.

75. T

76. F The decidual response is produced by the trophoblast.

77. T

Clinical Questions

78. Fraternal twins (dizygotic twins) are produced when two different eggs are released during ovulation and each is fertilized by a different sperm. These twins are born at the same time, but are no more genetically similar than siblings born at different times. **Identical twins (monozygotic**

twins) are produced when one egg is fertilized by one sperm. As the zygote begins to divide by mitosis a small group of cells may detach from the original group of cells and *both* groups of cells implant in the uterine wall. This results in twins that are genetically identical.

79. Implantation needs to occur before hCG is produced, which generally happens between 6–12 days after ovulation. For this reason, a woman needs to wait at least seven days after ovulation. However, a significant percentage of women who are indeed pregnant will still show a negative result because the test may not be sensitive enough to detect low levels of hCG. A pregnant woman's hCG levels should double every 2–3 days, but many women may not have a positive result until the first day of a missed period or even a few days later.

80. Breast milk supplies the infant with antibodies, which confer some degree of immunity to the infant. There are also growth factors and hormones in milk that promote tissue development in the infant.

Challenge Questions

81. In humans, many sperm cells actually reach the egg. However, under normal circumstances, only one sperm will penetrate the egg and transfer DNA to it. **Polyspermy is the fertilization of one egg by more than one sperm cell.** This would most likely result in an inviable zygote with too many chromosomes. Under normal circumstances, **once a sperm has fused with the oocyte's plasma membrane, sperm-binding proteins are inactivated, and the zona pellucida hardens and pulls away from the plasma membrane. These actions prevent further sperm from transferring their DNA to the oocyte.**

82. The amniotic fluid is composed mainly of fetal urine that contains epithelial cells shed from the skin, respiratory tract, and urinary tract of the fetus. Therefore, sampling the amniotic fluid results in fetal, and not maternal, cells.

Labeling

83. a. zygote **b.** morula **c.** blastocyst **d.** trophoblast

Concept Map

84. a. Hypothalamus **b.** Anterior pituitary **c.** Prolactin secretion **d.** Posterior pituitary **e.** Oxytocin secretion **f.** Milk ejection

CHAPTER 22

THE IMMUNE SYSTEM

Matching

1. a. L **b.** PA **c.** LT **d.** I **e.** IR **f.** AD

Completion

2. a. leukocytes **b.** phagocytic **c.** neutrophils **d.** tissues **e.** monocytes **f.** macrophages **g.** eosinophils **h.** basophils **i.** lymphocytes **j.** T-cells **k.** null cells **l.** B-cells **m.** plasma cells

Short Answer

3. The granulocytic leukocytes are differentiated from one another based on the way their cytoplasmic granules stain with Wright's stain. The granules of **neutrophils** remain a neutral color. Neutrophils circulate through the body constantly, ready to identify any kind of foreign material or debris that they engulf and remove. **Eosinophils**, whose granules stain red upon exposure to *eosin*, primarily attack parasitic invaders that are too large to be engulfed. They do so by attaching to a parasite and discharging toxic molecules from their cytoplasmic granules. **Basophils**, whose cytoplasmic granules stain dark blue or purple, are nonphagocytic cells that are thought to defend against larger parasites, much like eosinophils, by releasing toxic molecules that damage the invader. However, basophils also release histamine, heparin, and other chemicals that contribute significantly to allergic reactions like hay fever.

4. Phagocytosis is the process by which a cell engulfs and digests microorganisms, abnormal cells, and foreign particles present in blood and tissues. Neutrophils, eosinophils, macrophages, and some T lymphocytes are phagocytic. Fixed macrophages are found in large numbers in **connective tissue**, in the **wall of the gastrointestinal tract**, in the **alveoli of the lungs**, and in the **walls of certain blood vessels in the liver** (called Kupffer cells in that location) and **spleen**. Of significance is the fact that the locations of these fixed tissues correspond to where substances enter the body, so that any foreign invader attempting to enter the body at these locations can be intercepted and disabled.

5. Each of the peripheral lymphoid tissues contains a dense network of cells that trap microorganisms and foreign particles, and **each is located at a place where lymphatic** vessels converge, making it ideally positioned to ensnare these invaders. Once trapped, these substances are eventually cleared by the actions of macrophages and lymphocytes. The macrophage and lymphocyte networks of the spleen and lymph nodes filter blood and lymph. The networks of the tonsils and adenoids trap inhaled particles and microorganisms, while those of the appendix and Peyer's patches trap substances that enter the body by way of ingested food or water. Central lymphoid tissues are so named because they are the sites of lymphocyte maturation. The central lymphoid tissues are the bone marrow, fetal liver, and thymus.

Multiple Choice

6. d **7.** e **8.** d **9.** d **10.** b

True/False

11. T **12.** T

13. F **Central lymphoid tissues** are the sites of lymphocyte maturation.

14. F When **B cells** contact antigens they develop into plasma cells, which secrete immunoglobulins.

15. F Neutrophils, eosinophils, **monocytes, macrophages, and some T lymphocytes** are capable of phagocytosis.

Labeling

16. a. adenoids **b.** tonsils **c.** lymph nodes **d.** spleen
e. Payer's patch **f.** appendix **g.** lymphatic vessels **h.** bone
marrow **i.** thymus

Clinical Question

17. Bacteria that are present in interstitial fluid are
carried by the flow of this tissue fluid into lymphatic
vessels and eventually into the net-like lymph nodes,
which swell **and become tender.** In the lymph nodes, the
bacteria come into contact with B lymphocytes and T
lymphocytes, thereby inducing them to generate efficient
and selective immune responses that work throughout the
body to eliminate the invaders. **A common sign of
bacterial infection is** *leukocytosis,* **a four- to five-fold
increase in the number of circulating neutrophils.** The
reason for this increase is that the cytokines that are
secreted by macrophages eventually reach the bone
marrow, where they stimulate the proliferation and
release of neutrophils and, later, monocytes into the
circulation.

Challenge Questions

18. Memory B cells help you stay well. As the viral
particles leave your daughter's body and enter yours, your
neutrophils attack each invading particle. Neutrophils
bring the viral particles and their antigens into regional
lymph nodes, or the viruses may reach the nodes alone.
In the lymph nodes the appropriate memory B cells
recognize the antigens, immediately mature into plasma
cells, and start secreting anti-chicken pox
immunoglobulins. These antibodies combine with the
viral particles, marking them for macrophages to engulf.
If any of the chicken pox virus successfully invades other
cells of your body and kills those cells, they too enter
lymph nodes, where cytotoxic T cells can attack the
infected cells, freeing more antigens to provoke more B
cells and macrophages.

19. The adult would lose the equivalent of a giant lymph
node and probably suffer no noticeable effects in the
immune system since, in all likelihood, memory B cells
to a large variety of antigens would already have
developed. In a child, since the immune system is still
maturing, you might notice a difference in immunity to
childhood diseases or in the development of immunity to
diseases not yet encountered, particularly pneumococcal
pneumonia. In most cases, an awareness of the increased
risks and taking penicillin prophylactically are enough to
avoid any problems. Some children who have had
splenectomies suffer vaccine failure as adults, when they
are vaccinated for diseases required for traveling to foreign
countries. As a result, they may acquire malaria, for
example, despite having been recently vaccinated for that
disease, since they lack the ability to become immune to
diseases not encountered prior to their surgery.

**20. Blood plasma circulates through capillary beds,
allowing solutes to enter the tissue fluid that surrounds
the cells.** This arrangement allows cells a more leisurely
pace of exchange of solutes than the circulation of the

plasma in capillaries could allow. In addition, **tissue fluid
also collects worn-out cells and/or their debris. The tissue
fluid, depleted of solutes and laden with cellular debris,
is funneled into lymphatic capillaries as fresh plasma
arrives in the capillary bed,** creating a "flow" into the
lymphatic vessels. **Once the fluid enters these vessels, it is
now referred to as lymph and, in turn, is channeled
toward the peripheral lymphoid tissues,** where they may
do their work as described in Question 5.

ORGANIZATION OF THE BODY'S DEFENSES

Matching
21. a. NS **b.** S **c.** NS **d.** NS **e.** S **f.** NS **g.** S

Completion
22. a. skin **b.** mucous membranes **c.** bacteria **d.** viruses
e. mucous membranes **f.** mucus **g.** skin **h.** sweat **i.** oil
j. bacteria

Concept Map
23. a. humoral immunity **b.** T cells **c.** plasma cells
d. CD4 **e.** cytotoxic T-cells **f.** cytokines **g.** activation
h. opsonization **i.** proliferation **j.** complement activation
k. lysis

Short Answer
24. Step 1) Macrophages near the injury site begin to
engulf debris and foreign matter, starting the inflammatory
reaction, releasing the first cytokines, and reducing the
amount of foreign material present.

Step 2) Capillaries near the injury site dilate, increasing
local blood flow and becoming more permeable to
proteins and fluid. As capillary walls become more
permeable, proteins and fluid move into tissue spaces,
bringing additional leukocytes and defensive proteins into
the local circulation, which allows these proteins to move
into the tissues where they are needed. Lastly, collected
leukocytes migrate from the blood into the tissue spaces.

Step 3) Foreign matter is contained, limiting the damage
done by the inflammatory process. Clot formation
continues and effectively walls off the region of damage
and infection, eventually forming a scab, if needed.

Step 4) Additional leukocytes migrate to the region.
Reinforcements arrive! About an hour after the injury,
neutrophils accumulate. Approximately ten hours later,
monocytes begin to move to the tissue, where they develop
into large, active macrophages.

Step 5) Recruited leukocytes continue to help clear the
infection mainly by phagocytosis.

**25. By interfering with viral replication, interferons
stem the spread of viruses within the body.** Virally
infected cells secrete two interferons called *interferon-α*
and *interferon-β*. The secretion warns surrounding cells of
the viral threat, inducing them to set the stage for their
own resistance. An infected cell accumulates viral nucleic
acid during reproduction of the virus, stimulating the cell

to synthesize and secrete interferons. These bind to nearby cells that are still healthy, thereby initiating a series of intracellular changes that cause the cells to become more resistant to the virus by the presence of RNA-degrading enzymes and protein-synthesis inhibitors in their cytoplasm. Because these enzymes and inhibitors are potentially dangerous to the cell itself, they only appear in the case of virus infection, and are thus temporarily poised to block the production of new viruses. Both the production of interferon and the anti-viral state it induces are non-specific; almost any viral nucleic acid can induce interferon production, and interferon-induced resistance can defeat virtually any virus that comes along.

26. The *complement system* got its name from the fact that it completes or fulfills ("complements") the actions of specific antibodies. A series of activation steps, each component activates the next step in the series. It ends with the development of a *membrane attack complex* (MAC), a channel-forming protein that pierces the bacterial membrane, with the result that it fills with fluid, swelling, and then lyses. The important outcome of these events is that complement-mediated lysis is the primary way by which antibody-coated bacteria die.

Sequencing

27. e, b, d, a, c

Multiple Choice

28. e   **29.** c   **30.** d   **31.** a

True/False

32. F Complement **consists of a set of about 30 different proteins** that normally circulate in the plasma.

33. F Opsonization is **not a required process** for foreign material to be ingested, but makes it easier for the phagocyte to engulf the foreign material.

34. T   **35.** T   **36.** T

Clinical Question

37. Strains occur when muscles and/or tendons are stretched beyond their normal limits. Strains are usually less severe than sprains. Sprains occur at joints, where more structures intersect for support. Thus, more structures are damaged when support fails. In addition to the tendon damage of the strain, sprains include over-stretching of ligaments and broken blood vessels, which allows the joint and surrounding tissues to fill with blood and fluid.

Rest prevents further injury and allows all of the treatments and immune system components time to do their job.

Ice deadens the pain immediately after the injury, and, with **compression**, contributes toward limiting the swelling, which may also reduce the pain. The damaged tissues and broken blood vessels set some of the initial responses into motion, however, reducing the blood flow and temperature may inadvertently hamper the cells of the immune system, both from the standpoint of their arrival to the site and the beneficial effects of the pyrogens, which

allow efficient working of phagocytes and other immune system components. Because of these factors, it is important to limit the application of ice to the first few hours after injury.

Elevation takes advantage of gravity and allows both the vascular and the lymphatic systems to drain the area and reduce the swelling.

Completion

38. a. specificity **b.** diversity **c.** memory **d.** self-tolerance **e.** humoral response **f.** cell-mediated response **g.** class I MHC **h.** perforins **i.** fragmentins **j.** class II MHC

Challenge Questions

39. Non-specific immune responses allow for an immediate response, marshalling defenses as quickly as possible. **Specific mechanisms, on the other hand, take time to get started,** as the appropriate cells are moved into position, or while cellular machinery prepares particular secretions for release. These redundancies are primarily a matter of saving time; cells are mobilized into action, then fine-tuned once the appropriate antigens, cytokines, and cells have had time to make contact.

40. Vasodilation and capillary permeability allow the components of the immune system—the variety of cells as well as chemical factors—to be delivered to the problem site and enter the afflicted tissues.

Compounds that Enhance the Mechanisms of the Immune System

Compound	Source	Action
Histamine	Mast cells	Improve vasodilation and capillary permeability
Complement proteins	Plasma	Some bind to mast cells
IL-1, IL-6, TNF-alpha	Leukocytes	Collectively increase adhesion molecules, neutrophils, and pyrogens
Selectins	Blood vessel walls	Improve attachment to blood vessels
Integrins	Leukocytes	Improve attachment to blood vessels

41. Pain tells you, "Stop doing that!" and "Fix this problem!" It serves as an attention-getter to help prevent further damage. Acknowledgement of pain caused by immune reactions may lead to resting the afflicted part or seeking medical attention to reinforce the efforts of the immune system.

Matching

42. a. Ag **b.** L **c.** L **d.** Ag **e.** Ag **f.** L

Short Answer

43. Clonal selection is the antigen-driven activation of lymphocytes. It gives rise to two populations of lymphocyte clones, effector cells and memory cells, essentially producing an army of identical cells capable of fighting a particular invader.

44. These terms all refer to parts of an antibody's structure. A typical antibody is a Y-shaped molecule consisting of four protein chains: two identical **heavy chains** and two identical **light chains**, joined by disulfide bridges. Two identical antigen-binding sites are located on each of the upper tips of the Y, forming the **variable regions** (V) of the heavy and light chains, as the amino acid sequences in these regions vary extensively from antibody to antibody. The tail of the Y-shaped antibody is made up of the *constant regions* (C) of the heavy chains. There are five kinds of heavy chains, and so, five classes of antibodies: IgG, IgM, IgA, IgE, and IgD.

45. In both humoral and cell-mediated immunity, different mechanisms exist that result in the destruction of the invader and the *memory* of its antigenic determinants, the essence of immunity. In humoral immunity, B lymphocytes develop into plasma cells that secrete antibodies, which circulate in the blood and lymph. Long ago, these body fluids were called "humors," giving rise to the term **humoral immunity**. In cell-mediated immunity, by contrast, certain T lymphocytes develop into cytotoxic T cells, which bind to and kill abnormal body cells, requiring the direct contact of living cells with their targets in order to act on them, thus the term **cell-mediated immunity**.

46. Specific immunity relies on specificity, diversity, memory, and self-tolerance, which are all based on the principles of *recognition* of an invader, as well as the *memory* of an invader. **Non-specific defenses**, in contrast, rely on *barriers*, be they chemical or physical, that hamper the progress of *any* invader.

Multiple Choice

47. b   **48.** d   **49.** c   **50.** d   **51.** c

Challenge Question

52. Humoral immunity occurs because of antibodies circulating in the plasma; when a person donates their blood, these travel with the plasma. The cells, however, are removed and, with them, go the capacity for CMI. Hence, it is absent from the donor's plasma.

Graphing

53. The secondary immune response starts sooner, has a greater magnitude, and lasts longer than the primary response.

HUMORAL AND CELL-MEDIATED IMMUNITY

Short Answer

54. As their respective names suggest, the primary difference in these antigens is in their relationship with T cells, specifically helper T cells. Both types of antigens can trigger B-cell proliferation and plasma cell production, but IL-2, which is secreted by helper T cells (along with other types of cytokines), IS required for the production of memory cells, and memory cells, of course, are required for long-term immunity. Thus, when T-independent

antigens are involved in causing a disease, you actually will become ill each time the antigen reappears, since your immune system would have no "immunological memory" of the antigen's prior appearance.

55. The five classes of antibody molecules are IgG, IgM, IgA, IgE, and IgD. All classes of immunoglobulins can mediate the simplest forms of antigen attack—neutralization and agglutination. IgG antibodies are specialized at opsonization because their tails bind to specific surface receptors on phagocytic cells, triggering the phagocytes to engulf both the antibodies and their target. Both IgM and IgG antibodies can activate the complement system, bringing about the lysis of bacteria to which the antibodies are bound. IgG antibodies can enhance the nonspecific killing action of natural killer cells. IgE antibodies function in allergic reactions, and IgA is especially suited for crossing epithelial cells and is, therefore, present on mucosal surfaces. Little is known about IgD.

56. The three major types of T lymphocytes are: 1) helper T cells, 2) cytotoxic T cells, and 3) suppressor T cells. Helper T cells are the primary regulators of specific immune responses. They operate indirectly by secreting cytokines that enhance the activity of B cells, cytotoxic T cells, suppressor T cells, and helper T cells themselves. They also secrete cytokines that enhance the actions of macrophages and NK cells essential to non-specific defenses. Cytotoxic T cells are directly responsible for cell-mediated immunity in that they kill cells infected by viruses or intracellular bacteria, and cells that are otherwise abnormal, like cancer cells and transplanted cells. Suppressor T cells are not well understood, but they are thought to produce cytokines that suppress the activity of B cells, helper T cells, and cytotoxic T cells. All three types of T cells have antigen receptors (T cell receptors or TCRs) that detect foreign antigens on body cells. They only detect antigens that are associated with a special class of normal self-proteins known as *major histocompatibility* (MHC) molecules.

Matching

57. a. A   **b.** O   **c.** N

Completion

58. a. MHC molecules   **b.** human leukocyte antigens, or HLA molecules   **c.** Class I MHC   **d.** Class II MHC   **e.** Thymus

Short Answer

59. Each of our cells is identified as "self" by *human leukocyte antigens* (or HLA molecules), of which **Class I MHC** molecules are found on the surfaces of all nucleated cells—that is, on almost every cell of the body. **Class II MHC** molecules are found on only a few specialized cell types, including macrophages, activated B and T cells, and the cells that make up the interior of the thymus. Class I MHC molecules capture foreign or abnormal antigens synthesized within infected cells or tumor cells, while class II MHC molecules capture foreign antigens that have been taken into cells through phagocytosis or receptor-mediated endocytosis. As young T cells are developing in the thymus, they come into contact with thymic cells bearing high levels of the body's own class I and class II MHC molecules. T cells develop into two different types: those cells that bind to class I MHC molecules develop into cytotoxic T cells, and those that bind to class II MHC molecules develop into helper T cells. Class I and class II MHC molecules differ in another way: Class I MHC molecules are recognized by cytotoxic T cells, whereas class II MHC molecules are recognized by helper T cells.

60. B and T cells provide for the features of specific immune responses: specificity, diversity, memory, and self-tolerance. In the humoral response, antigen-activated B cells develop into plasma cells that secrete antibodies. Antibodies bind to and target specific antigens but recruit other defenses, including macrophages and other types of phagocytic cells, to destroy the antigens. In the cell-mediated response, cytotoxic T cells detect antigens presented by class I MHC molecules (on virus-infected cells or tumor cells) and become active killers. Both humoral and cell-mediated responses are supported and regulated by cytokines secreted by helper T cells that have been induced by antigens presented by class II MHC molecules on macrophages or activated B cells. Here is where the immune system achieves its full potential: initially, the macrophages respond broadly but become more accurate as an ever-increasing population of T and B cells with the proper binding site become a higher proportion of the population through clonal selection. See Figure 22.12 in *Principles of Human Physiology* for a visual summary.

Sequencing

61. f, e, c, b, g, d, a

IMMUNE RESPONSES IN HEALTH AND DISEASE

Matching

62. a. P **b.** A **c.** A **d.** P

Antigen		Antibody
A	Type A blood	B
neither	Type O blood	both
B	Type B blood	A
both	Type AB blood	neither

Short Answer

64. Active immunity depends on the ability of the vaccinated person's own immune system to mount a response. Thus, it is "custom made" for the antigen and induces the formation of memory cells, which are necessary for life-long immunity to be conferred. By contrast, **passive immunity** does not require a response from the immune system, and does not induce long-term immunity.

65. HLA molecules are responsible for stimulating the rejection that occurs when tissue grafts are performed and organs are transplanted. To minimize the chance of rejection, doctors attempt to match the HLA molecules of the donor and recipient as closely as possible, using a procedure called *tissue typing*. In the absence of an identical twin, who would have exactly the same tissue type, siblings usually provide the closest HLA match. In addition to testing and matching HLA molecules, physicians also attempt to minimize the chance of rejection by prescribing drugs that suppress the recipient's immune responses. The complication with this strategy is that this renders the recipient more susceptible to infections and cancer during the course of treatment. Drugs such as cyclosporin A and FK506 have greatly improved the success of organ transplants. The main effect of these drugs is to inhibit production of the IL-2, which in turn, inhibits B- and T-cell activation and the mounting of specific immune responses.

True/False

66. T   **67.** T

68. F People with blood type O are considered to be universal donors.

69. T

70. F In bone marrow transplants, the greatest risk is that the **donated cells** will attack the recipient's immune system.

71. T

Completion

72. a. anaphylactic shock **b.** allergens **c.** mast **d.** dilation **e.** death

Multiple Choice

73. c

Clinical Question

74. A bee sting could bring on an allergic reaction and anaphylactic shock. **In anaphylactic shock, his blood pressure could drop so quickly that he may lose consciousness.** Anaphylactic shock could also close his bronchioles, making it impossible for him to breathe. **Dwight will have been given epinephrine. Epinephrine raises the blood pressure** by increasing the heart rate and contractility, causing vasoconstriction **while simultaneously causing bronchodilation so he can breathe.**

Challenge Question

75. The causes of autoimmunity are varied and complex. While there is still much to learn about these diseases, it is known that **people who inherit particular MHC molecules also are more likely to develop certain autoimmune diseases.** For example, individuals who inherit certain class II molecules are at higher risk of developing insulin-dependent diabetes mellitus, compared to the general population.

CHAPTER 23

PRINCIPLES OF PHYSIOLOGICAL INTEGRATION AND THE START: TRANSITION FROM REST TO EXERCISE

Matching
1. **a.** ALM **b.** CP **c.** ANG

Completion
2. **a.** energy **b.** creatine phosphate **c.** glycogen **d.** oxygen **e.** local metabolites **f.** neural **g.** autoregulatory

3. **a.** sympathetic **b.** parasympathetic **c.** glucose **d.** central command **e.** intensity **f.** anaerobic glycolysis **g.** the Krebs cycle

Short Answer
4. Central command is a feedforward mechanism involving an increase in heart rate due to anticipation of the run. Essentially, **John's brain is voluntarily increasing his heart rate in anticipation of running.** This mechanism is important because it causes an increase in heart rate almost instantaneously, and ensures that blood pressure remains high when blood is shunted to the exercising skeletal muscles.

5. During exercise, cardiac output increases blood flow to the lungs, which causes more of **the capillaries to open and increases perfusion in the lungs.** This increase in blood flow to the lung capillaries helps Barb by increasing the oxygen-carrying capacity of the blood (and ridding the body of carbon dioxide). In addition, **red blood cells spend less time in the capillaries of the alveoli.** This allows more red blood cells to pass by the alveolar capillaries and increases the efficiency of exchange of both oxygen and carbon dioxide.

Multiple Choice
6. b   7. c   8. d   9. c   10. e

True/False
11. T   12. T

13. F During heavy exercise, **blood is *not* shunted away** from the brain and toward the exercising muscles. The **blood that the exercising muscles receive comes from blood that is shunted away from visceral organs.**

14. T

15. F During moderate exercise in a hot environment, blood is shunted **to** the skin.

Clinical Question
16. By eating a meal rich in complex carbohydrates the **runners can store the glucose as glycogen in muscle tissue and have a store of energy to call upon during the race.** Complex carbohydrates are broken down by the digestive system into smaller, more usable glucose molecules. Glucose is an energy source that can be broken down to produce ATP through glycolysis under anaerobic or aerobic conditions. Glucose can also be stored in the muscle and liver as glycogen.

Challenge Question
17. During exercise, body temperature rises. In response, the negative feedback mechanism causes increased blood flow to the skin where heat is dissipated to the environment primarily by convection and evaporation (sweating), which lowers body temperature. To accomplish this, blood is shunted away from visceral organs and to the skin. **The sympathetic nervous system is responsible for 1) constricting the smooth muscle in blood vessels serving visceral organs, and, 2) increasing sweating during exercise.** Norpinephrine and epinephrine are the neurotransmitters released from adrenergic fibers serving the vessels of the visceral organs that have α_1 adrenergic receptors; this causes vasoconstriction. The sweat glands have muscarinic receptors and are the targets for acetylcholine released from cholinergic sympathetic fibers; this increases sweating.

THE LONG HAUL: ALMOST STEADY STATE

Matching
18. **a.** V **b.** S **c.** M **d.** M, S

Completion
19. **a.** glycogen **b.** glucagon **c.** cortisol **d.** insulin **e.** gluconeogenesis **f.** Lactate **g.** Fatty acid

Short Answer
20. Cellular metabolites can be harmful to working muscle. If they are not flushed from the muscle, muscle performance will suffer. **The higher blood pressure ensures that increased blood flow removes the metabolites from the capillaries surrounding the working skeletal muscle.**

21. In males, testosterone is produced in the testes by the interstitial cells surrounding the seminiferous tubules. In non-pregnant females, estrogen is produced in the ovaries by the developing follicles and the corpus luteum, while progesterone is produced primarily by the corpus luteum. Some research suggests that **testosterone might influence the rate of glycogenolysis in muscle and liver** via an increase in epinephrine. **Estrogen increases lipolysis in muscle and adipose tissue.** As a consequence, males burn a greater proportion of carbohydrate as a fuel source during exercise, and women burn a relatively greater proportion of fat.

Multiple Choice
22. a   23. c   24. c   25. b   26. d

True/False
27. T

28. F At the onset of exercise an increase in pulmonary ventilation is the result of **increasing the tidal volume.**

29. F By gradually increasing exercise intensity a person can help to conserve the body's stores of **glycogen.**

30. T

Labeling

31. a. Epinephrine is released from the adrenal medulla in response to stress. During the last few miles of the race, epinephrine release increases rapidly due to increased stress on the body.

b. Free fatty acids increase at the end of the race as they are liberated by the release of epinephrine from the adrenal gland.

c. Lactate concentration levels out at the end of the race as aerobic metabolism and gluconeogenesis increase.

d. Glucose concentrations are reduced at the end of the race because glucose is used by the body in response to the release of insulin from the pancreas.

e. Insulin levels also fall at the end of the race due to decreased stimulation by the sympathetic nervous system of the beta cells of the pancreas.

Clinical Questions

32. During light to moderate exercise, glucose concentrations increase slightly due to the stimulatory effects of epinephrine on glycogenolysis and gluconeogenesis. **Sympathetic nervous input to the beta cells of the pancreas decreases insulin plasma concentrations. At the same time, sympathetic nerve fibers stimulate alpha cells to release glucagon.** All three of these responses ensure that glucose is readily available to the exercising muscle tissue.

33. Because Jim did not continue to replace lost fluids after heavy exercise, his plasma became hyperosmotic. Normally, when one stands up after lying down, the baroreceptor reflex ensures that blood will not temporarily pool in the lower portions of the body, leaving the brain without a sufficient supply of oxygen. The drop in blood pressure is sensed by baroreceptors, which stimulate vasomotor centers in the brain. Sympathetic efferent fibers stimulate the heart to increase the rate and force of contraction and also stimulate vasoconstriction. This increases cardiac output and total peripheral resistance, which increases blood pressure and keeps blood flowing to the brain upon standing. This mechanism, however, requires adequate blood volume. **Because Jim was severely dehydrated, his blood volume was decreased and the baroreceptor reflex could not adequately supply the brain with oxygen-rich blood.** By administering intravenous fluids, the physician increased Jim's blood volume back to within normal limits.

Challenge Questions

34. Stronger contractions of the inspiratory muscles produce greater expansion of the thoracic cavity, reducing intrapleural pressure and creating greater transpulmonary pressure. This results in greater lung expansion and deeper inspiration. Active expiration can be achieved by contraction of the expiratory muscles, which produces a greater and more rapid decrease in the volume for the thoracic cavity, which increases intra-alveolar pressure and causes an increased pressure gradient for air flow out of the alveoli.

35. During exercise, the sympathetic nervous system uses epinephrine and norepinephrine to decrease the motility (α_1, α_2, β_2 adrenergic receptors) and secretions of the digestive tract (α_2 adrenergic receptors) while at the same time causing contraction of the sphincters of the stomach (α_1 adrenergic receptors).

Concept Map

36. a. Metabolic activity **b.** Heart rate **c.** O_2 concentration **d.** vasodilation **e.** Muscle **f.** Carbon dioxide concentration **g.** Venous

THE DECLINE TO THE END: "THE WALL" OR THE FINISH LINE? AND THE AFTERMATH

Matching

37. a. MF **b.** WI **c.** PEF **d.** DOMS **e.** SYN

Completion

38. a. fatigue **b.** intrinsic **c.** Glycogen **d.** hydrogen ions

39. a. syncope **b.** heat **c.** venous return **d.** swelling **e.** cytokine **f.** delayed-onset muscle soreness **g.** repair

Short Answer

40. Normally, approximately half of the neutrophils in the circulatory system adhere to the inside endothelium of veins. **Increased cardiac output** (as occurs during exercise) **dislodges the neutrophils and, as a result, the circulating neutrophil concentration increases.**

41. a. Muscles use **stored glycogen** for ATP production during the first few seconds of exercise. The pathway is **glyconeogenesis and glycolysis.**

b. Glycolysis is the predominant pathway that synthesizes ATP during intense, sustained exercise.

c. When a muscle is exercised at a moderate rate, most of the ATP is supplied by **oxidative phosphorylation.** The fuel source is likely to be **triglycerides.**

Multiple Choice

42. b   **43.** e   **44.** a   **45.** b   **46.** e   **47.** c

True/False

48. F Delayed onset muscle soreness is thought to be produced by the tearing of the myofilaments.

49. T

50. T

Clinical Questions

51. The cell membranes of the muscles are disrupted during trauma, which releases the intracellular contents, which then diffuse into the surrounding capillaries. Because the intracellular concentration of potassium is high relative to the plasma, potassium moves into the blood, causing hyperkalemia.

52. Female athletes may have little body fat. Fat deposits aid in the conversion of adrenal androgens to estrogen. Without the influence of estrogen, the endometrial lining of the uterus does not proliferate and is never shed. The lack of estrogen can also influence the plasma levels of LH, FSH, and GnRH. Sherri may have too little fat on her body to allow her to produce estrogen.

Challenge Questions

53. Karen probably has hyponatremia, or water intoxication. Because of the large volume of water that she drank, her plasma and interstitial fluids became hypo-osmotic and water moved into her cells (including those in wthe brain) by osmosis, causing them to swell. This caused her symptoms, which were quickly recognized by the park ranger. By eating foods high in sodium and taking in a modest volume of fluids, Karen replaces the lost electrolytes and combats the effects of water intoxication.

54. In high-intensity exercise, glycolytic muscle fibers are recruited. These fibers have a tendency to generate lactic acid because of their low oxidative capacity. This causes a rapid buildup of lactic acid in the muscles. **In low-intensity exercise, far fewer glycolytic fibers are recruited.** Fatigue occurs more slowly in Jane because she does not deplete her glycogen stores in the muscles as quickly as Bill does.

Concept Maps

55. a. vasoconstriction **b.** cardiac output
c. gluconeogenesis **d.** liver **e.** fatty acids **f.** glucagon
g. insulin

56. a. hypothalamus **b.** liver **c.** heme **d.** macrophages